Emailing Allie

by
Julie Lawson

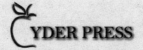

YDER PRESS

A Cyder Press Book

First published 2012
Copyright © Colin Thomas, 2012
The moral right of the author has been asserted

Cyder Press
Kenilworth Court, Lower Richmond Road,
London, SW15

www.cyder-press.com

A catalogue record for this book is available from the British Library

ISBN 978 0 9571877 0 2

Typeset by Regent Typesetting, London
Printed and bound in Great Britain by Clays Ltd, St Ives plc

For Ann Cameron Thomas;
My kind, brave, beautiful mother.

Hi there!

What follows is the story of my best friend Allie. It begins at the start of 2011 and is told mostly through her own words.

I hope you enjoy reading about her year now as much as I did then. As you'll see, Allie is a unique, disorganised, walking-talking disaster area. But she's also kind, caring and a wonderful friend.

Her adventures made me laugh and cry through many a long afternoon – I love her to bits.

With best wishes,

Julie Lawson

CHAPTER 1

Monday 3 January

From: Allie Rainsbury
To: Julie Lawson

Is there anything worse than a Monday morning? Happy New Year.

From: Julie Lawson

Happy New Year too. I'm tired and cranky – do not want to be here.

From: Allie Rainsbury

That makes two of us. Do you have meetings today?

From: Julie Lawson

Just one – an induction for some new starters. How can I properly convey the delights of the office environment?

From: Allie Rainsbury

I'm not sure there are words enough to do it justice. Maybe just point at a colour printer and smile at them knowingly?

From: Julie Lawson

Ingenious. Your creative powers are wasted in your role. :P

I'm off to get a coffee, catch you later.

From: Allie Rainsbury

Good luck with the newbies.

Tuesday

From: Julie Lawson
To: Allie Rainsbury

Want some gossip?

From: Allie Rainsbury

Always!

From: Julie Lawson

Some serious eye candy at the induction ☺ Two gorgeous guys, both starting in your UK department.

From: Allie Rainsbury

What, more gorgeous than Big Sweaty Kevin in accounting? Details please.

From: Julie Lawson

Yep, up there with him.

OK, as you know I was pretty tired yesterday and not exactly looking forward to taking bright new things over the do's and don'ts of 'career building at BMT Publishing'. But being the consummate professional I pulled myself together and walked into a meeting room with five fresh faces in it:

1. Graduate intern – young girl, black hair, slightly awkward.

2. Operations manager to replace Sandra.

3. New junior editor, very serious, reminded me of a younger Stephen Merchant (not a great look).

4. GORGEOUS!

5. GORGEOUS!!

So I perked up a bit.

From: Allie Rainsbury

Sandra's left? Where's she gone? Gorgeous isn't detail. What do they look like?

From: Julie Lawson

Borneo. Hmm, or Bangor. One of those two anyway – her husband was relocated so she followed. God knows why, I would have thought it a good chance to be rid of him ☺

Gorgeous # 1: Tall, dark and definitely handsome. His hair is wavy, but not in a foppish way, it just softens his perfect bone structure. He's witty; when I splashed my coffee over the intern he quipped that it was an interesting way to spill the beans. I'm not sure if he was flirting, but he has the most amazing smile and a great body and I think I'm in love.

Gorgeous # 2: A bit quieter. But he has this twinkle in his eye that, whenever I looked across at him, made it very difficult to look away. He's got sandy hair and has a boyish quality that made me want to protect and do terrible things to him at the same time.

Lunch today?

From: Allie Rainsbury

Ha – great descriptions. You're in love? I presume you told George all this last night? ☺

Lunch sounds good, you can tell me more about them then.

From: Julie Lawson

George forgot our anniversary last week (again!) – he's been on thin ice for a long time, the bugger ☺

See you at 12.30. I have another health and safety meeting before then.

From: Allie Rainsbury

You wouldn't swap him for Brad Pitt and you know it. 12.30 it is.

From: Allie Rainsbury
To: Julie Lawson

Have I missed the walk around?

From: Julie Lawson

Yes! Where were you? I hovered around your desk for ages but started getting funny looks from your boss.

From: Allie Rainsbury

Damn, damn, damn! Customer meeting overran.

From: Julie Lawson

So all our lunchtime scheming was for nothing? ☺ And there was I all set to introduce you as a diligent worker who spends her spare time reciting French poetry, attending MENSA and kick-boxing.

From: Allie Rainsbury

I do sound intimidating, don't I? Ah well, as believable as that would have been, I suppose it's irrelevant anyway. Firstly, they both sound completely out of my league unless they happen to go for 31-year-old women (with six pounds of Christmas weight newly added I might add) who lack the following:

- Dedication to the gym

- Interest in going to the gym, should dedication have ever existed

- Coordination (both before and after alcohol)

- A confident, strutting walk

- A basic of knowledge of most sports

- Any knowledge at all of politics

- A clear, focused career goal

- A solid dating history

I really must work on the gym I suppose. And politics is something that I've been meaning to get to grips with for a while, especially with that whole war thing recently.

But I digress. Secondly, it's irrelevant because, as you know full well, I have a date tonight with Arnold.

From: Julie Lawson

No one called Arnold can be a real person. It's impossible. You have a date with a cartoon character!

From: Allie Rainsbury

You're just jealous. :P Arnold is a solid, strong English name. I'm guessing he comes from a long line of landed gentry, plays polo and summers in the South of France.

From: Julie Lawson

I'm sure Udate.com have a database full of landed gentry.

Text me when you're home safe though, just in case he doesn't fly you off to Monaco. Good luck honey, and have fun ☺ x

Ps. Are we really meant to have a strutting walk?

From: Allie Rainsbury

Shall do. Enjoy your evening x

Ps. It couldn't hurt!

Wednesday

From: Julie Lawson
To: Allie Rainsbury

Now, you know me as well as anyone. I'd like to think I'm a pretty modest person, and I certainly would never profess to be an expert on dating. But (and forgive me if I'm wrong) a text message at 8.49 p.m. to announce, 'Home, I'm cursed. Will tell all tomorrow' isn't to my mind a good indication that dinner went well. At all. Or is that just me?

From: Allie Rainsbury

Morning! How much do cats cost? I shall buy all the cats my savings can afford and bask in undemanding feline company forevermore.

From: Julie Lawson

So, half a cat then. Not a good plan. Tell me!

From: Allie Rainsbury

You're the one in HR, you can sort out my lack of savings with a suitably generous bonus payment. We've talked about this!

From: Julie Lawson

But we haven't talked about last night. TELL ME!

From: Allie Rainsbury

OK, OK. I arranged to meet him at this Italian restaurant in Putney – he comes from Wandsworth so it was easy for us both – but he turned up 15 minutes late which, since I was half an hour early, meant that I'd managed to get through two glasses of white wine and was well on the way to constructing what I felt was a pretty sturdy fort from breadsticks by the time he arrived. The breadstick fort was the highlight of the evening. Easily.

He was wearing a bright yellow jacket and red trousers. He was completely bald. He was about 5'5" – at least an inch shorter than I am, out of heels (I was wearing heels). He looked a bit like Ronald McDonald without the wig.

Anyway, beauty is skin deep so, despite a discouraging start, I was prepared to give him the benefit of any burgeoning seeds of doubt. Except he'd brought a pot plant. A pot plant! Who does that? It wouldn't have mattered so much but it hadn't even flowered yet, so he basically handed me a pot with a stick in it. I was speechless. Which was actually quite convenient as I think I would have struggled to get a word in. Arnold, it seems, is very pleased with Arnold.

From: Julie Lawson

He he! Am giggling away down here at the thought of you dating a bald Ronald McDonald! ☺☺

From: Allie Rainsbury

Hmm. I think all thoughts of dating went out of the window when he was halfway through telling me about his Monopoly collection. I am not joking.

From: Julie Lawson

Aww, I'm sorry. You'll look back and laugh I'm sure. Worst case scenario, I'll look back and laugh anyhow.

Fancy a quick drink this evening? George is taking the kids to a football game so I have some time to myself.

From: Allie Rainsbury

That sounds nice, for them and you! Are you in meetings for the rest of the day?

From: Julie Lawson

Yes. :S Busy day, but the usual strong coffee should help get me through. See you in the lobby at six and we'll go to The Firestation for a natter.

From: Allie Rainsbury

It's a date (no yellow jackets allowed though). See you later.

Thursday

From: Allie Rainsbury
To: Julie Lawson

How's the head?

From: Julie Lawson

Sore! How are you?

From: Allie Rainsbury

A bit dizzy.

From: Julie Lawson

You always have been ☺ I've a huge bacon sandwich in front of me, but am now suddenly unsure if my stomach can take it.

From: Allie Rainsbury

How drunk did we get? I can hardly type the word bacon without feeling sick.

From: Julie Lawson

Drunk enough that I got into bed on the wrong side and fell asleep on top of George.

Chat to you in a bit. I need quiet, reflective, horribly ill time.

From: Allie Rainsbury

I shall wait here, curled up under my desk.

From: Julie Lawson
To: Allie Rainsbury

Doing any better? I'm now vaguely human again I think.

From: Allie Rainsbury

I have feeling back in my hands. I'm hopeful it will spread across the rest of me soon and normality will ensue. At least then I can stop answering all questions with 'Gaaaaaaarrrrghhhh!'

From: Julie Lawson

Ha, is your boss giving you his special evil look?

From: David Marshall
To: Allie Rainsbury

Hi Allison,

I've been handed your name as my point of contact for all things Non-Fiction.

As this is my first week at the company, would you be able to share some key information with me please, or point me towards where it's kept? In particular I'm looking for some Sales data across the following genres: Travel Writing, MBS and Humour. Are we able to broaden this out into narrative and non-narrative for humour? Would be great to see splits for backlist and frontlist as well. Any information of links you could send would be much appreciated.

Regards, David.

From: Allie Rainsbury
To: Julie Lawson

Hey, who's David Marshall? Is he the junior editor resembling Stephen Merchant?

From: Julie Lawson

That's James Grogan – and that description didn't come from me!

David Marshall is the new Marketing Director for digital. AKA the gorgeous dark-haired man from Monday ☺ Why?

From: Allie Rainsbury

I've just had an email from him.

From: Julie Lawson

Saying what?

From: Allie Rainsbury

Oh, just asking for data, a bit of market share information... Everything a girl wants to hear really :P

From: Julie Lawson

Hmph. I'm still jealous.

From: Allie Rainsbury
To: David Marshall

Hi David,

Welcome to the company! You can find all the relevant information in the shared drive Sales Data folder, by following the relevant genres. It's worth noting that Travel Writing has dipped considerably year on year across the market, although our share has held up well against the competition.

I'm unsure whether this is true for digital Sales as well; I cover traditional trade accounts only – perhaps the slant here is different than at retail. For detail there you'd be better to chat with Richard Booth who currently looks after all things e-book.

Let me know if I can help further though.

Kind regards, Allie x

From: Allie Rainsbury
To: David Marshall

Hi David,

I've just noticed I added an 'x' onto the end of my email to you.

I have spent the last half hour wondering whether to draw further attention to this. I've only decided to now because I thought you might think it had been deliberate. It wasn't at all, it was entirely accidental as anything else would have been inappropriate and unprofessional. Please disregard the kiss. But the Sales Data information should still be OK, I've double checked it.

Best regards, Allie.

From: Allie Rainsbury
To: Julie Lawson

Bugger.

Friday

From: Julie Lawson
To: Allie Rainsbury

A note to all employees: Although Fridays are dress down, please remember to be appropriate and professional throughout x ☺

From: Allie Rainsbury

Ha. Ha.

From: Julie Lawson

Sorry, couldn't resist! George nearly choked on his dinner when I told him.

From: Allie Rainsbury

Perfect. Please remember to tell the neighbours too next time I'm mortified.

From: Julie Lawson

Oh shush, it's nothing. It will be fine. I doubt he's even noticed.

Anyway, you can't be cross with me. I've got meetings all day today and am on this stupid course all of next week. I'm the one in need of sympathy here.

From: Allie Rainsbury

Hmph. Well, I suppose so, but only because I'm such a nice person.

All of next week? How on earth am I meant to survive without you for a whole week?

From: Julie Lawson

I know! I'll be on my BlackBerry at least, but not sure how often I'll be able to use it.

What a waste of a week. I'll have a mountain of work, no further understanding of 'How HR should better interact with the company's online site' and a shorter fuse!

From: Allie Rainsbury

Ugh. I don't even understand the title.

From: Julie Lawson

Exactly! I have to dash now, but I'll call you over the weekend.

Fancy coming over on Saturday evening for dinner with the family? Let me know. Don't work too hard :P xx

----

From: David Marshall
To: Allie Rainsbury

Hi Allison,

No worries at all. Thanks for the tip on Richard, I'll make sure to follow up with him over e-books.

You don't happen to be free for a quick coffee now do you? Not sure how much interaction we'll have, but no doubt there'll be some cross-over and it would be good to get a broader understanding of your area, along with putting a face to a name of course.

Best, David

From: Allie Rainsbury

Hi David,

Yes, as it happens, I do have a small window in my calendar now. A great idea to meet up – the induction process here is terrible really; what do they do in HR?

Downstairs café in ten minutes?

Thanks, Allie

From: David Marshall

Sure, sounds good. D

From: David Marshall
To: Allie Rainsbury

Allie, thanks for your time earlier – was a pleasure to meet you and a very useful overview of current trading conditions on the high street.

Hope to catch up again soon, cheers, D

From: Allie Rainsbury

Hi David,

You're very welcome. In turn I was impressed by your digital marketing plans and whatever else it was you talked about. If I can help you in any other way please do say.

From: David Marshall

I should be OK I think. After a while you'd just confuse me with poetry or break my back with a kick-boxing move.

From: Allie Rainsbury

No. Never in the workplace.

From: David Marshall

Only outside the workplace then. Duly noted.

Enjoy the weekend x

From: David Marshall
To: Allie Rainsbury

Apologies, please delete the 'x'. Obviously.

From: Allie Rainsbury
To: David Marshall

Have a good weekend too ☺

From: Allie Rainsbury
To: Julie Lawson

What an AMAZING week! See you tomorrow for dinner x

CHAPTER 2

Monday 10 January

From: David Marshall
To: Allie Rainsbury

Richard Booth is rather dull.

From: Allie Rainsbury

Hi! You caught up with him? Well, I suppose after meeting me he had a tough act to follow.

From: David Marshall

True, it must just be that.

How was your weekend?

From: Allie Rainsbury

Relatively uneventful, but relaxing. I caught up on some reading and went over to a friend's for dinner on Saturday night. You?

From: David Marshall

That does sound relaxing.

I took some work home and dived into some numbers over Saturday. By Sunday I was seeing things in binary so played tennis and went to the gym.

From: Allie Rainsbury

How active. It's a bit cold for tennis though surely?

From: David Marshall

It was indoors, at the David Lloyd centre. Do you play at all?

From: Allie Rainsbury

A bit. I mean, I wouldn't be much good really. I used to have a bat though, and could hit the ball occasionally.

So probably average, I'd say. Good to average.

From: David Marshall

You're funny. I'm heading off now – see you later.

Tuesday

From: Julie Lawson
To: Allie Rainsbury

Course rubbish. Temper fraying. You?

From: Allie Rainsbury

I had a very boring meeting in the morning, but I think I managed to look alert enough to convince Garry that I was actually listening.

Plus, I've had an email from David asking after my weekend! I've so far followed your advice from Saturday and not made anything up. Are you sure about this? I might sound a bit boring. Maybe I should tell him I've taken up rowing – he looks like a rower. He definitely has the body of one ☺

I was so excited last night I hardly watched *Desperate Housewives*! What if this is the start of something? What if he asks me out? I'm reading way too much into this, aren't I?

From: Julie Lawson

Yes :P

From: Allie Rainsbury

I hope your course gets longer and harder.

From: Julie Lawson

Stop thinking about long hard things and get on with some work ☺

From: Allie Rainsbury

Outrageous! I'm calling HR :P

From: David Marshall
To: Sales EMEA; Marketing EMEA

Dear all,

As from next week, I am instigating a fortnightly cross-departmental (and cross-platform) strategy meeting. I see this as an ideal forum to communicate more fully with colleagues within Marketing, Sales and Operations enabling all teams to gain a clearer understanding of where priorities and time frames sit.

Please ensure you come prepared with the necessary data to allow analysis and discussion of the full first quarter, Jan–March.

A more detailed agenda to follow. I look forward to seeing you all there.

Regards, David Marshall.

From: Allie Rainsbury
To: David Marshall

I look forward to seeing you there too ☺

Wednesday

From: Allie Rainsbury
To: Julie Lawson

No reply, what do I do? WHAT DO I DO?

Stupid Allie, stupid Allie. I hardly know him. I need to calm down. No big deal I know. But I thought we were flirting a bit. I mean, not much, but a bit maybe. And there was definite eye contact when we met last week. And not just because he was talking to me. Real, proper eye contact – more than needed eye contact. I think.

Should I email him and apologise? But for what? Silly. Sorry. It's nothing, it never was, so it doesn't matter.

WHAT DO I DO?

Ps. Oh, how's your course?

From: Julie Lawson

Find a brown paper bag and breathe deeply. Then, and only then, re-read your email and pay particular attention to the phrase 'calm down'. Give it time and *don't* email him, I'm sure he's just busy (unlike some people, mentioning no names). Do NOT email him.

My course is even more dull yet perversely even more hectic than yesterday.

From: Allie Rainsbury

You're right. I know you're right, sorry for interrupting the course. Thanks for the advice, I won't email him.

From: Allie Rainsbury
To: David Marshall

Did you get my email yesterday? Sorry, obviously not expecting a reply but, well, I suppose I was half expecting a reply to be honest.

Anyhow, apologies. I don't mean to bombard you, I'm sure you're very busy. I am too of course. In fact, I need to go and work now, I have lots to do.

From: David Marshall

Hello! Yes, I got your email. I'm sorry but I've been in back-to-back meetings for the last 36 hours. It's so busy and there's masses on. I hate to speak badly of a predecessor but he was as organised as a gnat (admittedly I'm assuming that gnats are incredibly disorganised creatures).

Anyway, horrible, horrible excuse. Please do forgive me.

Thursday

From: Allie Rainsbury
To: David Marshall

After careful consideration I've decided you're forgiven ☺

Of course I understand! I completely realise you must barely pause for breath at the moment.

You were working late into the evening as well by the looks of when you sent that email.

From: David Marshall

Unfortunately yes. Stayed past 11 p.m. in the end – not quite the rock and roll lifestyle I imagined I'd have when I was a teenager!

Even more disastrously I'm in a directors' meeting most of today (your director Garry – nice guy?) so won't be able to chat I'm afraid.

From: Allie Rainsbury

He's a complete sexist. But he is good at his job. I suppose if you don't have to directly link the two then you could find him useful. Hope it's not too heavy going!

From: David Marshall

Nine directors and an MD talking about the annual budget? I guarantee it will be heavy going.

From: Allie Rainsbury

Anything I can do to help? (Aside from actually attending of course.)

From: David Marshall

Well, I still know nothing about you. Other than you deal with Waterstone's for BMT Publishing and feign an interest in kick-boxing (the giveaway was when you paused for breath climbing the stairs on the way back from our meeting).

From: Allie Rainsbury

Right.

From: David Marshall

If you have time today – and want to of course – why not tell me a bit more about the real Allie Rainsbury?

From: Allie Rainsbury

You want to know more about me?... As in, outside of work?

From: David Marshall

Sure. Preferably real interests, but imaginary hobbies are acceptable too I suppose.

From: Allie Rainsbury

Ha! Well, yes, OK, kick-boxing isn't actually a big hobby of mine.

Will you promise not to judge me?

From: David Marshall

Of course not. I've already labelled you as a daydreamer at best and a schizophrenic at worst.

From: Allie Rainsbury

Oh, you're trouble!

Maybe if I find some time this afternoon, I'll write you a little bit. No promises though, and no laughing if I do.

From: David Marshall

I look forward to it.

Yours, in seriousness, David

From: Allie Rainsbury
To: David Marshall

See below, which pretty much sums me up. I hope it makes for interesting reading. See you tomorrow maybe.

I've been at BMT for six years and I've account managed Waterstone's throughout that time (initially I was an assistant to the senior account manager, then promoted to oversee the whole account). The job is OK, but ultimately unrewarding – it's not what I thought I'd end up doing.

When I graduated (Sussex University, BA in English) I had hopes of becoming a literary journalist – I even secured an internship for two months at a local paper near where my parents live in Oxford. It was unpaid though which meant that I either needed to find work elsewhere and move out or stay and be eventually arrested for parenticide. So I applied for a role as an assistant at Clowes Publishing.

I got it, and moved down to London two weeks later. I think that was the beginning of the end for my journalism dreams. I ended up staying at Clowes for three years.

Initially I had been more editorially based, but account management seemed better paid and I was still able to read all the books we published – I just had to talk them through with customers instead. It seemed an obvious route.

I moved to BMT when a headhunter phoned the wrong extension number. He'd been trying to get through to another girl, but ended up convincing me to join a 'bigger, brighter company'. It's definitely bigger anyway. Six years later and I'm still here; if I wasn't so comfortable I'd think more about what I really want to do.

Julie, my best friend, works in Human Resources here which helps. We have a giggle and confide and gossip. You've met her I think – she took the induction meeting. She always thinks clearly when I cloud up, which can happen (hopefully you're not nodding knowingly at this!).

I'm 31, although friends say I can pull off 30. I live by myself in a little place in Putney, not far from the Thames. I like it as at the weekend I can wander down to the river with a cup of tea and watch all the cyclists and joggers and rowers. I feel very active, without actually being active, which is nice. The river police even toot their horn at me now, if they see me. At least I like to think it's me they're tooting.

Julie lives 15 minutes away so I often go round to hers and keep her company when she's not too busy with her family (George, her husband, and her two kids Cale and Elly). Apart from that and reading, sometimes going out for a drink or two with friends, occasionally visiting Oxford, I don't know, I must sound very boring actually!

I've been single for three years now, since my ex-boyfriend Tony. He came up to me in a bar and told me I looked like Rachel Weisz, which just shows that flattery works. We dated for two years and I thought we were getting pretty serious. In fairness, so did Tony – it was the reason he gave when he split up with me.

I haven't been abroad in four years and when I did I broke my leg skiing. Well, it wasn't skiing, I was sitting on the ski-lift and fell off. And the airline lost my luggage on the flight back. I don't know why I'm finishing with that story. There you go though.

Enjoy your evening, if you get one.

From: David Marshall

What a nice surprise to come back to. Your ex sounds like an idiot, although he's right – you do look like Rachel Weisz.

Friday

From: Allie Rainsbury
To: David Marshall

Thank you. Although she'd be terribly insulted by that comparison. Especially this morning, I slept terribly! I'll need at least three cups of tea to wake up. And another two hours' sleep.

From: David Marshall

Hang on in the knowledge that it's Friday and you're a day away from being tooted by the river police.

From: Allie Rainsbury

Hey, this is unfair! You now have lots of things to tease me with and I have nothing on you.

From: Julie Lawson
To: Allie Rainsbury

Last day of the course, hurrah! Any longer and I'd be stabbing the coordinator with my biro.

From: Allie Rainsbury

Chat later, Jules, busy at the mo.

From: Julie Lawson

Busy with what? Are you coming over this weekend?

From: Allie Rainsbury

Later. Shush. Emailing.

From: Julie Lawson

Who?

From: Allie Rainsbury
To: David Marshall

David, go away.

From: David Marshall

??

From: Allie Rainsbury

No! No, no! Not you. I was emailing Julie. I don't want you to go away.

From: David Marshall

Ah, OK. I was thrown there for a minute.

From: Allie Rainsbury

No, don't be. As I say, you have far too much information on me. I can't let you go anywhere before I find out a bit more about you.

From: David Marshall

What do you want to know?

From: Allie Rainsbury

Whatever you care to share.

From: David Marshall

I'm 35. I look at least that. I've never worked in publishing before, my background is through more traditional FMCG companies. I spent a few years at Coke, a couple of frustrating ones at a small consultancy called IPQC, before moving back to the multi-nationals with P&G. Spent seven years there, heading up their online marketing team before being approached with this role. I wasn't sure about it at first, but eventually saw it for what it is, a new challenge and opportunity.

The personal stuff – I used to be married. Unfortunately, like a lot of young marriages it didn't work out. Anyway, you live and learn. I stay pretty active – I play tennis most weeks and squash when I don't. I enjoy mountain biking, off-road, it's tough on the knees but very exhilarating. I have a passion for history, especially the Plantagenets. I have a rather hectic social life, which is no doubt the by-product of a rather hedonistic University existence along with a knack (and desire) to still keep in touch with a lot of the people I met there.

I think that will do for the moment!

From: Allie Rainsbury

Wow. A lot of interesting things there. And a lot more questions to ask as a result.

From: David Marshall

I figured there would be. If you're lucky, maybe you'll get to hear more some time.

From: Allie Rainsbury

Maybe...

Are you planning on joining with company tradition and heading to The Firestation after work?

From: David Marshall

The Firestation being the local pub I presume. But no, I can't this evening – I have previous arrangements with a friend, a squash court and a large dose of testosterone.

From: Allie Rainsbury

Really? OK... Not even for one? I was thinking of going for a bit.

From: David Marshall

No, I really can't, I'm sorry. Another time though, it would be nice to get to know people in the company a bit more.

From: Allie Rainsbury

OK. Well, one more question, as I don't think you mentioned it in your brief biog.

Are you single?

From: David Marshall

No, I'm not seeing anyone at the moment, why do you ask?

From: Allie Rainsbury

Just curious :P

Chat next week! X

From: Julie Lawson
To: Allie Rainsbury

WHO ARE YOU EMAILING?

From: Allie Rainsbury

Maybe, just maybe, the man of my dreams ☺☺

CHAPTER 3

Monday 17 January

From: Julie Lawson
To: Allie Rainsbury

Have you asked him for a drink yet?

From: Allie Rainsbury

No. I'm working on it.

From: Julie Lawson

Just do it!

From: Allie Rainsbury

I will. You're sure you think I should?

From: Julie Lawson

Yes! What's the worst that can happen?

From: Allie Rainsbury

There are too many answers to that question.

From: Julie Lawson

I'm giving you until 3 p.m. If you haven't done it by then, I'm emailing him on your behalf.

From: Allie Rainsbury

That's not helping with the pressure!

From: Julie Lawson

3 p.m.

From: Allie Rainsbury

OK, OK, I'll do it. I promise. I'll put the kettle on first though.

From: Julie Lawson

You're lucky – that's the one thing that I can't argue with!
Good luck, tell me how it goes.

From: Allie Rainsbury
To: David Marshall

Did you win your squash match?

From: David Marshall

It was an honourable draw (which is guy speak for 'I got badly beaten').

How was your weekend and river life?

From: Allie Rainsbury

Congratulations on being honourable at least.

My weekend was good fun, a friend of mine had tickets to a photography exhibition at the Natural History Museum and, deciding it was time to broaden my interests, I went along with him. It was incredibly inspiring and, in my opinion, visually spectacular.

From: David Marshall

Ah, I've read about that on tube posters. It's the one advertised as 'An inspirational display, visually spectacular'.

From: Allie Rainsbury

Um, yes, that sounds about right...

From: David Marshall

You were bored, weren't you? ☺

From: Allie Rainsbury

SO BORED. Chris kept on going on about the lens diameter and the number of pixies, and my legs started to ache after a while so I sat on a seat that turned out to be a rather large fossil and security got awfully touchy over what's basically a rock with a squiggle on it.

From: David Marshall

Pixels. Security can be very anal over things like that :P

Who's Chris then?

From: Allie Rainsbury

Chris is no one. I mean, he's someone obviously! But no one in that sense.

I've known him since I was nine. We used to play Kiss/Chase (where the boys try to catch the girls and get a kiss when they do. Looking back, it's possibly the most chauvinistic game one could think of; quite why primary schools aren't clamping down on it is a puzzle). Anyway, break time was only 15 minutes long and Chris never caught anyone. He just started breathing a bit heavily and going slightly red in the face. I suppose I felt a bit sorry for him, so one day I slowed up a little and let him catch me. He went down on his knee (I think he was still gasping for air) and kissed my hand.

Sadly, I'm pretty sure that remains the most romantic moment of my life. Chris is sweet, but we're just friends, nothing more.

Why are you so curious?

From: David Marshall

Just wondered. Thought it might have been a date.

From: Allie Rainsbury

Not a date, no. I told you – I'm not seeing anyone at the moment.

From: Allie Rainsbury
To: Julie Lawson

I'm going to ask him.

From: Julie Lawson

You haven't already?

From: Allie Rainsbury

I'm going to ask him!

From: Julie Lawson

I thought you had! Do it now or I will.

From: Allie Rainsbury

Eeekkk! I'm actually going to ask him!

From: Julie Lawson

NOW!

From: Allie Rainsbury
To: David Marshall

Do you want to go for a drink later?

From: David Marshall

I was wondering if you were going to ask me that. I can't later, sorry.

From: Allie Rainsbury

No, of course – silly idea. It was only on the off chance that you'd want to.

Apologies.

From: David Marshall

Are you free on Thursday evening? Maybe we could go for one then?

From: Allie Rainsbury

Yes, I'm free! That sounds nice.

From: David Marshall

Probably best to keep it under wraps though; wouldn't want to be the subject of office gossip – not that there's anything to gossip about, of course.

From: Allie Rainsbury

It will be our secret.

Tuesday

From: Julie Lawson
To: Allie Rainsbury

Have you planned an outfit yet?

From: Allie Rainsbury

No, not yet. I was looking through my wardrobe last night but I couldn't find anything. I'll go shopping this evening, that's my only hope.

From: Julie Lawson

Hair up or hair down?

From: Allie Rainsbury

Hair down? Hair up? Hair cut?

From: Julie Lawson

Hair down I think. Coquettish but classy at the same time. Want me to come to the shops with you?

From: Allie Rainsbury

Yes please! Are you able to?

From: Julie Lawson

Let me check. Elly has a piano lesson this evening, but George might be able to take her.

From: Allie Rainsbury

He's so good. We're both so blessed!

From: Julie Lawson

You stop thinking about wedding dresses; we are *not* shopping for one of those.

From: Allie Rainsbury

I wasn't! I meant, in general we're blessed. Honestly.

From: Julie Lawson

Uh-huh. Chat later, lover girl.

From: Allie Rainsbury
To: David Marshall

Hi, how's your day going?

From: David Marshall

Crazy busy. I'll be tied up for most of the next couple of days I'm afraid.

From: Allie Rainsbury

Sounds a bit kinky ;)

From: Allie Rainsbury
To: David Marshall

Sorry... a joke there. I'll tell better ones on Thursday!

From: Allie Rainsbury
To: David Marshall

Which I'm still really looking forward to by the way ☺

From: Allie Rainsbury
To: David Marshall

I'll leave you in peace now. Hope work isn't too stressful.

Wednesday

From: Julie Lawson
To: Allie Rainsbury

Can I take a bet that you went home and tried everything on again?
☺

From: Allie Rainsbury

You know, for someone who ended up buying two new pairs of boots, that's an awfully brave jest.

From: Julie Lawson

They were my reward for being such a good, selfless friend and accompanying you.

From: Allie Rainsbury

I'm sure that's just how George saw it too :P But yes, since you mention it, I may have had another quick look in the mirror wearing the outfit and the boots. With my hair curled. All necessary preparations!

I think you've forgotten all this because when you got married it was customary to have but two baths a month.

From: Julie Lawson

Ha! And one shoe was shared amongst the whole family.

From: Allie Rainsbury

It's such a shame photography was only invented six months later, I would have loved to have seen your wedding photos.

From: Julie Lawson

You wouldn't. George got absolutely hammered the night before. He had bloodshot eyes and beer breath throughout the ceremony. Just how every girl imagines it.

You don't need to worry, you look smoking hot in the dress you bought.

From: Allie Rainsbury

Aw. Thank you. Now I feel bad.

You did get married post photography. Just pre-colour :P

From: Julie Lawson

That's it. I am boycotting you for the rest of the day. Unless you're free for lunch (in which case you can buy)?

From: Allie Rainsbury

Canteen at 12.30?

From: Julie Lawson

Deal.

From: Allie Rainsbury
To: David Marshall

Hi, I hope your day's going OK. I know you said you were very busy, but thought I'd see if you were about. I've just spent the last hour on the phone to Waterstone's sorting out delivery slots for *A Bear in Summer* – one of our new books for June (if you don't yet know our schedule) and am now at a loose end.

From: Allie Rainsbury
To: David Marshall

Didn't really expect you to be free. I hope we're still on for tomorrow though?

From: Allie Rainsbury
To: David Marshall

Enjoy your evening x

Thursday

From: David Marshall
To: Allie Rainsbury

Hi – still mad here. Hopefully will clear a bit next week, but budget setting is proving somewhat tortuous (and frustratingly limiting from a creative marketing perspective). I'll tell you about it later (if all other conversation has run dry ☺).

I've booked a table at La Maison Blanche for 7.30 p.m. It's a little bistro off Charlotte Street near Tottenham Court Road. Can we meet there?

From: Allie Rainsbury

It sounds wonderful. I shall see you in front of La Maison Blanche at 7.30 p.m.

I'll be the nervous girl in the green dress ☺

From: Allie Rainsbury
To: Julie Lawson

Why am I so nervous?

From: Julie Lawson

Ah, sweetheart. You're only nervous because you see this as your last chance to escape the solitude and loneliness of perpetual singledom; to avert the otherwise stark inevitability of a lifetime of television dinners for one; to fall asleep secure and comfortable in someone's warm embrace as opposed to the frosty spaciousness of an empty bed.

That's the only reason though.

From: Allie Rainsbury

You're mean :P But actually quite astute.

From: Julie Lawson

Hush, and toughen up. I told you yesterday, I'll tell you today: You look gorgeous. I'd be very surprised if he wasn't the more nervous.

From: Allie Rainsbury

He doesn't strike me as the nervous type. But thank you – and for your patience this week.

Any last minute advice?!

From: Julie Lawson

Lots of eye contact.

From: Allie Rainsbury

I love his eyes! Gentle yet strong, like a whimsical soldier's.

From: Julie Lawson

Um... OK...

Ask about his interests.

From: Allie Rainsbury

Interests, check.

From: Julie Lawson

In fact, keep conversation flowing in general. No one likes awkward silences. Flirt a little, but not heavily. Show him you're keen, but not too keen. Make sure you come across as thoughtful but independent and self-motivated.

From: Allie Rainsbury

Talking, check. Flirting and not-flirting, check. Independent... Should I pay for dinner?

From: Julie Lawson

No way! Rule number one of dating: Worst case, you get a free meal.

Relax, and he'll relax - imagine it's your second date with Arnold!

From: Allie Rainsbury

Eeuww! OK, that's good advice. I can do this! I'm a relaxed, independent woman and a natural conversationalist. All systems check.

From: Julie Lawson

One last thing.

From: Allie Rainsbury

?

From: Julie Lawson

If everything's going wrong and nothing's working as you thought it would...

From: Allie Rainsbury

Yes??

From: Julie Lawson

Show some leg ☺ x

Friday

From: Julie Lawson
To: Allie Rainsbury

Tell me EVERYTHING.

From: Allie Rainsbury

Good morning ☺

From: Julie Lawson

Never mind about the morning, I want to know about the night!

From: Allie Rainsbury

It was a very nice evening, thank you.

From: Julie Lawson

? You better start talking, Miss Rainsbury, or I'm marching straight up there and getting it out of you in person!

From: Allie Rainsbury

Well, you did help me with my dress I suppose, so I guess it's only right to share a detail or two.

From: Julie Lawson

I'm counting down from ten...

From: Allie Rainsbury

OK, OK, give me a chance to write about it!

Nine...

:P Five minutes.

From: Allie Rainsbury
To: Julie Lawson

Firstly, I'm so glad I bought a new dress; it was a really smart restaurant! But intimate too, which meant we could talk easily. He looked amazing. He was wearing a dark-blue jacket over a white shirt and I'm pretty sure was mistaken for Pierce Brosnan by more than one person – albeit a younger, better-looking version.

He asked me lots of questions, which is always a good sign. He wanted to know about my hobbies (I need to get more hobbies – I don't think I impressed enough in this area), about places I've been and would like to visit (is he already thinking of holidays away, do you think?) about my family (perhaps in anticipation of meeting them one day?). He seemed genuinely interested in me.

I ordered the spaghetti, which in hindsight was silly. Have you tried eating spaghetti in a seductive way? It's impossible. I mostly got away with it though and only had one or two drops of sauce on me by the end.

He's very funny. He made me laugh and relax. He told me about his first ever day at work when his boss took him to lunch and he shook the ketchup bottle to loosen it, entirely forgetting to check whether the cap was on the bottle. It wasn't. He covered the man in tomato ketchup!

Other things. He's very clever, without trying to sound pretentious with it. He talked about lots of different news stories. I nodded along and tried to make a couple of intelligent sounds. He told me at one point that I had a very intent look and it made him feel vulnerable! I suppose I must have looked rather intent – he was talking about the state of the economy and I was trying hard to concentrate.

And then it all ended. The evening passed so quickly that we were still talking when they were closing up. But the last thing he did was reach across the table and brush my hair away (hair down, good call!). When we got up to leave he helped me into my coat and when we got outside he hailed a cab and gave me a kiss on the cheek. He looked into my eyes just before he did though and I'm sure I saw more than just friendship in his.

What do you think? I had such a good time. Does it sound like he's keen? Do you think he had fun too? I'm pretty sure he was flirting with me.

From: Julie Lawson

Just a kiss on the cheek?

From: Allie Rainsbury

Yes, but remember the long look into my eyes before that.

From: Julie Lawson

Lest we forget.

I think it sounds like a lovely evening. I'm sure he had a fun time.

From: Allie Rainsbury

What do you mean? You think he's not keen? You think he's letting me down gently?

I'm looking into what hobbies I can do this weekend. I shall be an active, can-do person who challenges life and pushes extremes. It is very cold out at the moment. But still, I will look into this!

Is he keen? Should I call him?

From: Julie Lawson

Yes, I'm sure he's keen. And if he's not then he's an idiot. Maybe he's just taking his time and being a gentleman. You already said he embodied that very approach throughout the evening.

Don't call him! Leave him to sweat over the weekend and see what happens next week.

From: Allie Rainsbury

True. Maybe he's just being patient. Damn it! This is going to be the longest weekend ever.

From: Julie Lawson

Well, your new-found sense of pro-activeness should help pass the time.

You just wait. By Monday morning I'll be diverse, intriguing and energised, laden with the confidence that a sparkling array of interests imbue.

He'll be so impressed he'll have to ask me out again.

CHAPTER 4

Monday 24 January

From: Allie Rainsbury
To: Julie Lawson

I hate Mondays. I'm sure time skipped at least four hours during the night.

From: Julie Lawson

Will it cheer you up further to know I'm working from home today? ☺

From: Allie Rainsbury

What? You never mentioned that!

From: Julie Lawson

Elly has flu, poor little mite, so I'm nursing her back to full fitness.

From: Allie Rainsbury

Well, that's doubly annoying, I can't even get outraged now. Is she OK? Anything you need me to do?

From: Julie Lawson

She'll be fine. She's coughing and sneezing and running a slight temperature, so I've prescribed a large dose of bed-rest and a hot-water bottle. She's well enough to ask her mum for jam on toast and is awake enough to watch *The Princess and the Frog*. So I'm confident she'll pull through.

Ah, bless. Send her a big kiss and a hug from me. I'll leave you to play nurse and find someone else to annoy on email.

From: Julie Lawson

I wonder who that might be :P

From: Peter Rainsbury
To: Allie Rainsbury

Hey sweetheart,

How's life in big old, dirty old London?

I just thought I'd drop you a quick note to say hello. I can't believe that it's almost the end of January already. Time just flies by.

The jumper you gave me for Christmas has come in very handy the past couple of weeks, it's been incredibly cold up this way. Perhaps it's milder in the city. Even so, I don't know how anyone can think the world is heating up when this frost has already meant that my garden will be threadbare in summer. The vegetable plot is ruined.

Your mother is still working her way through the tea selection you gave her – even at the rate she goes through tea, she hasn't managed to finish it. Although it would help if she shared some occasionally.

She has just called out to say hello (she's in the living room watching England play someone at cricket) and is asking when you'll next be up. Our neighbour Mike has his 60th birthday party next weekend, which you're invited to. I doubt you'll be around, but do come if so. You always brighten our days when you do.

Speak to you soon poppet.

Lots of love, Dad x

From: Allie Rainsbury
To: David Marshall

Hi, how was your weekend?

From: David Marshall

Quiet and uneventful. You?

From: Allie Rainsbury

Mine was good, thanks. I spent it considering new things I could do in the evenings and weekends – a late resolution list I suppose. Want to hear it? ☺

From: David Marshall

Another time, not enough hours in the days this week I'm afraid.

Tuesday

From: Allie Rainsbury
To: David Marshall

You know, if you'd rather not chat or see me again you could just say. It would make things easier for me.

From: David Marshall

? Allie, I'm in meetings for most of this week, I said that yesterday!

From: Allie Rainsbury

You just seem a bit off. I'm big enough to take no as an answer.

From: David Marshall

I didn't think I'd been asked a question.

From: Allie Rainsbury

You're acting differently, that's all. Are you busy all week then?

From: David Marshall

Yes. I have a schedule that would make grown men cry. I have, in fact, welled up slightly myself.

From: Allie Rainsbury

And in the evenings?

From: David Marshall

Again, I'm busy this week, sorry.

From: Allie Rainsbury

Did you not have fun on Thursday? Why didn't you just say and I'd at least have had the weekend to recover.

From: David Marshall

That's not it! Look, I really do have to go - we'll chat later, OK?

From: Allie Rainsbury

Fine. If you want to.

From: David Marshall

You can send me your resolution list in the meantime ☺

From: Allie Rainsbury

No, that's OK. I feel foolish enough already thanks.

From: David Marshall

Don't sulk :P

From: Julie Lawson
To: Allie Rainsbury

Are you feeling any better? I could hardly understand you between all the sobs.

From: Allie Rainsbury

Sorry. The last thing you needed was a hysterical phone call from me when you've got your hands full with Elly. And I didn't even ask how she's doing.

From: Julie Lawson

You did too! I told you, she's working her way through her Disney collection and has a bit of colour back today.

She'll be good enough for school tomorrow, or Thursday at a push (since she has me round her little finger).

From: Allie Rainsbury

Oh, OK. I must have been on autopilot. Good, I'm glad she's doing a bit better.

From: Julie Lawson

You weren't even listening to me? Unforgivable! ☺

So you're OK now?

From: Allie Rainsbury

Yes, thanks. I feel a bit silly but I'm fine. I've only been on one date for goodness' sake so I shouldn't even be upset. I was just... excited, I suppose, for the first time in a while.

From: Julie Lawson

Well, still be excited. You don't know what might happen.

From: Allie Rainsbury

I do. But that's fine. I'm really fine about it. He was never going to be interested in me anyway.

From: Julie Lawson

Hey, enough of that self-pitying rubbish. I'm not allowing that. He's not 'not interested'. You don't know, so don't waste time guessing.

In fact, don't waste time on him until you do!

From: Allie Rainsbury

I just think he'd have said if he'd wanted something. And he didn't. Wouldn't you have said something if you were keen?

From: Julie Lawson

Oh no, no, no, this is not a subject that's up for debate, sorry. There is only one thing that we should currently be discussing. Everything else should be fading into insignificance for you right now.

From: Allie Rainsbury

?

From: Julie Lawson

Isn't it your cookery class this evening? The one Chris got you for Christmas?

From: Allie Rainsbury

Oh BALLS! No, I'm cancelling. I don't feel like it and I'm not in the mood to be told that there's yet another thing that I'm horribly inept at.

From: Julie Lawson

Stop wallowing. You're getting no sympathy.

From: Allie Rainsbury

I'm not going.

From: Julie Lawson

If you don't go, it means I need to march round to yours and drag you there myself. Which, since George is taking Cale to football practice, means that I'll need to bring Elly along. This will no doubt set back her recovery.

So either go and enjoy it and learn something new, or don't and make a sick child even sicker.

From: Allie Rainsbury

I hate you.

From: Julie Lawson

I know ☺

Wednesday

From: Julie Lawson
To: Allie Rainsbury

So, does Delia Smith have a new rival?

From: Allie Rainsbury

Ha! She doesn't, but it was fun. How's the patient?

From: Julie Lawson

Better by the minute, thanks. The cheeky little devil could have gone in this morning, but gave me such a doe-eyed look and put so much effort into her cough that I decided one more day couldn't hurt.

What did you learn?

From: Allie Rainsbury

Ah. And you always thought she took after George :P

We learnt how to fillet a fish. There were only seven of us there (three couples and me, but did I let that bother me? No, hardly at all) so it made it easier for the teacher to show us what we were doing, and what we were doing wrong. You'll be proud to know that one person cut their thumb open, and that person was not me ☺

From: Julie Lawson

Truly, you have conquered the culinary world.

From: Allie Rainsbury

I know! I don't really understand what all the fuss is about. Cooking's easy. Although, my fish did look like mash by the end of my filleting. And I couldn't honestly tell you what type of fish it was. But I did it and that's the main thing.

Time to move on to resolution number two.

From: Julie Lawson

As in, that's it? You're done cooking?

From: Allie Rainsbury

I think so, yes. It was fun, but I don't think it would hold my interest for very long.

From: Julie Lawson

So your future dinner parties are going to consist of mashed fish?

From: Allie Rainsbury

If you're lucky enough to receive an invitation :P

From: Julie Lawson

And it had nothing to do with the fact that there were three couples and you?

From: Allie Rainsbury

That has nothing to do with it.

From: Julie Lawson

No bearing on the situation at all?

From: Allie Rainsbury

No, not even slightly! Although, in all honesty, it didn't help.

From: Julie Lawson

There's my girl ☺

Thursday

From: Allie Rainsbury
To: Julie Lawson

Find your way in OK?

From: Julie Lawson

I've spent the last half hour trying to remember where my desk was, but everything's starting to come back.

From: Allie Rainsbury

Well, we're all immensely proud of you for dropping by :P

From: Julie Lawson

Ha! I do too much, I know.

Busy day ahead?

From: Allie Rainsbury

So-so. A couple of internal meetings and then a customer meeting out of the office tomorrow.

Presumably you have a few work emails to sift through?

From: Julie Lawson

A few hundred, yep :S

I imagine that for once you're pleased to have a few meetings.

From: Allie Rainsbury

So I can resist emailing you-know-who? Yes, I guess that's true. I've been very good though, I haven't contacted him at all this week.

From: Julie Lawson

Not at all?

From: Allie Rainsbury

No, honestly, not once. Although he hasn't contacted me either, so I suppose it's not that difficult.

From: Julie Lawson

Hey, you keep that morale up. I was chatting with George last night and he mentioned that his colleague has a friend who might be single.

From: Allie Rainsbury

Hmm. As magical as that sounds, I'm a no thanks! I've been on two dates this year and I'm already dated out.

From: Julie Lawson

Maybe you're right; see how things go for a bit. I'm sure this guy will keep anyway. To be honest, he sounded a bit of a loser.

From: Allie Rainsbury

And yet you still thought of me? You're too sweet sometimes.

From: Julie Lawson

☺ Onto the email trail I go! See you Sunday if not before x

From: Allie Rainsbury

Sunday?

From: Julie Lawson

Cale's first football match. Lunch after (bring your own fish).

From: Allie Rainsbury

Let's hope he shoots as well with his feet as you do with your mouth :P x

From: Julie Lawson

☺ x

Friday

From: Scott Cooper
To: Allie Rainsbury

Hi Allison,

I'm organising catch ups with every Account Manager and Marketing Manager over the next two weeks to run through the current sign-off procedure that exists across customer invoices. In particular I'm conscious that there needs to be greater visibility, allowing an ultimately smoother sign-off process and ensuring that customers get paid as efficiently as possible. This will also negate the duplication of POs across Sales and Marketing which at the moment is causing a lot of confusion internally.

Please can you spend some time next week reviewing what trade marketing payments you have outstanding for the first quarter, along with a complete breakdown of all payments made (and owed) across your account base for the last full financial year. It would be great if we could release some of our accruals.

I'll ask my assistant Holly to schedule in a meeting for us.

Regards, Scott.

From: Chris Trail
To: Allie Rainsbury

Hey Raspbury! it's Friiiiiday! You up to much this weekend? I'm wanting to do something fun but am at a loss. Promise there won't be any museums involved ☺ Let me know your thoughts or drop me a text. Maybe a few cheeky drinks down at The Boathouse on Saturday?

From: Ann Rainsbury
To: Allie Rainsbury

Hello darling,

I hope your week has gone well and they're not working you to the bone over there. It did all sound terribly busy from what you were telling us at Christmas. I do wonder sometimes if you should come back to the country where life seems more... gentle? Is that the word I mean? Anyway, your father says I worry too much. I'm sure I do; but then, that's what mothers are for so don't get cross please ☺

Very little news here. I think your father wrote to you the other day, so I shan't repeat his rant about the weather and the garden. But you know how precious he gets about his flower beds and his cabbage (or the vegetable plot as he calls it), so I think he's slightly despondent at the moment.

We have Mike's birthday this weekend, which I'm not really looking forward to, but etiquette dictates that we must pop in I suppose. I could do with you there to giggle with – I fear it might all be rather austere, as they are slightly snobbish and more than slightly tedious!

What else? I met up with my girlfriends and we had our usual annual brainstorm over what charity we could support this year. As usual we decided to delay the decision on the charity but agreed to support whichever one we finally do decide upon by hosting another summer village fête. It does always seem to raise money.

I have been watching far too much television. I suppose that's the danger when there are thousands of channels and it's cold, dark and raining outside!

That's really all I have for now – sorry it's so boring. Do call if you get the chance. I don't imagine we'll see you this weekend, but I hope it won't be long.

Don't work too hard or too late. All my love, Mum xx

From: David Marshall
To: Allie Rainsbury

Hello, stranger...

CHAPTER 5

Monday 31 January

From: Allie Rainsbury
To: Julie Lawson

Has George seen the funny side yet?

From: Julie Lawson

Hmm. He certainly saw the angry side of me when we got home! Men, honestly.

From: Allie Rainsbury

What did you say?

From: Julie Lawson

I told him I thought he was pathetic. Showing disappointment in his five-year-old son's footballing ability? Really!

From: Allie Rainsbury

I thought Cale played well. Although I must admit, I didn't really know what was going on. It was very sweet though seeing all those little lads taking it so seriously.

From: Julie Lawson

Not, it appears, as seriously as the parents were taking it. And what's the poor boy to think when his father says, 'I'd say well played, but I wasn't raised a liar'?

From: Allie Rainsbury

George said that? Aw, that's mean. Although, in fairness, I thought it was worse when the other team's parents applauded. If I'd been Cale, that would have confused me too.

From: Julie Lawson

Exactly! No wonder he shot at the wrong goal! Anyway, thanks for coming (even if you were a bit worse for wear :P)

From: Allie Rainsbury

Don't remind me, I'm still suffering. I'm going to keep my head down today and struggle through it.

From: Julie Lawson

So, much the same plan as every Monday morning then?

Any update on the David situation?

From: Allie Rainsbury

No, not really. To quote a wise old woman, 'Men, honestly.'

From: Julie Lawson

You meant wise bold woman clearly.

It's such a shame Chris is gay, isn't it? He'd be perfect for you otherwise.

From: Allie Rainsbury

Chris isn't gay! Monday is too early in the week for a wind-up. We're not getting into that debate again.

From: Julie Lawson

What did he wear on Saturday evening?

From: Allie Rainsbury

He isn't gay! You *know* he's had girlfriends before. You can be elegant and straight, that's allowed!

From: Julie Lawson

So he donned...?

From: Allie Rainsbury

A purple polo neck and red corduroys.

From: Julie Lawson

Have a good day ☺

From: Allie Rainsbury

Go hire a football coach :P x

From: David Marshall
To: Allie Rainsbury

Dear Ms Rainsbury,

Your silence suggests that I've inflicted a wound not to be soon forgotten. Please confirm by first light tomorrow and I shall forebear from contacting you in future.

Yours faithfully,

Mr David Marshall.

Tuesday

From: Allie Rainsbury
To: David Marshall

No wound inflicted. I've just been busy as well.

From: David Marshall

OK. Are you too busy now for a canteen coffee?

From: Allie Rainsbury

Now's not a good time I'm afraid.

From: David Marshall

You're definitely cross with me.

From: Allie Rainsbury

No, I'm not in a position to be cross with you. We don't know each other well enough for that.

From: David Marshall

Maybe just mildly annoyed then :P

From: Allie Rainsbury

Why do you even want to go for a coffee, David?

From: David Marshall

I want to explain why I was so distant last week.

From: Allie Rainsbury

So explain.

From: David Marshall

Over email?

From: Allie Rainsbury

...

From: David Marshall

OK, over email then. And hopefully I can convey this with the right emotion...

The thing is, I like you. I think.

From: Allie Rainsbury

I'm blown away, David.

From: David Marshall

Hey! You're the one who said email! ☺

I think I might like you a lot. But when my marriage failed... I got really hurt, let's put it that way. No doubt a psychoanalyst would have a field day with me, but the upshot is that I'm very cautious now when it comes to starting something new.

I worry about moving too far too fast; probably because I did just that, got married and it all fell apart. I suppose, after having so much fun with you on Thursday, that my instinctive reaction was to back off as a result. That probably makes no sense to you, and I understand if you want nothing to do with me but at least I can give you an insight into where I'm coming from.

From: Allie Rainsbury
To: David Marshall

OK, I've had a bit of time to digest that email. Why didn't you just say that's how you felt? I totally understand; it's not like I haven't been hurt before and anyway, we're far away from jumping into anything serious (or anything at all yet).

I think I could really like you too; but I know that it will be a while before we know that for sure – if it ever gets to that stage. How about we cross that bridge when and if we come to it?

From: David Marshall

That sounds like a plan.

I'm sorry, I should have said something straight away. But I didn't want to disappoint you by saying I could offer you something that I can't.

From: Allie Rainsbury

Well I appreciate your honesty. So, just to clarify:

We both like each other

We both want to see where this might lead

We're both keen to go slow and not jump into anything

From: David Marshall

Apart from a bed maybe ;) Yep, that sounds about right!

From: Allie Rainsbury

!!

From: David Marshall

Apologies, that was far too forward!

From: Allie Rainsbury

Can a girl ask for dinner first? ☺

From: David Marshall

What are you doing after work this Thursday?

From: Allie Rainsbury

I'm free.

From: David Marshall

Fancy a second try? Now that the strange behaviour has been accounted for? ☺

From: Allie Rainsbury

It's in the diary x

Wednesday

From: Allie Rainsbury
To: Julie Lawson

Where were you last night?

From: Julie Lawson

Out visiting the in-laws. I'm shattered. What's up?

From: Allie Rainsbury

Balls! That reminds me – I need to reply to my parents, I completely forgot.

Ask me why I'm so happy!

From: Julie Lawson

Not because you need to reply to your parents, surely?

From: Allie Rainsbury

Ha. No. I really do need to do that today though. Are George's parents well?

From: Julie Lawson

They're fine. His mother cooked her speciality: overdone chicken and underdone vegetables for main course, tasteless apple sponge for dessert.

From: Allie Rainsbury

Wow. You're such a bitch ☺

From: Julie Lawson

Any woman who's able to buy my children's affections with boiled sweets has to be my enemy. It's practically law.

Now, you were about to tell me why you were so happy.

From: Allie Rainsbury

Date. Two. Number. David. With. Rearrange the words.

From: Julie Lawson

That's amazing news! When did this happen? I can't believe you've been chatting to him on the sly and not telling me!

From: Allie Rainsbury

I know! How exciting! It only happened yesterday, I haven't spoken to him apart from that. I followed your advice and resisted all temptation to get in touch.

A second date and your advice worked! Two miracles at once ☺

From: Julie Lawson

Ha, ha. When is it? Where is it?

From: Allie Rainsbury

Tomorrow. I'm not sure where.

He said he thinks he might really like me! ☺

From: Julie Lawson

Ah, I'm so happy for you! And excited too. If ever news called for a celebratory cup of tea, this is it.

From: Allie Rainsbury

Ha! Go make your morning brew – sorry to make you wait for it, I just had to tell you.

From: Julie Lawson

I want more details later. But after tea, please. After a strong cup of tea ☺

Hey Mum, hey Dad,

How was the party last weekend? Hope you had a good time. Sorry I wasn't able to make it. London life is fine, just busy as always (although, having said that, I don't really have much news).

Work's good (Mum, stop worrying). We're bringing out a book about gardening in March, which made me think of you, Dad – I'll try and grab a copy and bring it up with me next time (it's more a forestry book really, but there might be some tips you could use).

I'll call you this weekend and we can catch up properly. And I'll schedule in a visit soon I promise.

Love, Allie xx

Thursday

From: David Marshall
To: Allie Rainsbury

Shall we keep it less formal this time and go for a drink in Putney?

From: Allie Rainsbury

Lovely. You're based further up north though, aren't you? Are you sure that's OK?

From: David Marshall

I'm sure. But perhaps I should leave the bar choosing to the local resident.

From: Allie Rainsbury

Done! We can go to a little pub called the Duke's Head on the Lower Richmond Road.

From: David Marshall

It sounds very quaint and no less appealing. Is it by the river perchance? ☺

From: Allie Rainsbury

It is and it is. You'll love it. ☺

From: David Marshall

I have no doubt. Shall we meet at Putney Bridge and walk along from there?

From: Allie Rainsbury

7 p.m., see you there x

From: Allie Rainsbury
To: Julie Lawson

Hey, how's your day going?

From: Julie Lawson

In a word, ugh. My boss has just called us into her office and given everyone a talking to for not following up anything from that course the other week. She's expecting us to detail our initial thoughts by the end of the week along with ideas for integration. I thought the course *was* the idea session. Now we have to think of further things too? I zoned out for the whole last day of it and all I remember now from the first four was that the facilitator had an irritatingly high-pitched voice.

From: Allie Rainsbury

So, you've had better then? ☺

Can you not discuss it with other people who attended as well, and send something in jointly?

From: Julie Lawson

Hmm, piggy-back on the listening skills of colleagues... Interesting! It's certainly worth a try.

How are you?

From: Allie Rainsbury

Nervous again. But excited!

From: Julie Lawson

OF COURSE. I forgot entirely! What on earth is happening to me? I almost prioritised work there for a minute :P

Where are you going to go?

From: Allie Rainsbury

A pub in Putney.

From: Julie Lawson

Ooh, is he going to stay over?

From: Allie Rainsbury

No! Well… No! I don't think so. I'm not the sort of girl who'd let that happen after just two dates!

From: Julie Lawson

Ha. With him, I reckon you're the sort of girl who would let that happen after just two drinks, let alone two dates ;)

Which pub are you going to? Perhaps George and I can come along and keep you company…

From: Allie Rainsbury

You stay away! No way I'm telling you and no way you're coming to spy on us.

From: Julie Lawson

Hmm… The Duke's Head?

From: Allie Rainsbury

Go get on with your work! No, not there – I wouldn't be that obvious.

From: Julie Lawson

It is, isn't it? I know you far too well!

Hmm… What to wear? ☺

From: Allie Rainsbury

Julie, don't you even dare. I mean it!

From: Julie Lawson

He he. I'll leave you be, don't worry! It would be fun to see though.

From: Allie Rainsbury

I'll be nervous enough without you and George giggling away in the corner.

From: Julie Lawson

☺ Fine! Good luck then, kiddo. Details tomorrow. If you make it in on time :P

From: Allie Rainsbury

Put your imagination to better use in the meantime and go think up some ideas for your project!

Till tomorrow x

Friday

From: Julie Lawson
To: Allie Rainsbury

So, what does he think of your flat?

From: Allie Rainsbury

I wouldn't know, he hasn't seen it.

From: Julie Lawson

What happened? Didn't it all go well?

From: Allie Rainsbury

I love how you think that him not staying over is suggestive of the evening being a wash-out.

It was a fun night and I think we both enjoyed ourselves (although since I've said that before I'm trying to be slightly more cautious this time around).

From: Julie Lawson

So...?

From: Allie Rainsbury

So, we just talked. We went to the Duke's Head (I half-expected to see you there anyway :P) and chatted over a bottle of wine. He told me a bit more about how his job is going so far and what he's finding frustrating. We talked more about his hobbies and what they all involve. He really does seem very active, which is a good thing, if slightly daunting.

Then we spoke a bit about my dreams, my family and friends (yes, your name was mentioned!). A lot of topics that we'd spoken briefly about before really, but started to detail more thoroughly this time. Conversation just seemed to flow very easily again. Then he caught the last train home.

From: Julie Lawson

And was there a kiss this time?

From: Allie Rainsbury

That's personal information ☺

From: Julie Lawson

So personally tell me!

From: Allie Rainsbury

There might have been a little kiss.

From: Julie Lawson

I KNEW IT. How was it?! Is he a good kisser? Were there tongues involved? :P

From: Allie Rainsbury

I'm not telling you that! Suffice to say that I was very happy with it ☺

From: Julie Lawson

There were tongues! Amazing. Were you not tempted to invite him in?

From: Allie Rainsbury

Hush. I'm telling you no further details. It was a lovely kiss, that's all you need to know :P

From: Julie Lawson

Hmph. Fine. I'll get details out of you later.

You were tempted!

From: Allie Rainsbury

So much so! Chat later ☺

From: David Marshall
To: Allie Rainsbury

Thanks again for yesterday, I had a really good time ;)

From: Allie Rainsbury

You're very welcome! I did too. Maybe we should do it again sometime?

From: David Marshall

Definitely. Have a good weekend and we'll chat next week.

From: Allie Rainsbury

Busy today then?

From: David Marshall

Busy every day. I'm terribly important, didn't I say that last night? ☺

From: Allie Rainsbury

I suppose you did manage to convey how special you are :P

Fine, I'll leave you to it today then. Maybe catch up next week?

From: David Marshall

Sounds good. Enjoy x

From: Allie Rainsbury

OK. Maybe later in the week then, if you're free.

Enjoy yourself too, hope you have a lovely weekend x

Ps. I've just had a flashback to last night – standing in front of my front door as you leaned towards me. It sent a shiver down my spine x

CHAPTER 6

Monday 7 February

From: Julie Lawson
To: Allie Rainsbury

Are you cross with me?

From: Allie Rainsbury

Furious :P

From: Julie Lawson

Thanks! And I'm sorry, I was just a bit shocked (and still am).

From: Allie Rainsbury

That's because you're sooo innocent.

From: Julie Lawson

Hmm, we both know that's not true. But does it not change things slightly?

From: Allie Rainsbury

The fact that he's been married? The fact that (shock, horror!) he's led a life before he met me? I don't see that it's a big deal. And I don't really see what it changes either.

From: Julie Lawson

Well, who is she for a start? What happened? You hung up in such a huff yesterday I didn't even get the chance to ask you anything.

From: Allie Rainsbury

That's because you started doing a passable impression of an army interrogator.

From: Julie Lawson

I'm sorry! I was surprised, that's all. But I have a calming cup of tea in front of me and no meetings until this afternoon, so I'm in a much more sedate state of mind to digest things now.

From: Allie Rainsbury

I don't know much about her. He doesn't like to talk too much about it and I don't like to ask. From what he has said, they met at University and had been dating for six months before they graduated. They both applied for jobs in London but she didn't get the one she wanted and was set to take a job in Manchester instead. David thought that if they were living in different cities then they wouldn't survive so he proposed.

His parents thought he was nuts. It turned out they were right. David was married to her for just over a year and when the split did come it wasn't particularly amicable. That was twelve years ago.

From: Julie Lawson

Is he still in touch with her?

From: Allie Rainsbury

I don't think so, no.

From: Julie Lawson

Where is she now?

From: Allie Rainsbury

I've no idea, and anyway it's completely irrelevant! If it was twelve months ago, maybe, but it was another lifetime. I think you're fixating way too much on this!

From: Julie Lawson

I suppose so.

Just looking out for you that's all ☺

From: Allie Rainsbury

He was married. He got divorced. That's that! What about all the girls he's no doubt dated since then?

From: Julie Lawson

OK. Point made. I won't ask any more.

From: Allie Rainsbury

Jules, you really don't need to worry. For one, it was a long time ago. Two, it has nothing to do with me (or, potentially him and me if things progress at all, which they are far from doing).

We're taking things slowly. He's already said that he can only offer that at this stage, which is great! I don't want to jump into something unless I'm sure about it either.

From: Julie Lawson

Why does he want to take things slowly?

From: Allie Rainsbury

Because he was hurt so much by his marriage. I just told you, it wasn't a good break-up. That's obviously going to effect how someone behaves in the future.

From: Julie Lawson

Well, don't bite my head off for this, but for someone who got divorced a 'lifetime' ago, he seems to have her very much front of mind still.

From: Allie Rainsbury

Julie! Not everyone has the perfect little life that you have. It's not fair for you to sit in your little cocoon and pass judgement on things you know nothing about.

From: Julie Lawson

I'm just saying. You've been on a couple of dates with this guy and he's mentioned his ex-wife both times.

From: Allie Rainsbury

So what? It was a major part of his life! A part that I asked him to talk about and, despite the fact he obviously felt uncomfortable doing so, he did. I'm guessing in an effort to be open and honest and decent.

From: Julie Lawson

OK, fine. Let's chat about this another time.

Are you free for lunch later?

From: Allie Rainsbury

No, let's not chat about it later. I'm done chatting about it.

From: Julie Lawson

OK, so no divorce chat. Lunch though? You can advise me on holiday destinations for Easter ☺

From: Allie Rainsbury

No, thanks. Another time maybe.

From: Julie Lawson

Allie, don't be like that! Come on, don't make a meal of this (if you'll pardon the pun :P).

From: Allie Rainsbury

I'm not making a meal of anything. Sorry, I have too much work on. Perhaps later in the week.

From: Julie Lawson

Fine, suit yourself. I give up!

Tuesday

From: David Marshall
To: Allie Rainsbury

How's the week treating you so far?

From: Allie Rainsbury

I've had better really.

From: David Marshall

Hardly a ringing endorsement. What's up?

From: Allie Rainsbury

Oh, it's nothing. I had an argument with Julie yesterday and that's made me a bit sad as we never argue. Plus I didn't sleep particularly well (probably because of that) so now I'm tired as well as sad.

Anyway, none of which I want to bore you with. What's new with you?

From: David Marshall

News is light, work is heavy.

What were you arguing about?

From: Allie Rainsbury

Nothing. Girl stuff. All very silly ☺

You can have the role of cheering me up if you like?

From: David Marshall

Well, I've already had a two-hour meeting this morning with Garry, your boss. Such a charming man and incredibly enlightened. Want to hear the joke he led with today?

From: Allie Rainsbury

Go for it.

From: David Marshall

What do you give a woman who has everything?

Pause.

A man to show her how to work it.

Boom, boom.

From: Allie Rainsbury

How completely appropriate. I bet you all laughed though!

From: David Marshall

Only very awkwardly. There were seven of us in the room, four of them female. He hardly picked his audience.

From: Allie Rainsbury

Oh dear, what a ridiculous little man.

From: David Marshall

Think of the positives. All you need to do is wear a short skirt and you'll be in line for a promotion ☺

From: Allie Rainsbury

Great, exactly why I've worked so hard for the last decade. (And you're dangerously close to joining Garry in the 1950s by the way!)

From: David Marshall

Maybe I was just looking for an excuse to picture you in a short skirt ;)

I have another meeting to go to. Hope I at least partially succeeded on the cheering-up front.

From: Allie Rainsbury

You did, thank you!

Hope the meeting goes well. No imagining me in a tiny skirt ;)

Wednesday

From: David Marshall
To: Allie Rainsbury

Tell me three things I don't yet know about you.

From: Allie Rainsbury

Three secrets, you mean?

From: David Marshall

Exactly!

From: Allie Rainsbury

At a loose end today are we? ☺

From: David Marshall

On a train to Cardiff for a meeting with a potential third-party partner. I was torn between catching up on some sleep and emailing you. You just won out :P

From: Allie Rainsbury

So charming.

How long are you down in Cardiff for? Just the day?

From: David Marshall

And tomorrow too. Back in on Friday, with more meetings to look forward to.

Stop stalling!

From: Allie Rainsbury

I'm not! I was just wondering if we'd get a chance to meet up this week at all?

From: David Marshall

It could be difficult this week. Maybe we can chat a bit at The Firestation on Friday?

From: Allie Rainsbury

Ah, you're being dragged down to our end-of-week drinking club, are you? They get everyone eventually, there's no escape!

From: David Marshall

I foolishly agreed to a quick pint there with my team. I figured it was probably time to socialise slightly.

From: Allie Rainsbury

Uh-huh. You'll be peeled off the floor by closing time I bet. I'll come for a drink though, if everyone's going.

From: David Marshall

Great. Short skirts are allowed ;)

From: Allie Rainsbury

Duly noted.

Do you want to get together next week? (I'm not expecting it to be Valentine's Day, don't worry!)

From: David Marshall

Yes, absolutely. Let me check my diary and come back to you with a day. Monday would have been fine, but I'm already booked in for tennis.

From: Allie Rainsbury

How romantic :P

OK, let me know. I can come further up north this time if you like.

From: David Marshall

Let's see. I did like Putney after all ☺

Are these secrets worth the wait by the way? :P

From: Allie Rainsbury

Definitely not. Here you go – but these stay between us please!

1. I stepped on an upturned nail when I was four and it went right through my foot. I have no memory of it, but my father remembers getting cross that I didn't come out when he called me for dinner. He felt guilty when he found me bleeding in the garden shed. I still have the scar.

2. I used to smoke in my first year at University. I suppose that's not exactly revelatory as lots of students do. I did it to impress a guy that I liked. He smoked all the time and I thought it would give me a good excuse to ask him for a light. Three months later I still hadn't worked up the courage to say anything but was addicted to Marlboro Lights.

3. In my interview for Clowes Press I called my interviewer 'Mum' twice. I was incredibly nervous and couldn't think straight. But I obviously appealed to her maternal nature since I got the job in the end. She is a lovely lady and we laugh about it now (and I cringe less and less each time).

From: David Marshall

Interesting, and funny. Somehow I can completely imagine you doing all of those things. All very innocent secrets though.

From: Allie Rainsbury

Well, I'm a very innocent girl!

From: David Marshall

I think you have a dark side lurking about somewhere.

From: Allie Rainsbury

Ha! You do, do you? I'm saying nothing more until I get three secrets of my own!

From: David Marshall

Not even a little one to keep me company in wet and wintry Wales?

From: Allie Rainsbury

Nope! ☺

From: David Marshall

You're tough. I'll have to have a think.

From: Allie Rainsbury

Think away. You can ponder for the rest of the train journey – the time will fly by! :P

From: David Marshall

You have all the best ideas.

Safe travels, email me later if you can x

Thursday

From: David Marshall
To: Allie Rainsbury

Hi, reception here is terrible! I'm standing in the far right-hand corner of the hotel room to send this. I thought of three secrets last night. Can't imagine why I thought of them as I was lying in bed ;)

1. I saw you before you saw me. On my first day I was taken around the office (by your friend Julie I think) and we went past the external meeting rooms on your floor. You were in one of them, sitting around a table with several other people. From where I was standing, I could just about make out the doodles on your notepad.

2. I knew who you were when I emailed you. I was given a company planogram by my assistant and it had photos of everyone to help jog the memory (it's proved invaluable – I still glance at it most days). Anyway, it may not be your most flattering picture, but I recognised you from that meeting room. I didn't invite every account manager for a coffee.

3. I definitely have a 'type'. I'm drawn to people who aren't particularly self-aware. I think shyness is a very endearing and sexy trait. Brown hair, big eyes, great smile. A bookish Rachel Weisz perhaps.

For your reference ;)

From: Allie Rainsbury

Interesting secrets there. And very devious. I had no idea you'd seen my photo!

I will keep my eyes peeled for your 'type' ;)

From: Julie Lawson
To: Allie Rainsbury

Hello...

From: Allie Rainsbury

Hi.

From: Julie Lawson

It's been such a long week without you to chat to and I feel horrible and guilty and a bit of a bitch as well. Please can I be forgiven?

From: Allie Rainsbury

Do you promise to be a bit less judgemental?

From: Julie Lawson

Yes! No judging at all I promise.

From: Allie Rainsbury

Seriously? Because I have a really good feeling about David and you were being so unfair the other day. I know it was all said with good intentions, but I'm a big girl and I'm not stupid (despite there often being evidence to the contrary).

From: Julie Lawson

I know. You're right. I'm sorry, I was being patronising and utterly molly-coddling! What more can I say?

From: Allie Rainsbury

Fine. Then you're forgiven. But only because you managed to use the word 'molly-coddling' in a serious sentence.

And, I've missed you too, a little bit :P

From: Julie Lawson

Of course you've missed me! How is everything? Do you have time for a coffee in the canteen?

From: Allie Rainsbury

Not really. Meeting in an hour that I haven't prepared for.

From: Julie Lawson

So come for half an hour and prepare after that ☺

From: Allie Rainsbury

You're such a wonderful example to follow :P

See you down there in five minutes.

Friday

From: David Marshall
To: Allie Rainsbury

You know what I hate more than anything?

From: Allie Rainsbury

I have a feeling you'll say...

From: David Marshall

People who talk gibberish. The amount of time that's wasted at work through people constantly feeling the need to spout ridiculous Americanisms and jargon-splattered phrases that mean absolutely nothing.

From: Allie Rainsbury

As opposed to the amount of time wasted at work through emailing co-workers over non-work matters, you mean?

From: David Marshall

Touché :P

Over the course of the past two days I've heard (and these are all verbatim – I took notes):

'Let's get our ducks in a row'

'A cradle-to-grave approach'

'Not enough bandwith' – this wasn't in reference to a computer, I have no idea what it was in reference to

'We're in a sand trap'

Absolutely. Ridiculous.

From: Allie Rainsbury

Good trip?

From: David Marshall

You are not creating a positive energy at the moment (another one!).

I'm glad to be back although no doubt I'll be subjected to more patience-sapping meetings this afternoon. Such is the lot of a marketeer.

Are you OK?

From: Allie Rainsbury

I'm well. Looking forward to the weekend as always. Chris has invited me to go around Portobello Market on Sunday, which should be fun. You're very welcome to join us if you'd like?

From: David Marshall

Your friend Chris who took you to the photography exhibition? Doesn't really sound my thing. Plus I'm busy on Sunday unfortunately.

Those two reasons apart, I'd be there in an instant! ☺

From: Allie Rainsbury

Good reasons both.

So what are you up to then? Any big plans?

From: David Marshall

I'll be in Suffolk with some friends. It has some great countryside for off-road cycling so we'll spend most of the weekend on the bikes.

From: Allie Rainsbury

Wow. Active as ever.

Are you still going for a drink after work today?

From: David Marshall

Yes, although we're driving out of London this evening so I'll just be there for the one.

From: Allie Rainsbury

That's a shame. I was looking forward to seeing how little you thought of the Firestation!

From: David Marshall

Another time. With everyone else around, it would be difficult to chat for too long anyway. Perhaps if we found a quiet corner we could grab a few minutes alone ;)

From: Allie Rainsbury

We can chat with other people about. No one knows I've seen you outside the office or that I've even spoken to you at work for that matter (apart from Julie and she doesn't count).

From: David Marshall

Sure. But better to be safe on these things I always think.

Right, I'm going to crack on with some work, I'll see you in the pub later.

Another one I've just remembered: 'Let's give 110%'. What the hell does that mean? Since when was giving my maximum capacity of 100% not good enough? Now we have to give an impossible percentage commitment and achieve the unachievable. Absurd.

From: Allie Rainsbury

Not sure talking to each other is anything other than polite? Don't see how 'safe' comes into it. Safe from what anyway?

From: David Marshall

I didn't mean it like that, sorry.

From: Allie Rainsbury

It's just an odd thing to say, that's all. Talk later – assuming you feel it's allowed.

CHAPTER 7

Monday 14 February

From: Julie Lawson
To: Allie Rainsbury

Good morning! How was Portobello with gay Chris yesterday? ☺

From: Allie Rainsbury

You sound sprightly considering a whole week is lying right ahead of us.

It was good fun. He bought an extremely heterosexual shirt and I snapped up a silver corkscrew decorated with an angel on top. It's either an angel or a streaker anyway, depending on whether they're wings or an open coat. I think angel is more likely though.

A streaker by the time you've finished the bottle maybe?

My Sunday was mostly spent listening to rather painful and oft repeated recitals of Elly and Cale's musical pieces for their end-of-term play. If they haven't improved in a month's time then I'm volunteering you to go along in my place.

I couldn't possibly deprive you of that ☺

So, come on then – let's get this over with. What did George do this year?

What do you mean? It's not every year.

Every year! And every year I have to listen while trying not to throw up in a corner :P

Ha! Well, I don't have to tell you. But since you asked...

It began with breakfast in bed: scrambled eggs on toast, orange juice and a cup of tea. He insisted that I have a lie in while he got the kids ready for school (I obviously resisted heavily, but eventually relented). By the time I was finally up and coming out of the shower, he'd placed a bouquet of 12 red roses on the bed (cheesy but impossible to beat all the same), along with an envelope. Inside it was a very sweet card with two tickets on the Eurostar to Paris! I have a long weekend to look forward to in three weeks' time!

Which reminds me – are you free to babysit on 4, 5 and 6 March? ☺

Aw, that sounds very romantic. So no dinner out tonight then, and you'll leave it for Paris?

Three days of babysitting? Do you pay well?

Elly has swimming after school today so we thought we'd wait and make a more special night of it in France. Perhaps a little bistro under the Eiffel Tower, perhaps a restaurant near the Champs-Élysées... *Je ne sais pas* ☺

Monetarily the pay is dreadful, however I cannot quite put into words how much it will enrich your character and soul. Plus, they both get so excited when they know their Auntie Allie's coming over.

From: Allie Rainsbury

Oh, that's such low emotional blackmail!

Fine, I'll do it, but if I end up calling one, or all three, emergency services then I don't want to hear any moaning.

From: Julie Lawson

I would almost be disappointed if they weren't put to use.

From: Allie Rainsbury

And copious amounts of red wine is to be brought back.

From: Julie Lawson

Agreed!

So... Have any Valentine's cards appeared for you yet? ☺

From: Allie Rainsbury

No. I don't think they're likely to either. I mentioned it to David last week, but I think we're both agreed that it's too early for all of that. Plus, it's all terribly commercial really.

From: Julie Lawson

Yes, that's true. It is all a bit silly to be honest. A big money spinner for flower shops and card makers.

From: Allie Rainsbury

Definitely. I mean, not to say that George's presents weren't very thoughtful and lovely. But personally I'd be a little freaked out if David did anything like that. We're at a very different stage though, obviously!

From: Julie Lawson

Exactly; it was nice to get them, but it's not something to shout about. Valentine's Day isn't for every couple, irrespective of where you are in a relationship.

Precisely. All in all, it's a considerable relief. I was panicking that I'd turn up to work and see hundreds of flowers on my desk!

From: Julie Lawson

Oh, no! That would have been awful! Lucky you then.

Right, I must get on, I have meetings this morning and now also need to decide whether I'd prefer a hotel in central Paris or further out? Decisions, decisions!

From: Allie Rainsbury
To: David Marshall

Happy Valentine's Day x

Tuesday

From: Scott Cooper
To: Allie Rainsbury

Hi Allison,

Good to meet you briefly on Friday. As mentioned then, I'm still waiting for your PO information and history for any trade marketing payments you've made across the past year.

Please can you get back to me by the end of the week on this. At time of writing you are one of only two account managers to have not already done so.

Regards, Scott.

From: Allie Rainsbury

Hi Scott,

Apologies for the delay. I will send these across to you by Friday.

Thanks, Allie.

From: Allie Rainsbury
To: Julie Lawson

Who's Scott Cooper?

From: Julie Lawson

He's a big cheese. He's the Financial Director, reports to our CEO, so he's on a joint level with the MD. Why?

From: Allie Rainsbury

Bugger.

From: Julie Lawson

What have you done?

From: Allie Rainsbury

Nothing! Really, nothing – actually that's the problem. He emailed me a couple of weeks ago asking for some information on POs and I entirely forgot about it. I've just had a crappy reminder email from him.

From: Julie Lawson

Well, that's retrievable. Just forward him the information and apologise! From what I hear he's a nice guy.

From: Allie Rainsbury

From what I can tell he has his head too far up his own arse.

From: Julie Lawson

Allie Rainsbury! If you do feel the need to mention his arse, you must reference the cuteness of it as well. It's only fair ☺

From: Allie Rainsbury

Aren't you busy booking romantic hotels for you and your husband? :P

From: Julie Lawson

Hotels always get trumped by butt perving!

From: Allie Rainsbury

Hmm, cute behind or not (!) I went to the Firestation on Friday for a drink and was introduced to him by Erica from finance. I just assumed he was another analyst. He is, admittedly, rather incredible to look at. However, that's only before he starts talking. He said very little, nothing of note and seemed incredibly awkward the whole time. He was just plain boring, utterly distant and, I thought, rather rude.

What made it all the worse was seeing David over his shoulder being the life and soul of the party. My wits were being so dulled that I couldn't think of a single reason to excuse myself and move away. By the time I did escape David had left.

So Scott Cooper can take his butt and he can toddle off!

Plus, I don't have any of the information he wants because I haven't kept any records.

From: Julie Lawson

Ah. And there in lies the real reason you're annoyed.

From: Allie Rainsbury

No! Well, yes, OK, I suppose a bit... I don't have any PO numbers! I just sent them over to the customer and forgot about them. I thought that's what everyone did. What should I do?

From: Julie Lawson

I'm not really the person to be asking. But don't worry – nothing's ever as bad as it seems. I reckon just go see him and explain the situation.

From: Allie Rainsbury

The truth never works in situations like this. I should know, I've been in them before.

I should have thought of a decent excuse before saying I'd get them to him on Friday. Lesson learnt for next time!

From: Julie Lawson

May I venture to gently suggest that the lesson to learn should revolve more around the matter of keeping POs filed?

From: Allie Rainsbury

That's just useless, sensible talk. Now hush whilst I think how to best get out of this!

Wednesday

From: David Marshall
To: Allie Rainsbury

You're not the most observant.

From: Allie Rainsbury

What does that mean?

Happy Valentine's Day to you again by the way. I wasn't expecting a card, but a response would have been nice.

From: David Marshall

You weren't expecting a card? Well then, I'm as inappropriate as you are unobservant ☺

From: Allie Rainsbury

Are you talking in code? You've lost me completely.

From: David Marshall

Look in your desk drawer.

From: Allie Rainsbury

When did you put that in there? It's such a cute card, thank you!! Signed by '?' Hmm, I wonder who it could be? ☺

From: David Marshall

I'll ask around and see what I can find out ☺

Are you around tomorrow evening? I was thinking I could come down to Putney again. We can either go to the Duke's Head (yes, I've been won over by it already) or somewhere else if you'd rather.

From: Allie Rainsbury

Yes, come down! Let's play it by ear, maybe we can start at the Duke's and move on elsewhere. Unless you'll be in a hurry to get off...

From: David Marshall

No, tomorrow I'm all yours ;)

From: Allie Rainsbury

So I can do with you whatever I please?

From: David Marshall

Whatever you desire.

From: Allie Rainsbury

That sounds like the best Valentine's present ever! ;)

From: David Marshall

Glad you approve ☺ See you tomorrow.

From: Allie Rainsbury
To: Julie Lawson

Valentine's Day is officially amazing!

From: Julie Lawson

Because you get to spend three days looking after my kids as a result?

From: Allie Rainsbury

Ha! Of course not :P

I did get a card after all. David had put it in my desk drawer!

From: Julie Lawson

Ooh, what did it say?

From: Allie Rainsbury

I can't tell you that! Well, I shouldn't.

But OK, just between us, it says, 'I can't bear-lieve it – somebody wants to be your Valentine!' There's a picture of a bear holding a heart-shaped balloon and he signed the card with a question mark and two kisses. TWO kisses!

From: Julie Lawson

How clever...

Aw, I'm so pleased for you! Are you seeing him soon?

From: Allie Rainsbury

Tomorrow evening, in Putney. And no, you can't come.

From: Julie Lawson

But it might be fun to have a double date! It could take some of the pressure off.

From: Allie Rainsbury

No way! This evening is going to be all mine. Plus, after careful consideration, I have decided that sexy lingerie shall be worn this time. I'm pulling out all the stops.

Well, that sounds determined. And shall sexy lingerie be seen? ;)

From: Allie Rainsbury

Only if I can possibly help it ☺

Thursday

From: Ann Rainsbury
To: Allie Rainsbury

Hi darling,

I was just talking with your father and he mentioned that he thought you were visiting this weekend. I can't remember if that's what you said when we last talked, so thought I'd check first before putting fresh sheets out.

It would be lovely to see you if so, but we do understand that you don't have much spare time these days – no doubt the last thing you'd want to do is spend it with your silly old parents.

We are going into Witney this afternoon to have a stroll around the shops. The sun is out for once and I feel like stretching my legs. I've been feeling terribly stiff recently – no doubt a by-product of the cold winter weather. I'm so looking forward to the summer months.

Your father wants to visit Brittany around June. He has suggested going back to the farm we used to stay at when you were young. Do you remember? It's where that boy took a shine to you and I had to have a word with his parents. He was far too forward for a ten-year-old! Even if he was French.

I'm not so sure it will be the same now. I've suggested America instead, especially since I suspect that, more than any trip down memory lane, what he really wants to do is play the local golf courses. We shall see. Perhaps you could come along too if we do go? That French boy would be all grown up by now!

Anyway, must go and wrap up for the outside world. Hopefully see you this weekend.

Lots of love, Mum xx

From: Julie Lawson
To: Allie Rainsbury

I know I speak for both of us – in all probability I speak for every woman in the office – when I say 'Eeeeekkkk!'

From: Allie Rainsbury

Stop it! I'm more nervous now than I was yesterday. I can't really think about anything else.

From: Julie Lawson

Skimpy underwear on? :P

From: Allie Rainsbury

Not yet, no. I'll change in the toilets after work.

From: Julie Lawson

Classy ☺ Anything I can do?

From: Allie Rainsbury

No, I don't think so. I just need to remember to... Wait! What must I remember to do? I've completely forgotten. I gave myself a pep talk last night and definitely had to remember something!

From: Julie Lawson

Remember to calm down? Remember to be yourself?

From: Allie Rainsbury

Jules, that's the one thing I don't need to remember! This evening I will be a far more glamorous, sophisticated me than myself.

From: Julie Lawson

Offer to split the bill? Remember to laugh at his jokes?

From: Allie Rainsbury

No, no!

From: Julie Lawson

Remember not to choke on a cocktail olive as you try to seductively roll it around your mouth?

From: Allie Rainsbury

No! I'm just going to have to forget about it, aren't I? Hopefully it wasn't too important.

From: Julie Lawson

Remember to get drunk and invite him back to yours?

From: Allie Rainsbury

No, that still wasn't it. Although in lieu of anything else I suppose I'll have to use that instead.

Thanks!

From: Julie Lawson

☺ Good luck, gorgeous!

From: David Marshall
To: Allie Rainsbury

Hey, I'm going to leave in a few minutes, so I'll see you at Putney Bridge, OK?

From: Allie Rainsbury

OK. I've decided that we'll go to the Boathouse this time. It's on the Wandsworth side, only a few hundred metres up the road from the Duke's Head (so we can head there if we start to miss that place too much).

From: David Marshall

Perfect.

Friday

From: Allie Rainsbury
To: Julie Lawson

I think I might have a boyfriend. I think I might just have the most jaw-droppingly beautiful, incredibly talented, successful, outdoor-sports-going boyfriend! ☺

From: Julie Lawson

He said that? You're officially an item now? So much for taking things slowly!

From: Allie Rainsbury

Well, we're not officially a couple, no. Obviously we don't want anyone at work to know. And he's still cautious about moving too quickly. But we exchanged mobile numbers and I think we'll be arranging another meeting pretty soon ☺

From: Julie Lawson

You didn't have his mobile number already?

From: Allie Rainsbury

No! We've spent so much time emailing each other over the past few weeks that we didn't think to.

From: Julie Lawson

Well, nothing says love like an email :P

Did he stay over?

From: Allie Rainsbury

You really are terribly nosey, aren't you?

From: Julie Lawson

Did he?!

From: Allie Rainsbury

He did ☺

From: Julie Lawson

And? Any details you'd like to share? Was he good in bed? ☺ I bet he was! He looks as if he would be.

From: Allie Rainsbury

Hey! Stop thinking about my maybe-boyfriend in bed please.

He was amazing. No more details :P

From: Julie Lawson

What? Amazing! How was he amazing?

From: Allie Rainsbury

He was tender and attentive. He made me feel very special.

From: Julie Lawson

And he had the stamina to last all night long, didn't he?

From: Allie Rainsbury

Sorry, my lips are firmly sealed.

From: Julie Lawson

Unlike last night I bet. That's not fair, I want more details! Lunch later, and tell me more then?

From: Allie Rainsbury

You're so rude! Lunch sounds good. See you there x

From: Allie Rainsbury
To: David Marshall

Just to say thank you again for last night. It really was an incredible evening. I had so much fun (both inside and outside the bed ;)).

Shall I call you over the weekend? It would be nice to have a chat and maybe arrange another date for next week if you're free?

I hope you have a lovely weekend. Be careful with your biking, don't go too fast (unless that's the point of it in which case go very fast, but safely) xx

----

From: Scott Cooper
To: Allie Rainsbury

Allison, how are you coming with those POs?

Scott.

CHAPTER 8

Monday 21 February

From: Allie Rainsbury
To: David Marshall

Hi, how was your weekend?

Hopefully Hampshire wasn't as rainy as London otherwise I don't see how you could possibly cycle bikes down a hillside without slipping off. Since all bruises will be kissed better though, maybe I'm secretly hoping you've got one or two!

I left you a message on your phone on Saturday – did you get it? It probably didn't make an awful lot of sense – I think I may have babbled since I didn't really have much news.

My Saturday mostly consisted of a bubble bath (which was where I called you from, in case you are interested ;)) and curling up on the sofa reading a murder mystery set on the Isle of Wight. It wasn't great, but it was a good page-turner. After that I opened a bottle of wine and watched the new series of *Masterchef* which very nearly inspired me to cook dinner. But in the end I ordered butterfly prawns and Singapore noodles from my local Chinese (which you should try – if you like Oriental food, you'll love them).

On Sunday I tidied the flat and put on a couple of washes – all very boring! But, since I washed the bed sheets, I've now lost all traces of you being there. Perhaps you should come back again soon to remedy this? ☺ In the afternoon I went for a walk to Richmond Park. Well, actually, I didn't quite make it that far, the park was further away than I realised. I suppose that slightly ruined things, but it was good to get some air all the same. Next time I'll get the bus first. We should go there one day (if you haven't been before). There are wild deer and wild boar running around and it's all very picturesque. There are definitely deer anyway – I'm not sure about the boar come to think of it. But it's terribly pretty either way.

So, that was my weekend. When did you get back? Do you have a busy week ahead? I'm free on Wednesday, Thursday and Friday (and this weekend too) if you're around. Tuesday's the only day I can't do; Chris is taking me out for a jog, which should be interesting (although I could probably cancel if you wanted).

Chat later xx

From: Allie Rainsbury
To: Ann Rainsbury

Hi Mum,

Thanks for calling on Sunday. I'm sorry I didn't get in touch earlier to let you know I couldn't make it up this weekend. Why don't I come visit on 12 March? I've checked my diary and that's the first date I'm free. Perhaps we could go out for lunch?

You never told me how your holiday plans are progressing? (I think because you were slightly annoyed at me for not calling before. Now I've got my apologies in though, maybe you can let me know more? ☺) I think you should keep on at Dad over America. Do you know where exactly you'd like to go?

Anyway, I have another busy week ahead so I should go and get on with publishing another best-seller! I'll call you this week, I promise, and try to drop you another note too.

Send my love to Dad, and love to you,

Allie xx

From: Allie Rainsbury
To: Scott Cooper

Hi Scott,

Apologies (again) for the delay here. I've looked diligently through my filing system for all records of purchase order history, however I cannot find any trace of them.

Having spoken with our IT department, they reminded me that the server went down in December for a day, which actually meant everyone had the day off and, from a Christmas shopping perspective, helped me out hugely. But that, unfortunately, was the only good that came out of it, as several files seem to have been lost or deleted in the process including the one that stored all my financial data.

I'm not sure what else to do now as I've spent several hours trying to find this information but, disastrously, to no avail.

I hope that when we meet again it will be under happier circumstances.

Best of luck with your project, Allie

From: Allie Rainsbury
To: David Marshall

Are you in meetings all day today?

From: Scott Cooper
To: Allie Rainsbury

Allison,

Disastrously we will have to meet under difficult circumstances as this can't just be left.

If the file's gone, it's gone. However we might be able to pull the relevant information from our own financial SAP system. We will need your help in validating it though.

I will send a meeting request through for early next week. Please accept, irrespective of shopping plans.

Regards, Scott.

From: Allie Rainsbury
To: Julie Lawson

I hate Mondays.

Tuesday

From: David Marshall
To: Allie Rainsbury

Yep, in meetings – back and forth for most of this week. Not sure whether it's reflective of me or this company that, two months into the role, I already need a holiday.

From: Allie Rainsbury

During the evenings as well? They're working you hard!

I could really do with a holiday too. I didn't go abroad at all last year, unless you count Jersey, and I don't really think you can.

From: David Marshall

I'll definitely have to work late most evenings, yes. We're way behind the pace on trade presentations – I'm surprised you haven't been chasing me for them yourself!

From: Allie Rainsbury

I've been too busy chasing you for other things ;)

From: David Marshall

True.

OK, I've got to go, sorry. Emails are becoming an insurmountable problem. I wouldn't mind but most of them are utterly unnecessary.

From: Allie Rainsbury

OK. Should I stop emailing you for a while then?

From: David Marshall

No, sorry – not referring to you, obviously! Yours are crucial ☺

From: Allie Rainsbury

Glad to hear it!

I might give you a call later.

From: David Marshall

Sure. Apologies in advance if I don't answer. I generally switch my phone off in the evening so I can concentrate on actually getting some work done. We'll chat very soon though, OK?

From: Julie Lawson
To: Allie Rainsbury

Sorry, I was out for most of yesterday afternoon so didn't pick up my emails until this morning. Why did you hate Monday so much?

From: Allie Rainsbury

Tuesday isn't much better ☹

From: Julie Lawson

Oh dear, you don't sound very happy. What's up?

From: Allie Rainsbury

Ah, nothing. Just very busy. Everything's getting a bit on top of me, that's all. Thank you for being concerned though.

From: Julie Lawson

Of course! I'm always worried if you're down. Why is work so busy? Do you want to come around this evening for dinner?

From: Allie Rainsbury

I'd love to, but I can't tonight – I promised Chris I'd go jogging with him. Can you rain check the offer and I'll come over tomorrow?

From: Julie Lawson

What? You're going jogging?

Ha, ha, ha! You don't jog!

From: Allie Rainsbury

Stop that laughter! I do jog, I've just chosen not to for a while. I need to get fitter and more active. And if I don't go now, I know I'll just end up postponing it for another twelve months.

From: Julie Lawson

Uh-huh. And this new-found fondness for exercise has just coincidentally reared its head with the appearance of a tall, dark, handsome man on the scene…

From: Allie Rainsbury

David has nothing to do with it. It was a belated New Year's resolution. No more, no less.

From: Julie Lawson

You make me laugh! You do realise it's raining outside, don't you? Heavily.

From: Allie Rainsbury

The rain will be refreshing. And you won't be laughing when you see a svelte new me in a few months' time!

From: Julie Lawson

You're already svelte, silly girl.

Fine, come over tomorrow then. In the meantime, please make sure your running route takes you past our house and I'll get ready with the camera ☺

From: Allie Rainsbury

No problem. I'll be a picture of health :P

From: Julie Lawson

Now I'm groaning as well as laughing. Enjoy the elements!

Wednesday

From: Julie Lawson
To: Allie Rainsbury

How'd it go? Did you actually make it out in the end?

From: Allie Rainsbury

Oh. My. God. How is it possible that people run a marathon?

From: Julie Lawson

He, he! How far did you manage?

From: Allie Rainsbury

According to Chris's pedometer, 460 metres the first go. 527 metres the second. We ran across Putney Bridge and into Waterside Park, up towards Fulham's football ground. It was exhausting. I had to sit down for ten minutes after the second run before I could move; and even then it was only because Chris started to cramp up. I think he was slightly annoyed with me, although he wasn't much better himself.

From: Julie Lawson

Ha! Does he have a gay run?

From: Allie Rainsbury

What's a gay run?!

From: Julie Lawson

You know - did he run limp wristed with his heels kicking out?

From: Allie Rainsbury

No! At least, no, I don't think so. I was partially blacking out after the first two hundred metres though, so I'm not the best person to ask.

From: Julie Lawson

Ah, well, I'm very proud of you. However, I trust this foray into the dangerous world of exercise will be as short-lived as your culinary adventure was?

From: Allie Rainsbury

Maybe. I'll gather my thoughts and my strength across the next week and see if I can muster the energy again. I must admit that, before the whole red-faced, heavy breathing, nearly fainting started, I was feeling rather smug.

From: Julie Lawson

So you were self-satisfied right up until the end of the driveway?

From: Allie Rainsbury

Almost that far, yes :P Now stop making me laugh. I have a stitch, a cricked neck and can only type with one finger.

Am I still invited over to yours this evening?

From: Julie Lawson

Absolutely. George is cooking a fish casserole. Do you want me to collect you or can you make it over by yourself?

From: Allie Rainsbury

Hmm. I think being chauffeured could prove to be the final indignity. I'll make it over by myself, don't worry.

From: Julie Lawson

OK, see you later, Zola Budd.

From: David Marshall
To: Allie Rainsbury

Hi, how are things?

From: Allie Rainsbury

Hi, not bad thanks – a bit sore still though.

From: David Marshall

Still? I'll have to be more gentle next time!

From: Allie Rainsbury

Get your mind out of the gutter, mister. I went for a run yesterday, so I'm feeling the after-effects now.

From: David Marshall

How far did you manage?

From: Allie Rainsbury

Oh, it was only a quick jog really, nothing major. A few miles, no more than that.

From: David Marshall

Wow, I'm impressed.

Look, I'm so sorry about this week, it would have been nice to meet up, but there's absolutely no chance now. I've just been asked to attend a Marketing Expo in the ExCeL Arena on Friday. I'll be out of the office for the rest of the week.

Are you free next week at all?

From: Allie Rainsbury

I'm free every day except Friday; I'm looking after Julie's kids for the whole weekend (her husband's taking her to Paris for a late Valentine's treat).

From: David Marshall

That makes my 'card in a desk drawer' surprise look pretty tawdry.

How about next Thursday then? That seems to be our day after all!

From: Allie Rainsbury

OK, I can do that.

Can I ask you something though?

From: David Marshall

Sure...

From: Allie Rainsbury

Is that all we're going to get? One day a week? I know we're taking things slowly and everything, but it would be nice to maybe see you outside of just Thursday at some point.

From: David Marshall

That is a big question! Or a lot of little ones, depending on how you view it ☺

I reckon that's too big a subject to start discussing now, Allie. I don't say that to dismiss it – I'd just rather take it away and talk it through face to face. OK?

From: Allie Rainsbury

Yep, that's OK. I don't mean to pressure you. I completely understand that you want to move slowly, and I don't want to rush things either. I just wanted to share my thoughts with you, that's all.

From: David Marshall

And I'm so glad you did. I really respect you for it, and totally respect your thoughts too.

OK – till next week then!

From: Allie Rainsbury

OK. Or text me/call me sooner if you want x

Thursday

From: Julie Lawson
To: Allie Rainsbury

Are you still humming the tune to *The Entertainer*?

From: Allie Rainsbury

Ah, thanks for yesterday. It really cheered me up! And I actually thought both Elly and Cale were great on the piano. They're definitely musically inclined. The last time I heard them they couldn't play at all and now they're (Elly especially) able to play all sorts of tunes.

From: Julie Lawson

All sorts of tunes, out of tune unfortunately.

From: Allie Rainsbury

I thought they were very impressive. And I loved their bow to the audience – Cale's was very solemn ☺

From: Julie Lawson

Perhaps we'll extend our trip to Paris next weekend. I'm not sure three days will give you enough time to truly appreciate how impressive they are (although I do like the bows too, apparently their teacher has them all practising it).

Now, George mentioned something to me last night, and I thought it worth repeating...

From: Allie Rainsbury

A Georgism is always worth repeating :P

From: Julie Lawson

But this one involved David. And I know I promised to stay away from that particular area, certainly in regards to my thoughts on the subject anyway.

From: Allie Rainsbury

Well, these are George's thoughts, not yours so it should be fine. Go ahead, I'm all ears.

From: Julie Lawson

I don't doubt he's a fantastic guy and this is completely uninformed and speculative, and George wouldn't have even brought it up at all if you hadn't mentioned David last night and how he was making you feel a little down this week.

From: Allie Rainsbury

Go on. I won't bite, I promise...

From: Julie Lawson

Well, just after you left George said that if he was really keen on someone, he'd make time for them. Irrespective of how busy and hectic other things in his life were. He said that by the sounds of things, David wasn't doing that (yet) for you. And that, as tough as other relationships of his might have been in the past, they shouldn't really impact on how your relationship moves forward.

From: Allie Rainsbury

OK. I think that all sounds pretty rational and hard to argue with. What was his advice?

Well, I'm not sure really. I thought about what you'd say in those circumstances, so I told him to mind his own business and that David sounded lovely!

From: Allie Rainsbury

What did George say to that?

From: Julie Lawson

He shrugged and went into the living room to watch football highlights.

From: Allie Rainsbury

Brilliant.

From: Ann Rainsbury
To: Allie Rainsbury

Hi darling,

Thank you very much for your email. I'm sorry I was a bit grumpy when we chatted last weekend, but it was only because I was disappointed not to see you. 12 March would be lovely though! Will you just come up for the day, do you think, or are you able to stay over? If you are, I'll ask your father to pick up a beef joint for a Sunday roast.

There is little news since we last spoke. Oh dear, I do always seem to be saying that, don't I? In fact the only things I've done of any note across the past few days are all medically inclined. I now have a dentist's appointment next week and a check-up with the doctor at the end of March. How perfectly dull!

Your father is at the driving range. He came back on Monday in a fearful mood having missed several swings, or shots, or something like that. I smiled and nodded and carried on peeling potatoes.

Write soon, speak soon, see you soon!

Lots of love, Mum xx

Friday

From: Chris Trail
To: Allie Rainsbury

My thighs are still tighter than a nun's unmentionables.

From: Allie Rainsbury

Amazing. In one short email, you've managed to conjure two horrible images in my head to start the morning off with.

From: Chris Trail

There's also a slight rash running down my left leg. It's either chapped from the cold or simply rubbed too vigorously against my running shorts.

What are you doing this evening? Fancy a cheeky beverage someplace or are you spending it smooching in a corner with David?

From: Allie Rainsbury

Christian! No more thigh talk!

I was going to have a quiet night in, but I could be swayed. Would the conversation be more erudite?

From: Chris Trail

Does a bear shit in woods?

From: Allie Rainsbury

Fantastic, I'm in.

Where do you want to go?

From: Chris Trail

How about venturing out of Putney for once and coming up to Maida Vale? We can go to The Warrington (the Gordon Ramsay pub just round the corner from mine) or the Prince Alfred further up towards Warwick Avenue?

From: Allie Rainsbury

Isn't the Prince Alfred where I hit my head on the door frame?

From: Chris Trail

Which actually sparked a learned conversation of the sort you're so craving. You asked why the bloody hell the door frames were so bloody low and I carefully explained that they were dividing walls, part of the décor from a bygone age when many pubs were split into sections determined by class.

From: Allie Rainsbury

Let's go to The Warrington and get pissed.

From: Chris Trail

It's perhaps, needless to add, appropriate that we sit down in the section of the pub traditionally frequented by the lower classes.

From: Allie Rainsbury

Careful, or I'll prod your thigh.

See you there, straight from work.

From: Chris Trail

Have mercy, have mercy! ☺

From: Julie Lawson
To: Allie Rainsbury

One final meeting to go before the week is done – hurrah! Even having it chaired by my boss cannot dampen my positive mood.

I thought I'd drop you a quick email and wish you a fun, relaxing weekend. Give me a call if you want to chat. We're away visiting my parents this time (our lives seem to be a constant yo-yo between one set of grandparents and another) but I'll always be around for a natter if needed.

From: Allie Rainsbury

Ah, thanks, Jules. Actually, I'm feeling more positive too. Lots of good things are happening right now, and I should be feeling happy and excited rather than worried.

I'll chat to David next week and I'm sure everything will be sorted out. After all, if he wasn't keen we wouldn't have come this far.

I'm a jogging machine, a course-qualified cook and a social animal who's off for a drink with Chris this evening.

All in all, I can chalk up another successful week ☺

From: Julie Lawson

Quite right!

Plus, this time next week you'll be able to add babysitter extraordinaire to your resumé as well.

From: Allie Rainsbury

Bugger! I haven't asked Garry if I can work from home on Friday yet. I'll do that now.

From: Julie Lawson

Go, go, go! He'll be all right about it, won't he?

From: Allie Rainsbury

Yes, absolutely, he's knows how disorganised I am. Your romantic get-away will not be scuppered!

From: Julie Lawson

My children are in safe hands.

From: Allie Rainsbury

Don't ruin my positive mood :P

Enjoy the weekend xx

CHAPTER 9

Monday 28 February

From: Allie Rainsbury
To: Julie Lawson

Just to let you know that Garry was fine with me working from home this Friday. A quick joke about not spending too much time in the kitchen was all I had to suffer.

From: Julie Lawson

You're a legend, thank you!

How was your weekend?

From: Allie Rainsbury

Another relatively quiet one. I'm obviously gearing myself up for this coming one, hey?

How about you? Did the kids announce who their favourite grandparents were? ☺

From: Julie Lawson

Whichever ones happen to have the more Haribo out on display. It's a pretty close race.

The parents were actually on reasonable form, operating on an annoyance level of 'almost tolerable' for most of the visit. Only a couple of bursts of 'irritating beyond words'.

My mother asked after you – she always does!

From: Allie Rainsbury

I'm not sure how much fondness she places behind the question though. I still feel guilty for ruining her dress, along with her Christmas no doubt.

From: Julie Lawson

It was an accident – she knows that! Besides, *she* tripped over *your* foot! It was just bad luck that a ditch ran along the side of the road. I reckon she was secretly chuffed to be centre of attention at the church service.

From: Allie Rainsbury

I think she'd have been happier if there'd been time for her to go home and change. The priest must have thought there was a Yeti sitting amongst his congregation.

From: Julie Lawson

Ha! I'm sure he thought it was merely the nativity donkey. Anyway, what's Christmas if not a time for forgiveness? It was forgotten by that same afternoon.

From: Allie Rainsbury

I notice I didn't get an invitation this year.

From: Julie Lawson

Because – lots of reasons! Which we've been through already. Let's talk no more of it.

From: Allie Rainsbury

Hopefully I'll be a less clumsy babysitter...

From: Julie Lawson

You'll have to do better than that to get out of it!

Actually, I still need to take you through everything, don't I? You probably know where most things are kept but I'll type you up a check list just in case.

From: Allie Rainsbury

Sounds good, although I presume it's the normal rules: all the sweets they can eat, a minimum of five hours on the computer a day, all arguing and answering back to be rewarded with bonus chocolate and in bed by 2 a.m.?

From: Julie Lawson

Perfect. Maybe add on loud late-night music to annoy the neighbours, but I'll leave that to your own judgement.

(You do realise that, come the actual weekend, I'll be worried and anxious and that joking should be put away? :P)

From: Allie Rainsbury

This will be fun ☺

From: Julie Lawson

Stupid George and stupid Paris – forcing me to leave my precious children with an accident-prone surrogate aunt!

From: Allie Rainsbury

Hush, while I go shop for Haribo.

From: Scott Cooper
To: Allie Rainsbury

A quick reminder that we have a meeting in place for tomorrow afternoon – just in case your diary had been deleted by an IT error.

Regards, Scott.

Tuesday

From: Allie Rainsbury
To: David Marshall

Do you know Scott Cooper at all?

From: David Marshall

Finance Director. A complete tool. In my humble opinion.

From: Allie Rainsbury

I wouldn't disagree. But what makes you say that?

From: David Marshall

I've only spoken to him a couple of times, but he's incredibly arrogant and has a vastly high opinion of himself. He's barely brought himself to look at me in the meetings that we've been in together.

Plus, from what I hear (admittedly the office grapevine isn't always the most accurate) he has spent his first few weeks here constantly trying it on with the female members of his team.

From: Allie Rainsbury

I have a meeting with him later today.

From: David Marshall

You should watch yourself ☺

What's the meeting about?

From: Allie Rainsbury

Oh, all dull financial stuff. I won't bore you with the details.

How's your week going?

From: David Marshall

Not bad, thanks. I have a presentation to make tomorrow to a couple of digital agencies; other than that this is proving a useful week for catching up with admin for once.

From: Allie Rainsbury

Oh, that's good. You should have emailed me yesterday if you weren't busy. I don't like to disturb you because I know how hectic things are.

From: David Marshall

Well, when I say 'not bad', that's still relative. I had a number of one-to-one's with my team yesterday (one of whom is thinking of handing in her notice) so I've still got a lot on. It's just I've got time to breathe as well this week, which doesn't often happen!

From: Allie Rainsbury

Ooh, that's good gossip! Who's thinking of quitting?!

From: David Marshall

I can't tell you that! Not here anyway. Maybe if you get me drunk on Thursday I'll give you a hint or two.

From: Allie Rainsbury

OK, that sounds like a deal. Although not too drunk – I don't want you falling asleep on me ;)

From: David Marshall

I'm sure you've got a plan for how to keep me awake...

From: Allie Rainsbury

You'll just have to wait and see won't you? :P

Right, I should start preparing what I can for this meeting with Scott bloody Cooper. I'm not looking forward to it at all.

From: David Marshall

Remember to be terribly deferential; speak only when spoken to and sit out of groping range, just in case he decides to get fresh.

From: Allie Rainsbury

Well, as irresistible as I clearly am (?! ☺) I think I'll be safe on that front!

From: David Marshall

Don't be so sure. From what I hear, groping has occurred to someone already.

From: Allie Rainsbury

What? That's not true! Are you joking? That can't possibly be true!

From: David Marshall

I'm serious. This guy is a properly nasty piece of work by all accounts. I'm sure it's just more office rumour, but there's not often smoke without fire is there?

From: Allie Rainsbury

Well, I don't believe it for a second. That's outrageous!

And anyway, even if it was true, if he tried that with me then he wouldn't have an arm left. Not to mention he'd be out of a job so fast he wouldn't know what had hit him.

From: David Marshall

Ha! I'm sure you're right, I don't believe it either. Worth bearing in mind, that's all.

From: Allie Rainsbury

I'm not likely to forget it!

I'll be fine, I'm sure x

Wednesday

From: Julie Lawson
To: Allie Rainsbury

Did you survive your 'meeting from hell'?

From: Allie Rainsbury

It was strange. Despite all previous evidence to the contrary, he seemed quite nice. He was very quiet again, as he was when we met in the pub the first time, but not in an arrogant, aloof way. If anything, he seemed slightly timid and shy.

Maybe I misjudged him. I certainly can't imagine him groping anyone.

From: Julie Lawson

He groped someone??

From: Allie Rainsbury

NO! Office rumour, that's all. Ignore me and ignore that – it all sounds terribly unfair on him. He came across as a thoughtful, sensitive person. And actually, he was surprisingly helpful which was a huge relief as I really don't have any idea what I've done with my POs. As it turns out, we should be able to track most of them down – he just needs to get his team to work on them for a bit. And he asked me to try and be a bit more careful in future and recommended a more methodical way of filing things. Which is fair enough.

It's funny – I wasn't sure sometimes if he was being serious with a few of his comments or whether he was teasing.

From: Julie Lawson

How do you mean?

From: Allie Rainsbury

Well, the deleted files – when he first emailed me about them I thought he was just being obnoxious, but when he brought them up in his office, I could have sworn there was a hint of humour in his voice. And in his eyes for that matter.

From: Julie Lawson

Uh-oh. Somebody isn't getting a crush on her big evil Finance Director, is she? ☺

From: Allie Rainsbury

No! Goodness, no! He's not even near David for charm or intellect or humour or looks.

From: Julie Lawson

Excuse me while I get a bag to vomit into.

From: Allie Rainsbury

Well, it's true! Anyway, I've no doubt completely misread it; Scott probably is a bastard and I'm just being overly charitable.

From: Julie Lawson

You do make us mere mortals look bad, tis true :P

From: Allie Rainsbury

Precisely! More than anything, I'm just relieved to have it out of the way. And, whether he was teasing or not, I can't see that I'll have much more to do with him now. So I suppose it doesn't matter either way.

From: Julie Lawson

Unless he gropes you in the corridor at some point.

From: Allie Rainsbury

Julie, quit it! You didn't hear that from me, and I shouldn't have heard it in the first place. Who would he have groped?

Plus, if he did (which he didn't!) then that person would surely have come straight to you and filed for sexual harrassment.

From: Julie Lawson

I suppose so. Unless he threatened her with the power and influence he wields.

From: Allie Rainsbury

You're right. We don't know how far this goes. Call the president.

From: Julie Lawson

Your sarcasm is wasted on me :P

From: Allie Rainsbury

As, it seems, is logic.

I have a meeting to go to – lunch later on the grassy knoll? :P

From: Julie Lawson

Clever. See you in the canteen at one.

Thursday

From: Allie Rainsbury
To: David Marshall

How did the presentation go yesterday?

From: David Marshall

Fine, excepting that large number of rather fundamental questions at the end of it. But then agencies do have a tendency to ask the blindingly obvious on occasion.

Do you feel like watching a film this evening?

From: Allie Rainsbury

A DVD and a take away, with a couple of cuddles for dessert? I could be persuaded.

From: David Marshall

Actually, I was thinking more of going to the cinema. There's a little theatre right by your place, isn't there? There's a new Russell Crowe film out which I'd like to see...

From: Allie Rainsbury

Yes, we can do that. Have you run out of things to say to me already then? ☺

From: David Marshall

Never! But since I was forced out for a couple of drinks after the presentation last night, I'd rather stay away from the pub this evening.

From: Allie Rainsbury

Ah, so you're feeling a little fragile? Well, we can always postpone tonight for another time if you're too tired?

From: David Marshall

Absolutely not. I've been looking forward to this for two weeks!

From: Allie Rainsbury

Good answer ☺

See you at Putney Bridge after work?

From: David Marshall

You certainly shall.

I'll get on with booking some back-row tickets in the meantime ;)

From: Julie Lawson
To: Allie Rainsbury

I'm so excited I could burst! I know we've been through this a hundred times already, but humour me once more please. You're coming round tomorrow morning at 10.30 a.m., right? We need to catch the Eurostar from St Pancras at 12.30 p.m., so that should allow us plenty of room for error, and a drink in the champagne lounge beforehand.

From: Allie Rainsbury

I'll be there at 10.15 a.m. Any later and I'm scared you'll be too nervous to travel.

From: Julie Lawson

Thank you, thank you! I'm so looking forward to a break without the kids. As much as I love them of course.

I can't believe I've left it this long without going to Paris. My list of things to do gets longer with every page of the guidebook I turn. I just hope there's time enough to see everything I want to see!

From: Allie Rainsbury

Um, George is going with you, isn't he? There seems to be an awful lot of 'I' and not much 'we' at the moment ☺

From: Julie Lawson

This is my Valentine's Day treat. It should be all about me!

But of course George is coming. Someone needs to carry the bags.

From: Allie Rainsbury

Ha! Poor guy. Just make sure he gets to do at least one thing he wants to.

From: Julie Lawson

If he plays his cards right, I might let him do me. Beyond that I make no promises.

From: Allie Rainsbury

Eww. Spare me that thought!

Does Paris have a football team? Maybe you could watch them play?

From: Julie Lawson

If you even mention that to George then we are no longer friends.

See you tomorrow morning!

Oh, and good luck tonight (sorry, how self-centred of me).

Ha, that's OK, you can be selfish once in a while. I'll tell you how it goes tomorrow.

You just think about Paris and what the view will be like from the Eiffel Tower!

From: Julie Lawson

Julie has just fainted with excitement. She will see you in the morning, but wishes you all the best for your date tonight ☺ x

Friday

From: Allie Rainsbury
To: David Marshall

Well, it's now 9 a.m. and (between us) I could get used to the whole 'working from home' idea. I'm still snuggled under the duvet, with a cup of tea and a crumpet on the bedside table.

The sun is beginning to peek through the clouds, which suggests you probably caught the worst of the weather when you left. I think the rain stopped around an hour ago (how early were you up?).

I'm going to get up in about quarter of an hour and make my way over to Julie's. Hopefully she hasn't combusted with nervous energy overnight.

I know you mentioned you were busy this weekend, but if any of your sports fall through and you do want to keep me company then give me a call. I promise I won't make you help out with the kids too much!

Thanks again for a lovely evening; the film may not live long in my memory but the rest of the evening will.

Ps. I think I could get used to having you in my bed more often as well xx

----

From: Allie Rainsbury
To: Julie Lawson

Hey Julie (and George!),

Just a quick note to update you. Everything's fine here in Blighty — in fairness, since you've only been gone less than a day I shouldn't really chalk that up as too much of an achievement.

The kids have been safely and efficiently picked up from school and delivered home (with lots of traffic but minimum road rage). Elly is reading quietly in front of me as I write this and Cale is watching a cartoon which looks bafflingly complicated but seems very action packed (Robot Future? Space Robots? Something like that anyway). Don't worry, the TV's being turned off soon and we're going to play Kerplunk before dinner.

I won't add anything further as I may intrude too much into what will no doubt be a wonderful weekend. Suffice to say, all is well and really, nothing should go wrong.

Love Allie, Elly and Cale xxx

From: Julie Lawson

Thanks for the email! Paris is amazing so far.

What road rage? What do you mean 'nothing should go wrong'?

From: Allie Rainsbury

I'm just kidding. Go enjoy yourself! I'll call if there's a problem.

From: Julie Lawson

Why would there be a problem?...

From: Allie Rainsbury

There won't be! Well, there shouldn't be anyway.

From: Julie Lawson

Has something happened?

From: Allie Rainsbury

No! Or, in language you may better understand, '*Non*'. I'm going now before you get even more paranoid.

From: Julie Lawson

You're sure? You will call if there are any issues, won't you? You won't be disturbing us and we'd rather know!

From: Allie Rainsbury

I'll call if I need to. Now go away and stop bothering me. Enjoy your dirty weekend!

From: Julie Lawson

Thank you.

And you saw the emergency contact list on the side of the fridge, didn't you?

From: Allie Rainsbury

I memorised most of the numbers before the fire took hold, yes.

CHAPTER 10

Monday 7 March

From: Allie Rainsbury
To: Julie Lawson

I still can't believe you actually called!

From: Julie Lawson

In my defence, I was half a bottle of wine in and already emotional.

From: Allie Rainsbury

And suffering a sense of humour failure.

From: Julie Lawson

You need to work on your sense of humour, that's all!

From: Allie Rainsbury

Hmph, fine. To be honest, I'm just glad you haven't spotted the bump on Cale's head yet.

From: Julie Lawson

Ha ha. It's already improving.

From: Allie Rainsbury

☺ So, tell me your stories of Gallic charm, culture and charisma.

From: Julie Lawson

Yes, sorry for rushing you off last night but we were pretty much dead on our feet. We did try to keep it a relaxing weekend, but you don't want to go there and not see the main sights.

Are you free for lunch tomorrow (today is very meeting-heavy) and I'll tell you all about it?

From: Allie Rainsbury

Lunch it is.

From: Julie Lawson

With one funny story to keep you going until then.

It turns out George suffers from vertigo! How can you reach the age of 40 and not know that you're scared of heights? He found out the hard way anyway. We decided to climb the Eiffel Tower rather than take the elevator up. All the steps are iron-grate and you can see through each one (I don't suppose that helped much). We were halfway up the second level when I heard this slightly feeble cry of 'Stop' behind me and turned to see George curled up in a ball at the foot of a flight of stairs.

Initially I almost had a heart attack because I thought, well, I thought that he'd had a heart attack. But it turned out to just be a manly fear of the view beneath him. It took about ten minutes of coaxing to convince him to move at all, by which time a large and rather irate group of people had gathered behind, shouting and cursing at him in various languages to move out of the way.

From: Allie Rainsbury

Oh no! Poor George! Was he OK?

From: Julie Lawson

He was fine, the silly man! His pride was a bit dented and he looked a touch green for an hour or so afterwards but by the time we'd sat down on terra firma and had a cup of coffee he'd forgotten all about it.

From: Allie Rainsbury

Until you reminded him?

From: Julie Lawson

Well it wouldn't be funny if it wasn't constantly talked about!

See you later x

From: Allie Rainsbury
To: David Marshall

Hi, how was your weekend? Did you race down many hills and hit lots of tennis balls? If so, I hope they were separate sports!

I survived my weekend of playing the suburban housewife. In fairness Elly and Cale were both very well behaved so it wasn't too tricky. Perhaps I have a knack of getting on well with children while retaining their respect at the same time. It must be that, come to think of it.

We made chocolate-chip brownies on Saturday, making an awful mess in the process (although, I must admit, since I made most of it, I couldn't complain too much). And on Sunday we went to Putney Common where Cale kicked a ball about and Elly played on the swings.

Goodness – reading that back, it really does sound suburban housewife! All I needed to do was get a Golden Retriever and the illusion would have been complete. A husband as well I suppose. A husband and a Retriever.

Are you free one evening this week?

From: Allie Rainsbury
To: David Marshall

I tried calling again on Saturday by the way. Do you always have your phone off? Is there any point in you having one?

Tuesday

From: David Marshall
To: Allie Rainsbury

A husband, a Retriever and a Volvo. Definitely not the finished article without a hatchback as well.

Sorry, it was meeting central yesterday and very heavy again for the rest of this week. So I'm afraid either work or other social commitments are encroaching. Mostly work unfortunately!

From: Allie Rainsbury

You're busy all week?

From: David Marshall

Yep, unless you count a half-hour window on Wednesday afternoon ☺

From: Allie Rainsbury

So, you can't/don't want to see me again until sometime next week? If you're even free next week, which sounds unlikely.

From: David Marshall

Whoa, easy there, tiger! Where's that come from?

I'm busy, I'm sorry – I can't exactly change that can I? Next week we should definitely be able to get together.

From: Allie Rainsbury

Actually, you should be able to change that. If you really wanted to see me then you'd see me. You'd change your plans and you'd make some time for me.

From: David Marshall

Hold on a minute, Allie, that's unfair! Of course I want to see you. But I have other things on as well.

I'm very busy, and I appreciate that's frustrating but I did say on our first date that I wanted to take things slowly.

From: Allie Rainsbury

And I understand that. But I don't think I'm exactly upping the ante to a light-speed setting by asking to see you more than once a fortnight! Our first date was almost two months ago and we've seen each other three or four times since then. Hardly a shot-gun wedding.

From: David Marshall

Isn't a shot-gun wedding a forced marriage due to pregnancy?

From: Allie Rainsbury

Don't change the subject.

I haven't exactly been unreasonable, have I? Have I once put you under any pressure?

From: David Marshall

Until now, no! But then, I'd be slightly unnerved if you had. We've dated a couple of times over the course of a few weeks. We're not close to being at a stage where there'd be any pressure to build up. Surely we should just be enjoying each other? I know that's what I want anyway.

From: Allie Rainsbury

Well I want that too. But for how long? How long before we move to the next stage? I asked you this a couple of weeks ago and you stalled on it. I think I deserve an answer.

From: David Marshall

This is all getting far more intense than it needs to be.

I can't give you an answer, however much you may deserve one. How can I possibly say when something feels ready to move to the next stage? You don't ever know the answer to a question like that, you just feel it.

And you don't force that kind of thing either, which is why I want to carry on with my normal life and just see how things go.

That's not to say I don't like you (a lot); that's not to say I don't think about how things might be with you (I do) but I don't want to ruin something that could be very special just because I'm not ready to rush full steam into it. And the frustrating thing is that I've been really clear about this since the beginning.

I was very upfront and honest over what I could initially offer. And who knows where things might go from there?

From: Allie Rainsbury

I'm sorry. I don't mean to get intense. Or to rush you.

It's just… I like you a lot too and I think about you quite often. I'm not as busy as you always seem to be, so I suppose because of that I feel that we should be able to meet up more regularly. Probably more than is reasonable for the stage we're at.

I'll try and work on it. It's only because I enjoy spending time with you so much though.

From: David Marshall

I'm sorry too. Now I feel really guilty.

From: Allie Rainsbury

Don't feel guilty. Ignore me – I don't want you to feel guilty. I really am sorry. Forget we even had this conversation and let's start over.

Something about a Volvo?! x

From: David Marshall

We definitely shouldn't forget about it! I always want to hear your thoughts. Honesty's what a relationship is based on after all, irrespective of how formative it is.

Look, let's have a time out for now and digest all of this. I've got a meeting to go to anyway.

I promise we'll meet up soon though. I'd really like that. x

From: Allie Rainsbury

Sounds fine. Only when you're free though, please don't feel that you need to alter your schedule around me.

Chat later x

Wednesday

From: Chris Trail
To: Allie Rainsbury

Calling all running fans. Come in all running fans...!

From: Allie Rainsbury

What are you calling them? :P

From: Chris Trail

Ha! Stop quipping and put some trainers on. Tonight we run until we bleed!

From: Allie Rainsbury

Chris, that's disgusting!

Besides, it's freezing outside today and I'm not sure I'm in the mood.

From: Chris Trail

Rubbish. We went two weeks ago now, you can't still be stiff! Even my thigh rash has pretty much cleared up.

From: Allie Rainsbury

Really? I can breathe easy again then?

From: Chris Trail

I see somebody has her mean cloak on today. You need to cast it off and put on a sweatshirt instead. C'mon, Allie, I won't bother going if you don't come with me!

From: Allie Rainsbury

Or… we could stay inside with a big bowl of popcorn and watch *Armageddon* huddled on the couch under a warm duvet?

From: Chris Trail

Argh. That is my Kryptonite! Stupid Bruce Willis saving the Earth – who can resist that?

No, I must be strong. For both our sakes. I'm passing by your flat at 7 p.m. and I'm ringing your doorbell until you come out :P

From: Allie Rainsbury

You might be there a while. I'm really not in the most positive of states today.

From: Chris Trail

Then I'll be there a while.

You can either come out and tell me all about why you're being such a grump or you can stay inside and sulk, listening to a high-pitched monotone sound shriek relentlessly through your flat.

From: Allie Rainsbury

How long are we going to run for?

From: Chris Trail

We'll try for 1.5 kilometres this time, but rest if we need to.

From: Allie Rainsbury

Fine. But if I fall and break anything then you're paying my hospital bills.

From: Chris Trail

Not only that - I will quit my job and spend the following months nursing you back to full health!

From: Allie Rainsbury

And we're going to the pub afterwards for a glass of wine.

From: Chris Trail

A large glass. At least one.

See you this evening ☺

From: Ann Rainsbury
To: Allie Rainsbury

Hello darling,

Just checking that you're still definitely coming this weekend. I don't have any reason to think otherwise but know how you youngsters can have things thrown at you at the last minute. We are both really excited about seeing you. It's been nearly three months already. It's scary how quickly time passes.

I've made up your bed in the far left bedroom, where you normally sleep. Your father's spent the last week adjusting it, whatever that means, as I know you mentioned it was slightly soft when you stayed in it at Christmas. I don't think it can be the mattress, so perhaps a spring has gone somewhere in the frame itself. No doubt that is what your father's looking at.

So, give me a call or send me a little reply just so we know for sure. We have lots of food in the fridge; if you don't come then half of it will go to waste – I don't seem to have much appetite these days!

Much love, Mum xxx

Thursday

From: David Marshall
To: Allie Rainsbury

What if I was to ask you to come away for the weekend with me on Friday 25 and Saturday 26?

From: Allie Rainsbury

Of this month?!

Where would you want to go?

From: David Marshall

Yep, this month, around two weeks' time.

Not sure where yet – what do you think?

From: Allie Rainsbury

I think… yes!! ☺

From: David Marshall

You're sure?

From: Allie Rainsbury

I'm positive! But only if you really want to. You're not having to cancel anything else, are you?

From: David Marshall

I wouldn't ask if I didn't want to!

And no, not that you need to worry about that, but I'm not cancelling anything. I just thought it would be nice for us to spend a couple of days together. And nights as well. ;)

From: Allie Rainsbury

What a lovely surprise! I'd love to.

We don't need to do anything special though, so don't feel you have to go to any trouble organising it. I'd be very happy just to spend the weekend with you, whether that's at mine or yours. I could come up north if you wanted, since I haven't seen your flat yet.

From: David Marshall

Since when is organising a weekend away with a beautiful girl any trouble? Besides, it'll be nice to get out of London.

I'll make the reservations, you just have to come and look pretty – which should be very easy.

From: Allie Rainsbury

OK! I accept! It's in the diary.

Thank you so much. You've just made my day ☺ xx

From: David Marshall

I'm glad. I like it when you're happy. I hope that it goes someway to making up for the other day.

From: Allie Rainsbury

You have nothing to make up for. You really don't. Although if this is going to be the standard response then maybe we should debate things a bit more often!

From: David Marshall

True, I'm digging myself a hole here, aren't I?

OK, I'm not sorry for anything, but I am taking you for a weekend away. Bring yourself, your smile and some very skimpy underwear.

From: Allie Rainsbury

Let's hope it's not black tie at dinner then :P

From: David Marshall

I was thinking that room service might be preferable either way ;)

From: Allie Rainsbury

It would, it would. See you later!

Ps. You're gorgeous ☺ xx

From: Julie Lawson
To: Allie Rainsbury

You've been quiet this week. Are you still recovering from the weekend or have you just been busy? ☺

From: Allie Rainsbury

A bit of both.

Plus I went jogging again last night (no laughing – enough people did that en route) so it's been a rather hectic week by my generally sedate standards.

From: Julie Lawson

Good for you! I have resolved to be supportive of rather than poke fun at this new jogging craze.

How did you do this time?

From: Allie Rainsbury

We nearly ran two kilometres, with only one break in between.

I think I managed better than Chris expected because he'd drunk his whole water bottle after 500 metres. He suffered for the rest of the run, it must be said.

How are the post-Paris blues?

From: Julie Lawson

Silly Chris! I must come and watch next time.

Post-Paris blues aren't too bad; perhaps if I'd gone for a week the withdrawal would be slightly higher. It has made me crave another holiday though.

From: Allie Rainsbury

I was just thinking that. All I have coming up is this surprise weekend away, but I could really do with something longer and more exotic.

Are you going for Thursday drinks after work this evening?

From: Julie Lawson

I might go for one or two, yes. It's been a long week.

Hold on. A surprise weekend away? What do you mean?

From: Allie Rainsbury

Have I not told you about that?

From: Julie Lawson

No! What weekend away?

From: Allie Rainsbury

I could have sworn I'd mentioned it...

It's just something David's organising for me.

From: Julie Lawson

What the hell? Where? When exactly?

It had better not be Paris!

You dark horse. DETAILS!

From: Allie Rainsbury

See you at drinks ☺

Friday

From: Allie Rainsbury
To: David Marshall

We missed you at the pub last night (me especially ☺). Hope you had a nice evening though.

Have you decided where we're off to yet?!

From: David Marshall

I ended up working very late – incredibly unglamorous, terribly unfortunate but utterly necessary.

I haven't yet, no. There are a couple of places featuring on the short-list though.

From: Allie Rainsbury

I suppose it would sound terribly un-sexy to say I feel like a kid counting down for Christmas.

So I won't... and I don't... but I am still very, very excited!

Just so you know.

From: David Marshall

You do realise that using sexy and kid in the same sentence has probably automatically put you on an FBI watch list :P

From: Allie Rainsbury

Oop... I didn't even think of that!

That won't actually happen will it? I was just a bit over-excited.

From: David Marshall

If they take you for questioning then you've now admitted that using sexy and kid in the same sentence gets you over-excited.

You could be in for some hard time here, Allie.

From: Allie Rainsbury

If they take me for questioning when I should be on a weekend away then they'll be the ones in for a hard time!

From: David Marshall

I think you'll be OK ☺

I'm excited too x

From: Allie Rainsbury

You are? Good, I'm glad. I was saying at drinks that I wasn't sure how much you wanted to do this and how much it was guilt induced. I suppose it was mostly the former but then maybe the latter had a little bit of a say too. Which is fine, obviously.

From: David Marshall

You said what at drinks? You said we were going for a weekend away together?

From: Allie Rainsbury

No… only to Julie. She knows everything I get up to. You know that already.

No one else heard, don't worry!

From: David Marshall

How do you know? Were you sitting at a table with others or by yourselves?

From: Allie Rainsbury

We were off to the side. No one heard.

Not that anyone would have guessed if they did; I'm quite sure that everyone thinks you're completely out of my league!

From: David Marshall

That's not the point! I've already asked you – please DO NOT talk about us at work.

I know you think it's paranoia, but I do not want to be the subject of office gossip. It never, ever ends well for those involved and it absolutely impacts on the position people are in professionally.

Please don't do it, Allie – you can chat with Julie anytime; she lives right by you!

From: Allie Rainsbury

No one heard! I hardly said anything.

From: David Marshall

Don't say anything at all! Not when work colleagues are about. It's not a big deal, but I really hate people I don't know knowing about my personal life.

From: Allie Rainsbury

OK, I get it. I'm sorry. I won't talk about you in future.

From: David Marshall

And don't sulk. I'm not being mean, I'm just keeping our privacy. For both our sakes.

From: Allie Rainsbury

I'm not sulking. But you don't have to speak to me like I'm five years old though.

From: David Marshall

I'm sorry too then. It just must have been all the kid talk earlier :P

From: Allie Rainsbury

You're definitely on the FBI list!

From: David Marshall

Have been for a while, sweetheart.

How's it feel to be dating an outlaw? ;)

From: Allie Rainsbury

Ooh. I like it!

Unless this weekend away is just to skip bail of course...

From: David Marshall

Stop talking crazy and start looking into flights to Peru.

OK – I have a busy afternoon ahead. I'll let you ponder some more over where we're headed and crack on with work.

From: Allie Rainsbury

Enjoy your weekend. Feel free to call, as ever (although no doubt your phone will be buried in the bottom of your rucksack as you hurtle down a hill on a bike!) xx

CHAPTER 11

Monday 14 March

From: Julie Lawson
To: Allie Rainsbury

That weekend seemed to last two hours, not two days! There should be a law that lets people take Monday off if they feel as tired as I do.

From: Allie Rainsbury

You've already won my vote.

Strong cup of tea may come to the rescue?

From: Julie Lawson

Way ahead of you (and a chocolate croissant, just because I deserve it this morning ☺).

How was your weekend?

From: Allie Rainsbury

I spent it with my parents in Oxford. It was OK but I ran out of things to say after half an hour and spent the rest of the time discussing the weather and how bad the television schedule was. And I don't want to play another hand of rummy for a while. We must have played at least a day's worth of cards – I don't think I won once.

They seem well and happy though; on the whole it was relaxing!

From: Julie Lawson

Plus, you've now got enough brownie points to feel guilt-free about not visiting for another couple of months!

From: Allie Rainsbury

Wow, you're cynical when you're tired. Actually, that's unfair – you're cynical all of the time.

From: Julie Lawson

I just speak the truth. That's how I always think of trips home, anyway (even more so to the in-laws :P).

Did they ask you about your love life?

From: Allie Rainsbury

They always ask me about my love life. Although it's become more and more tokenistic over the years – I think I'm gradually wearing them down!

Plus, I've been single for so long that they now have to factor in the lesbian possibility. That started coming into the equation a couple of years ago when they stopped just quizzing me about a boyfriend and started tentatively asking whether I'd found a 'partner' yet. Now I always know it's coming because Dad clears his throat and starts to look distinctly uncomfortable. I feel bad for them; there's an awful lot of etiquette involved really.

From: Julie Lawson

Aw, the poor things. That's so cute and so English.

So, did you tell them about David? That huge strides have been taken towards providing them with grandkids over the past couple of months? ☺

From: Allie Rainsbury

Ha! No, not yet. It would have opened the way for too many other questions that I don't even know the answer to myself.

And those strides can be measured in millimetres by the way!

From: Julie Lawson

Fair enough – you will let me know if you want to talk anything through, won't you? I'm always here if you need me. Except for right now. Monday morning isn't a good time for a deep and meaningful. Besides, I need to find a quiet meeting room somewhere and see if I can sneak in a power nap.

From: Allie Rainsbury

Thanks, Jules, I will do.

Go enjoy some stealthy shut-eye. How come you're so tired?

From: Julie Lawson

Providing parents with grandchildren may help them rest easy, but it pretty much guarantees that you won't!

From: Allie Rainsbury
To: Ann Rainsbury; Peter Rainsbury

Dear Mum and Dad,

Just to say thank you so much for a lovely weekend. Dad, the bed was really comfy, although I do wish you wouldn't go to so much effort. I only mentioned it in passing last time!

I have a very busy week ahead of me, so I should get on with a couple of presentations that are outstanding (by outstanding, I mean they are still to do rather than already being fantastic – unfortunately).

I'll try and call this weekend and look forward to seeing you again soon.

Much love to you both, Allie xx

Tuesday

From: Chris Trail
To: Allie Rainsbury

Guess what I have in my possession?

From: Allie Rainsbury

I don't know, but if you're holding someone against their will then you really should let them go before you get into trouble.

From: Chris Trail

I have two tickets to the Green Day concert at Wembley this evening!!

From: Allie Rainsbury

Um... Exciting? You certainly sound pleased!

From: Chris Trail

I love Green Day! You know I love Green Day! I even made you listen to them when we first went running, remember?

From: Allie Rainsbury

Chris, I was seeing stars when we ran the first time. And the second time, come to that. So, no, I'm sorry, I don't really remember. But I'm sure they're very good.

From: Chris Trail

They are seminal! They're beyond good – they've educated an entire generation with their music.

From: Allie Rainsbury

Not my generation. Anyway, what do you want? You have my blessing. Go in peace and enjoy many a Green Day concert.

From: Chris Trail

I have two tickets. I have one best friend. And I'm on a mission to rock!

From: Allie Rainsbury

Have you regressed a decade over the past week? You're not wearing your jeans down around your bum, are you? If you are, please tell me how boys manage to keep them from falling down, they seem to defy the law of gravity. It's quite impressive really.

From: Chris Trail

Look, a colleague of mine had tickets but his girlfriend is sick (with flu – there's quite a bit of that going around at the moment, you should stock up on oranges). He asked if I'd be interested. I said, who wouldn't be? He said he didn't care who wouldn't be, he just wanted to find someone who would. I vocalised myself a bit more clearly and gave him twenty pounds for the pair. So come along!

From: Allie Rainsbury

That's very sweet of you to offer, but I think I might pass. I've always considered anything more hard core than Bryan Adams to be pretty alternative. I just don't think that Green Day is really me.

From: Chris Trail

Now you're sounding pathetic as well as sixty. What else do you have planned for this evening?

From: Allie Rainsbury

A hot bath and a new episode of *Grey's Anatomy*.

From: Chris Trail

There's a new episode of *Grey's* on? Hmm, I didn't know that in fairness.

But don't distract me with that! I will record it. You can record it. And a bath will wait until tomorrow.

Come, Allie – how often do we go to a concert at Wembley? This shouldn't be a difficult sell.

From: Allie Rainsbury

If I come, then we don't have to go on a run this week.

Deal?

From: Chris Trail

How are those two things even remotely linked?

From: Allie Rainsbury

They're not. But it remains a condition nonetheless :P

From: Chris Trail

Fine! No running then. We'll sweat off more weight by dancing to 'Jesus of Suburbia' anyway.

From: Allie Rainsbury

Oh, that's a bonus. Will we be dehydrated by the end of the evening too? You should have told me sooner.

From: Chris Trail

Rock on!

From: Allie Rainsbury

Piss off x

From: Allie Rainsbury
To: David Marshall

Are we seeing each other this week? I can't remember.

That's not meant to push you into something if we're not, but I'm free every day except tonight if you are around x

Wednesday

From: Julie Lawson
To: Allie Rainsbury

It sounded as if you were having fun last night...

From: Allie Rainsbury

Ha, I couldn't really hear a word you were saying, sorry! They were really good though. I'm glad I went in the end!

I mean, there was quite a bit of pushing and shoving, but I think that was all part of it. I felt like a component part of one big, heaving organism. Definitely the most uncoordinated part, but a part nonetheless!

I need to apologise to Chris today; don't let me forget.

From: Julie Lawson

Why, what happened?

From: Allie Rainsbury

Nothing – well, I trod on his foot a couple of times, so I should say sorry for that – but mainly because he's always trying to get me to do things, and I'm always so negative about them. And then I end up doing them anyway to keep him quiet and have a great time. I will henceforth try to be more positive.

From: Julie Lawson

Good philosophy! And wonderfully timed. Please remember you wrote those words when your team away day is announced later.

From: Allie Rainsbury

Um... huh? Am I meant to be confused?

From: Julie Lawson

Your boss, the lovely Garry, was in HR earlier today (along with the genuinely lovely Scott). They were double checking that we would be OK to sanction wake-boarding next Wednesday!

From: Allie Rainsbury

I'm still confused. What are you talking about?

And what's wake-boarding?

From: Julie Lawson

Your team away day on Wednesday next week.

From: Allie Rainsbury

Yes...

From: Julie Lawson

It's a team-building day that will involve an afternoon of brainstorming ideas with your colleagues to ensure that you as individuals and as teams are maximising your potential and output.

From: Allie Rainsbury

OK (and good corporate speak by the way).

From: Julie Lawson

Prior to the afternoon session there will be an activity in order to foster competitiveness, togetherness and general camaraderie (thank you).

From: Allie Rainsbury

What the hell is wake-boarding?

From: Julie Lawson

It's a bit like water-skiing, but with a snow-board.

From what I understand ☺

From: Allie Rainsbury

Are you joking? Where?

From: Julie Lawson

At a regal sounding place called the Prince's Club, just past Twickenham. They have a couple of purpose built lakes.

It all sounds very safe, so after ensuring the necessary precautions would be followed we were able to sign off a day of fun-filled frolics!

From: Allie Rainsbury

Twickenham? It's mid-March! We haven't had a day of sunshine yet this year – the water will be freezing!

You're joking, aren't you?

I'll leave it there until the email gets sent out this afternoon; I don't want to ruin the surprise for everyone.

From: Allie Rainsbury

I'm not doing it! They can't make me do it. Can they? What a ridiculous idea.

What necessary precautions?

From: Julie Lawson

Patience, my dear, patience.

Now I must go. I have work to do in a warm, snug office. Not all of us can have a day off to play water-sports, you know...

From: Allie Rainsbury

This isn't over. I know my rights!

From: Julie Lawson

Remember to stay positive.

From: Allie Rainsbury

I hate you.

Thursday

From: Ann Rainsbury
To: Allie Rainsbury

Hi sweetheart,

Thanks for your note. It was lovely to see you too. I hope we didn't overdo it with the card games, but the weather was pretty horrible outside, wasn't it?

I was at the dentist's earlier this week and had a new filling put on my top molar – apparently the first one was coming loose. Apart from that though they're a fine example of teeth for a person of my age. I almost thought I was going to get a lollipop.

I have this trip to the doctor's next week and then I'm done again for another few months, touch wood. I keep trying to persuade your father to go along for a check up, but he's so stubborn! I think he just knows he'll get a telling off over his cholesterol levels (and over-indulgence in red wine).

Anyway, enough of your old parents' medical updates. I wanted to ask you what your Easter plans were and thought I'd get in early. Your father and I are planning the usual trip down to Teignmouth to visit your aunt and uncle. I thought, with it being a couple of years now since you last came along, that you might want to join us.

Lots of fresh sea air and a few bracing walks down the beaches. It would make a nice change from the madding crowd of London. Something to think about; I know they'd love to see you as, obviously, would I (I know I'm being greedy having just had you up).

Enjoy the rest of your week, I hope it isn't too busy for you.

Lots of love, Mum xx

From: David Marshall
To: Allie Rainsbury

So, I have good news and bad news.

The bad news is that this has been another torrid week of work yet again ruining any chance of getting enough spare time to see you.

The good news is that a reference number has just been emailed to me for a booking confirmation: two nights in a sweet little bed and breakfast in Canterbury.

From: Allie Rainsbury

Shame about this week, although I've been busy with presentations myself so it's not a problem.

That's very good news to hear! I've only ever been to Canterbury once before and that was on a school visit. The only real memory I have of the trip is putting chewing gum in Emma Mortimer's hair.

From: David Marshall

I'm confident I can compete with Emma Mortimer.

I thought we could drive my car down there; it shouldn't take too long once we're past the Dartford tunnel if we leave a bit early. Do you reckon you'll be able to sneak out around 3 p.m.?

From: Allie Rainsbury

I'm sure I'll be able to manage it, yes!

An early finish and a weekend away – all my dreams are coming true.

From: David Marshall

Great. I've also reserved a table at a restaurant recommended to me, near the city centre. It's only half a mile from our hotel so thought we could have a relaxing meal and wander back to our bedroom across the cobbled streets.

From: Allie Rainsbury

That sounds lovely too.

Our bedroom, you say?

From: David Marshall

Yes, only one bedroom booked. I hope that wasn't too presumptuous ;)

From: Allie Rainsbury

No, no, it's not that! I just like how it sounds, that's all.

So, are you busy up until then with work?

From: David Marshall

Yes, work never stops, it merely accelerates.

I'll try and call you this weekend if you're around, although I might not get the chance – another trip out of London planned with two Uni friends, some mountain bikes and the Lake District.

From: Allie Rainsbury

A phone call from you will always be welcome, but I understand if you're too busy.

Another active weekend. Do you ever stop? I shall relax enough for the both of us and save my energies for next weekend. Just in case I need them ;) x

Friday

From: Allie Rainsbury
To: Julie Lawson

Are you busy with the family this weekend?

From: Julie Lawson

They'll no doubt take up an inordinate amount of my time by combining disorganisation with over-dependency, yes.

Why do you ask?

From: Allie Rainsbury

I just don't have any plans and hoped we might be able to go shopping.

From: Julie Lawson

Tell me more ☺

From: Allie Rainsbury

I want to get something new and revealing to surprise David with on Friday. A second opinion would be very useful!

From: Julie Lawson

A bit of role play, huh? Kinky! :P

What about Sunday morning while George takes the kids swimming? You can come back to mine afterwards and help with the roast chicken.

From: Allie Rainsbury

Sunday's fine with me.

And clean up your mind! Nothing kinky – something sophisticated and subtle.

From: Julie Lawson

Yeah, because men the world over are known for their subtlety and sophistication.

My opinion and judgement are obviously urgently needed.

From: Allie Rainsbury

You are clearly an adept dominatrix.

From: Julie Lawson

Ha! You know, I think George would be mortified if he ever caught sight of our email exchanges ☺

You can repay me by thinking of a good holiday destination for this year. I want to spend the weekend chatting through options with my gorgeously subservient husband and book something up next week.

From: Allie Rainsbury

Ooh, OK! What kind of holiday? A resort-type break where the children can play in the pool or a more adventurous one where inoculations are needed?

From: Julie Lawson

I'd rather not be jabbed if it can be helped.

From: Allie Rainsbury

The Caribbean?

From: Julie Lawson

Jamaica or Barbados? That would be incredible! But perhaps out of the price range – especially since the kids will hardly remember it in five years.

From: Allie Rainsbury

Ibiza?

From: Julie Lawson

I'm not sure about the Spanish islands. They are meant to be beautiful, but parts of Ibiza are filled with cheap alcohol and late-night partying. Since I didn't go when I was 18, I don't think I'll go now; too many chavs on the party side of the island (for want of a more diplomatic word).

From: Allie Rainsbury

A tough critic. I'll have a proper think and come prepared with more detailed suggestions on Sunday.

Maybe you could try the Egyptian coast? You'll have water-sports on the beach and the option of something more cultured if you make a trip to Cairo.

From: Julie Lawson

I like that idea. Let's discuss more at the weekend!

Speaking of water-sports – do you have a plan yet for the away day on Wednesday?

From: Allie Rainsbury

Yes, locking myself indoors and refusing to come out.

See you Sunday.

CHAPTER 12

Monday 21 March

From: Julie Lawson
To: Allie Rainsbury

I forgot to ask yesterday if you want to come to Elly and Cale's concert this week? Please don't feel obliged to, I'm only asking because you suffered their practising when you babysat.

From: Allie Rainsbury

I'd love to come! Thursday evening, isn't it?

From: Julie Lawson

Great, the kids will be so excited. Yes, it's on Thursday at 7 p.m. I'll put you down for a DVD of the evening too; you can treasure the unique sounds they create for ever.

From: Allie Rainsbury

When your children collect their first Grammy awards one day, you won't be thanked in their acceptance speeches.

From: Julie Lawson

I can live with that, providing I receive a percentage of the record sales.

From: Allie Rainsbury

Touching...

I'm going to make a cup of tea before I well up too much.

From: Julie Lawson

They'll thank me or I'll write a tell-all book about their formative years.

Go make your brew!

From: Scott Cooper
To: EMEA Sales; EMEA Marketing; Group Finance

Dear all,

Ahead of our department's away day this Wednesday, I wanted to share with you the shape of the day and the aim behind it.

After much discussion you'll all no doubt be excited to know that we've created a more energised and active day than previous away days have enjoyed. In the morning we are all meeting in Twickenham to enjoy the thrills and spills of wake-boarding. Not being an expert in water-sports, there is little advice I can give beyond saying that it is safe (!), fun and splashorific (according to the manager there).

I encourage you all to join in and enjoy the experience. Both Garry and I foresee a challenging year ahead and we feel that this day will be a great illustration of physically rising to challenges, thriving in new experiences and throwing yourselves in at the deep end. The hope and desire is that this energy will transfer itself onto the afternoon and create a vibrant and engaging atmosphere of ideas, suggestions and creative thoughts. We have reserved a private function room at a hotel nearby where, having dried off and enjoyed a buffet lunch, we can concentrate on how individually and collaboratively we can push the business forward across 2012.

A full agenda will be sent out this afternoon detailing directions and specifics for the afternoon discussions.

Thank you and best regards, Scott.

Tuesday

From: Allie Rainsbury
To: Julie Lawson

This is ridiculous. This is actually going to happen?

From: Julie Lawson

Um... and what would that be, pray?

From: Allie Rainsbury

Wake-boarding! Did you get the email that Scott Cooper, prince of idiots, sent out yesterday?

From: Julie Lawson

Ah, the mist is clearing.

Yes, I was cc'd, and I must say, I am incredibly excited at this approach and agenda. It's a good example of new people and new ideas at work.

From: Allie Rainsbury

Do not wind me up. How do I get out of this?! Am I the only person to have made an official complaint?

From: Julie Lawson

A doctor's note? A strategic sick day? Both of which will be viewed poorly I should warn.

A fair bit of our social budget has been put aside to run tomorrow and this new activity-based approach is generating a lot of attention and interest from various senior management.

(You're not really making an official complaint, are you?)

From: Allie Rainsbury

When I was eight, I was the only girl in my class who couldn't pick up a brick from the bottom of the swimming pool.

From: Julie Lawson

Tragic.

From: Allie Rainsbury

Exactly!

Do you think that will get me immunity?

From: Julie Lawson

Well, if you really don't want to then no one can force you into doing anything.

But you would be (at time of writing) the only person who isn't giving it a go.

From: Allie Rainsbury

Senior management might admire the courage I have to stand up against the majority and fight for what I believe in.

From: Julie Lawson

Yes, a true example of leadership and bravery. Undeniably they'll see you as a person to earmark for future greatness.

From: Allie Rainsbury

Unbelievable. I'm going to be pushed into this, aren't I?

If I end up getting a cold for my weekend away then I'm going to kill Garry, Scott bloody Cooper and the whole stupid senior management team.

From: Julie Lawson

Actually, that would probably be a better way to fast-track your career.

From: Allie Rainsbury

You are loving every minute of this, aren't you?

You'll feel guilty if I get flu, or fall off and flail about in the water, which I can guarantee will happen. It's always me who ends up making a complete idiot of themselves.

From: Julie Lawson

You'll be fine. It really does sound safe! Apparently there's a cable that drags you around the lake. All you have to do is hold on to it.

From: Allie Rainsbury

Along with my temper.

I'm signing off in a huff; you've offered me neither the support nor the get-out-of-jail options that I need.

From: Julie Lawson

Don't be cross – this could be the last time we talk after all. It would be terrible to leave things on the wrong note.

From: Allie Rainsbury

Bad stuff will happen to you.

From: Julie Lawson

Remember to swim across any rip currents, never into them ☺

Wednesday

From: Chris Trail
To: Allie Rainsbury

Up to much this evening?

From: Allie Rainsbury

Out of office reply: Allie Rainsbury is currently away from her desk until Thursday 24 March, unless a freak and easily avoidable accident determines otherwise.

If your query is urgent then I'm available intermittently on my mobile.

For information, I bequeath all my possessions to the Lifeboat Association.

Thursday

From: Julie Lawson
To: Allie Rainsbury

Hey there, intrepid adventurer! How was it?

From: Allie Rainsbury

Well, I did it!

I fell in.

I just about survived.

From: Julie Lawson

From what I hear that's a modest retelling.

From: Allie Rainsbury

What's that supposed to mean? What have you heard?!

From: Julie Lawson

Oh, nothing much...

Although there might be a rumour going around our floor at the moment.

From: Allie Rainsbury

What are people saying?

It's exaggerated, whatever it is. Use your influence and put a stop to it!

From: Julie Lawson

Did you really do a somersault off one of the jumps?

From: Allie Rainsbury

That depends. Does it sound cool? It sounds pretty cool to me!

From: Julie Lawson

I'm hearing the phrase 'airborne like a flailing elephant'.

From: Allie Rainsbury

I want to make that official complaint now.

From: Julie Lawson

☺ What happened?

From: Allie Rainsbury

I managed to stand up initially, that's what those gossips should be concentrating on. That's an achievement in itself! Unfortunately I had no control of the direction of the board.

This should be understandable because, as mentioned on numerous previous occasions, despite having little to no sense of balance, I'd been emotionally bullied onto a flimsy bit of plastic while holding onto a precarious overhead cable that proceeded to drag me around a gloomy piece of water at great speed.

Inevitably I veered off course, headed straight up a ten-foot ramp in the middle of the lake and took off like bloody Evel Knievel. Apparently I completed an unplanned somersault and emitted an ear-piercing scream mid-flight. I remember neither.

In fact the next memory I do have was being hauled out of the water by none other than Scott bloody Cooper who, surprise surprise, happened to have done the whole thing several times before and looked effortlessly cool.

I feel like I've been set up!

From: Julie Lawson

Yep, that more or less backs up the rumours!

From what I hear Scott was quite the white knight, fairly racing over the water to check you were all right.

From: Allie Rainsbury

To call him a white knight would be to ignore the pink elephant: He organised the stupid day in the first place!

Although I suppose it was nice of him to swim with me to shore. And he did get a couple of towels to put around me when we got back to the group. Plus he referenced my bravery at throwing myself into things as an analogy for positive thinking during the afternoon discussions.

From: Julie Lawson

Exactly! Good for you I say.

Have you seen the photos yet by the way?

From: Allie Rainsbury

What photos? You're kidding? What photos?!

From: Julie Lawson

Just a few of the very best across the course of the day. Those wet suits they give you can be really unflattering, can't they?

From: Allie Rainsbury

Please say you're joking.

Am I in any of them? There aren't any of me doing the jump, are there?

From: Julie Lawson

Well, I'd be lying if I said there weren't but actually you look OK. I think.

The fact that you're moving so fast has meant you're slightly blurred, so that helps.

They're being emailed round in a bit, so you can have a look then.

From: Allie Rainsbury

Scott Cooper has just cemented his place in my little book of people I despise.

I'm going to be the butt of all the jokes around the office!

From: Julie Lawson

Your butt will never be a joke around this office. I won't stand for it!
☺

From: Allie Rainsbury

Any pretence at svelteness and grace that I had remaining has now dissipated completely.

Friday

From: David Marshall
To: Allie Rainsbury

Good morning, gorgeous. Are you all packed and ready to go?

From: Allie Rainsbury

Good morning! I was just about to email you.

I was worrying that you were going to cancel.

From: David Marshall

Not at all! Why would you think that?

From: Allie Rainsbury

I haven't heard from you all week. I tried calling last night but it went through to answer phone.

Sorry, I was just being paranoid because I've been looking forward to this weekend so much.

From: David Marshall

Work has bested me this week. But the weekend remains very much on – it's what has got me through the past few days.

From: Allie Rainsbury

Hurray! I absolutely echo that.

I've had a long, long week too and can't wait for a couple of relaxing, stress-free days ☺

From: David Marshall

By long week, are you referring to the photos of your sports day that were sent round yesterday?

From: Allie Rainsbury

Well, a little bit maybe – but mostly because I've been so hectic with customers recently and some time away in the country will do wonders.

Did you see those pictures then?

From: David Marshall

I had a quick look. Was that you in most of them?

From: Allie Rainsbury

Yes, I suppose it was...

It's all terribly unfair though. I'm still debating whether or not to sue. But I'll look more glamorous this evening, I promise!

From: David Marshall

You always look glamorous to me, don't worry ;)

Besides, the whole agenda just sounded like another vehicle to drive our wonderful CFO's ego even further forward.

From: Allie Rainsbury

Yes, exactly!

Although, in fairness, he was rather kind and thoughtful after my crash – I can't really fault him there.

From: David Marshall

No doubt he was worried that his standing with his colleagues might be tarnished.

No more talk about Scott Cooper! I don't want to expend energy on him – not when we should be immersed in creating our very own Canterbury tale.

From: Allie Rainsbury

Agreed! I am literally hopping with anticipation under my desk.

From: David Marshall

Are you still able to leave a bit earlier than usual? I was hoping to avoid prying eyes as well as London traffic in Friday rush-hour.

From: Allie Rainsbury

I have a strategically placed 3-5 p.m. 'customer meeting' in my diary. But my boss normally has a genuine meeting on Friday afternoons so will be none the wiser anyway!

From: David Marshall

Perfect. I'll meet you in the car park. You can duck down in the passenger seat until we're well away from the office.

From: Allie Rainsbury

Ha! That's a joke, right?

Seriously?

From: David Marshall

Better safe than sorry!

See you down there at 3 p.m. x

From: Allie Rainsbury

Sounds more like I'm being secreted out of occupied France than being taken on a romantic weekend away.

But OK, whatever it takes. You'll just have to make it up to me this evening ;) xx

---

CHAPTER 13

Monday 28 March

From: Julie Lawson
To: Allie Rainsbury

So, how was it?!

From: Allie Rainsbury

It was everything a weekend away should be.

I have a beautiful, caring and wonderful boyfriend!

From: Julie Lawson

Good to middling then? :P

Tell me more please! I have my morning coffee, my morning bagel and my Monday morning feeling all in front of me.

From: Allie Rainsbury

It was a weekend full of stolen glances and of dancing shadows in the moonlight. I felt like I was in an Austen novel; a reverie – a luminous, glorious dream.

From: Julie Lawson

Yuh-huh.

From: Allie Rainsbury

It really was that lovely. Canterbury is such a romantic place with all its cobbled streets and medieval feel. You can imagine belonging to another time as you wander through the cathedral and take in the surrounding architecture. It was somewhat spoilt by two students stumbling out of the local pub and throwing up on the pavement as we walked past; but that apart, it was incredibly picturesque.

From: Julie Lawson

Such wonderful memories...

From: Allie Rainsbury

Students being ill won't be my abiding memory of the weekend.

It will revolve more around the charming little bed and breakfast we stayed in; the walks that we took through the market; the perfection of David's face as he looked at me across the dinner table, a candle flickering between us.

From: Julie Lawson

It didn't catch your hair again, did it?

From: Allie Rainsbury

No! And that was ONE time. A long time ago. And it barely caught light before you patted it out.

And stop ruining my story! The whole two days were incredibly romantic.

I've been slightly worried for a while (as you know and/or have guessed) because I haven't really felt that David wanted to take any steps forward, but after this I really feel so much closer to him. I think we're finally in a good place now to move on to stage two.

From: Julie Lawson

Aww. I'm sorry for teasing. I really am very excited for you! And it does sound as if you had a great time.

I presume that our shopping trip for revealing-yet-classy clothing proved useful? ;)

What does stage two entail?

From: Allie Rainsbury

Revealing clothes were worn, yes – thank you for asking :P

I'd like to think that stage two will involve spending a bit more time together and perhaps starting to integrate each other into our wider circles of friends.

That sounds quite officious really; but I just mean, as with every progressive relationship, maybe it's time we take things more seriously.

From: Julie Lawson

Wow. Very promising!

So this is something you discussed?

From: Allie Rainsbury

In a round about way. He's still slightly reticent; I think he's naturally cautious by nature (or previous experience has made him that way). But I was pretty adamant that now would be a good time to try taking things to another level.

From: Julie Lawson

Fantastic! We shall have to organise a dinner!

I can finally meet David when I'm not passing him in the corridor, both of us having to pretend that we don't have a mutual object of affection.

From: Allie Rainsbury

Absolutely! That sounds good.

No interrogating though :P

The thought never crossed my mind.

Let me have a word with George and we'll see when we can do.

From: Allie Rainsbury

Lovely! x

Tuesday

From: Peter Rainsbury
To: Allie Rainsbury

Hi sweetheart,

It's been a while since I've written so I thought I'd drop you a quick line. Spring is finally into full swing and the weather's allowing me to actually make some progress on the garden, although admittedly this is still very slow.

Your mother thinks I shouldn't worry so much about it, but I do think that the condition of a lawn reflects the condition of the people within. No doubt horribly outdated, but there you go – I'm too old to change my ways now. Plus (and this really grates) our neighbours down but two have an incredible display of hyacinths already and I can't understand how they've managed it.

Anyway, none of this much interests you I don't doubt. How's work? Your mum says you're busy as ever. Have you talked to her much recently? I've been a bit worried that she seems very tired a lot of the time, although her trip to the doctor went well and she's been given a clean bill of health.

All the same, that's the main reason I decided that it would be good to get her down to Teignmouth this Easter. Instead of carrying all the hosting duties, I'm thinking that for once she could relax a little and enjoy a change of scene.

Speaking of Devon, I really think your mum would appreciate the whole family getting together. If you're not already tied into something else then why not come down? The biggest argument I had to overcome to convince your mother that we should go was that she thought you'd be unlikely to make it. So, if for no other reason other than to keep your dad out of the bad books, please do try.

That's all for now; we have a bridge class this evening – apparently your mum is keen to try another game from rummy. I can't understand why, but I'll go along and see what all the fuss is about I suppose.

With love, Dad.

From: Allie Rainsbury
To: Julie Lawson

Have you booked your holiday yet? Still planning on Egypt?

From: Julie Lawson

Yes. We're booking it this week. George is just clearing his schedule first, but he can't foresee any problems (mostly because he knows that any problems he might foresee at work would pale in comparison to those of two disappointed children and one angry wife ☺).

From: Allie Rainsbury

Fantastic, you'll have so much fun. I'm very jealous!

Do you think it's too soon for me to suggest a bigger trip to David?

From: Julie Lawson

I think only you can answer that. It certainly sounds as if you've both turned a corner after the weekend just gone.

What were you thinking?

From: Allie Rainsbury

I don't know. I have a lot of holiday still to use and don't want to end up like last year, on a weird last-minute package deal to Jersey with Chris, spending a week driving each other crazy with our opposing views on what makes a good holiday.

Or, worse still, spending my free time with my parents, playing charades and discussing the rules of cricket, or golf, or something similar.

From: Julie Lawson

Perhaps you should suggest a week away to him then. After all, it's not as if you're asking a favour. A girlfriend asking her boyfriend to spend a few days together in the sun isn't going to make newspaper headlines, is it? I say, go for it!

From: Allie Rainsbury

Good points. I'll do it! I'll think about where to go first, do a crafty bit of research and present him with an offer he can't refuse ☺

From: Scott Cooper
To: Allie Rainsbury

Hi Allison,

I just wanted to drop you a quick email to check you were OK after last week.

I hope the experience wasn't too traumatic for you – as mentioned during the afternoon itself, I was sincerely impressed by the way you took on the challenge and continued through the day as if nothing had happened.

Thank you again for contributing so whole-heartedly throughout the course of the day. I hope you found it useful.

With best wishes, Scott.

Wednesday

From: Chris Trail
To: Allie Rainsbury

Now that you're a fully fledged extreme sports athlete I doubt I'll get much resistance to this suggestion: Running this evening? A 3k challenge? (I managed over 2.5 the other evening so this shouldn't be outside the realms of possibility).

From: Allie Rainsbury

You've been running without me? I feel cheated!

From: Chris Trail

One of us, my dear, is taking this resolution seriously :P

Speaking of which, I've looked into guitar lessons as well (which, once taken, will tick off all our resolutions and give us a warm glow of satisfaction and achievement).

Do you want me to try and book one in after jogging?

From: Allie Rainsbury

Wait a minute there, Hendrix, I haven't confirmed the running bit yet, much less guitar lessons afterwards!

From: Chris Trail

The running is for certain, the guitar learning merely probable.

Thirty pounds per person per hour.

From: Allie Rainsbury

Thirty pounds? Do they throw in a guitar for that as well?

Anyway, there's no way I'm going to a guitar lesson having just run three kilometres. I'll be red and shaking and in dire need of a hot bath.

Yes to running; no to the musical racket. And that's the best deal you'll get :P

From: Chris Trail

Your terms are acceptable (providing we book up a lesson for next week).

From: Allie Rainsbury

But, it's your birthday next week!

From: Chris Trail

The week after then. No excuses.

From: Allie Rainsbury

Bless you for your bloody-mindedness.

See you this evening.

From: Allie Rainsbury
To: David Marshall

Hello! You can imagine my surprise when I got a text message from you last night. Coming from someone who never seems to use his phone, I feel incredibly privileged!

From: David Marshall

You can't say I never do anything for you ☺

From: Allie Rainsbury

I'm still having the odd flashback to the weekend until I get pulled out of them by the reality of the workplace...

From: David Marshall

I won't ask what these flashbacks concentrate on ;)

From: Allie Rainsbury

Mostly the food. And the beautiful scenery of course. Definitely just those thoughts and nothing else.

From: David Marshall

I absolutely don't believe you for a second.

From: Allie Rainsbury

You don't? Hmm... well, maybe you're right.

I'm rather transparent, obviously!

From: David Marshall

With the underwear you wore at the weekend, I couldn't disagree.

From: Allie Rainsbury

OK, now I'm blushing.

From: David Marshall

You're cute when you blush.

From: Allie Rainsbury

And now I'm flustered. Stop it!

Although, while we're talking about trips away, I was wondering... I still have all my holiday to use and I don't have any plans at the moment. How would you feel about spending a few days in the sun somewhere?

What do you reckon? A good idea?...

From: David Marshall

Wow... I don't know!

When were you thinking?

I'm not sure exactly. I hadn't thought that far ahead. I was just sounding you out at this stage.

From: David Marshall

All right. Let me have a think. It's a maybe.

I don't want to say yes straight away and make things too easy!

From: Allie Rainsbury

OK. Have a think and let me know.

It wouldn't be for a while so there'd be plenty of time to organise work and any other commitments (cycling or otherwise!).

I just think if it gets anywhere near replicating last weekend then we'd have a great time, which is what a holiday is meant to be about really.

From: David Marshall

True. We'll see.

OK, I must dash now, meetings beckon x

Thursday

From: Julie Lawson
To: Allie Rainsbury

Sharm el-Sheikh is all booked!

Would you and David care to come to dinner on Friday so we can show off in more detail?

From: Allie Rainsbury

Ooh, that is huge news! When are you going? How long for?

Dinner would be lovely. Let me just double-check that David's free and we'll be there with bells on.

From: Julie Lawson

We're going for ten days in May, staying at a hotel by the beach that has both a kids' club and a cocktail lounge. I zoned out after that.

Great, let me know if you're both free and we'll book you in. George is incredibly curious about this man. As am I! ☺

From: Allie Rainsbury

I think George will get on well with him; they have a similar sense of humour.

From: Julie Lawson

If David has that and a knowledge of the Arsenal starting line up, they'll be best friends.

From: Allie Rainsbury

I'll forewarn him.

Chat later x

From: Allie Rainsbury
To: David Marshall

Happy Thursday to you!

What are you up to tomorrow evening?

From: David Marshall

I'd be happier if another major work project hadn't landed on my lap.

I'm meant to be playing squash tomorrow. Why, what do you have planned?

From: Allie Rainsbury

Julie and George have invited us over for dinner.

From: David Marshall

Ah, that's a shame. Another time maybe.

By the way, do you have updated customer plans for Waterstone's to hand? I could really use some of that information if you do. Any idea of their market trend this year so far or is it too early to tell?

From: Allie Rainsbury

That's a shame?! Can you not cancel squash this once?

From: David Marshall

It's already arranged and the court is booked – if we cancel we'll lose our fee.

Plus, what am I meant to say to my friend? 'Sorry but I'm bumping you for a more important engagement that's just come up'?

From: Allie Rainsbury

That's exactly what you're meant to say. Anyone would understand that!

Julie's my best friend and she and her family mean a lot to me; I'd really appreciate it if you can forgo your kids' game for one evening.

From: David Marshall

Allie, don't talk to me like that.

You can't come to me the day before and expect me to drop everything – it's not right or fair.

From: Allie Rainsbury

I cannot believe you're trying to take a moral high ground here.

I'm only asking you to not play bloody squash in order to meet my closest friend! I don't get how you can't see why that would be important to me and why you wouldn't want to make an effort to come. Especially when we talked about spending more time together last weekend.

From: David Marshall

For the record, you were the one who talked about spending more time together, not me.

From: Allie Rainsbury

What are you saying? What does that mean?

From: David Marshall

It doesn't mean anything. I'm just pointing out the facts before I'm painted as the bad guy here!

Look, I get that it's important to you. And I'm sorry I'm not around tomorrow because I would love to meet Julie and Greg.

Why don't I check when I can do next week or the week after and we can organise something for then? I promise I'll be especially charming with them ☺

From: Allie Rainsbury

You could start by getting his name right.

Don't bother, I'll find someone else to go with me.

From: David Marshall

Allie, don't be silly. I'll let you know when I'm free as soon as I can and we'll have a great evening with Julie and George. I did mean George, I'm sorry.

Let's not argue over this.

From: Allie Rainsbury

We just have. I don't get you at all sometimes. Do you not want to spend time with me?

From: David Marshall

Jesus! I can't have this conversation now. One, it's ridiculous and two, I've got too much on.

From: Allie Rainsbury

Why am I being ridiculous?

I ask you to prioritise an evening with me and you won't. I don't understand how else you can view it?

From: David Marshall

Allie, I'm not replying any more as we're going round in circles.

I like you a lot (Lord knows why sometimes! ☺). If you're unhappy with things then let's talk them through, OK?

But not when you're too emotional to think straight or talk rationally. There's just no point.

From: Allie Rainsbury

I'm not unhappy when I actually get to spend time with you, but I feel that I hardly ever do.

And after all this, I'm the one left feeling bad.

Friday

From: Julie Lawson
To: Allie Rainsbury

Are we still being graced by Putney's new hot couple this evening? ☺

From: Allie Rainsbury

Tragically not. I'm so sorry for not letting you know yesterday but I was tied up all afternoon and felt a bit tired and under the weather in the evening. Between all that, I just plain forgot.

From: Julie Lawson

Ah, that's a shame. But not to worry.

How come you were feeling ill?

From: Allie Rainsbury

I'm not sure. There are a few colds going round, so I'm probably coming down with one of those.

I'm really sorry, Julie, I was looking forward to dinner as well.

From: Julie Lawson

Don't worry about it, silly girl. I wouldn't want you coughing and spluttering over the kids anyway :P

You just look after yourself, relax and rest easy. I presume David is taking care of his patient?

From: Allie Rainsbury

No, he's busy this evening as it happens.

But he is checking to see when he's next free so we'll be able to organise something for then (assuming you're still keen?).

From: Julie Lawson

Of course we'll still be keen. We're both dying to meet him.

What do you mean, he's checking? Who's he checking with?!

From: Allie Rainsbury

Just... He's going to let me know. He has a very full diary, unlike me, so he's trying to free up a couple of dates.

From: Julie Lawson

This isn't a bad attempt at an April Fool's joke, is it? I've known you for too long to fall for that.

From: Allie Rainsbury

No, he's just a busy guy, that's all. I'm too tired to go into details today, but honestly, we'll let you know as soon as we're next free and take advantage of your hospitality then.

From: Julie Lawson

Sure, understood.

Are you all right?

From: Allie Rainsbury

I'm fine! I'm fine. Just looking forward to the weekend and a couple of lie-ins!

From: Julie Lawson

You'll let me know if you want to talk about anything, won't you? I always offer and you always stay silent, but sometimes it's good to share...

Do you want me to pop by later with some soup or anything? Flu tablets?

From: Allie Rainsbury

Aww. You're so sweet, Julie!

No, thank you, I'm OK – just need a bit of bed rest and I'll be back to my perky best by Monday x

From: Julie Lawson

I'll give you a call over the weekend.

Wrap up warm and head home early. That's an order x

From: David Marshall
To: Allie Rainsbury

Do we find ourselves more calm today? ☺ I didn't want to leave things on a bad note before the weekend x

Also (and apologies to bring it up again) but have you had any more thoughts on the market trends question I asked yesterday? Deadlines everywhere right now.

CHAPTER 14

Monday 4 April

From: Julie Lawson
To: Allie Rainsbury

Was it just me who got drenched this morning? Stupid April showers!

From: Allie Rainsbury

I narrowly avoided the downpour which helped my mood immediately ☺

From: Julie Lawson

Glad to hear it. Did you chat to David?

From: Allie Rainsbury

I didn't, no. I think I'll leave him stewing for a bit longer.

I hate playing that kind of game, but like I said on Saturday, he still doesn't seem to understand what I'm looking for. Which is so frustrating!

From: Julie Lawson

I think you're right to let him come to you. You're too good to be chasing around, demanding someone's attention when you deserve it without even asking.

From: Allie Rainsbury

I know, I know (☺). Anyway, I'm not going to think about David for a while. It's Monday morning and it's raining; that's depressing enough in itself!

Plus, it is Chris's birthday on Wednesday and I need to organise a few drinks for his nearest and dearest. This shall be my sole focus of attention for today (apart from work, obviously). You free to come?

From: Julie Lawson

Absolutely! Fancy dress theme again?

From: Allie Rainsbury

After last year's photos?

Actually, as we're all getting older now, I was thinking of something classier and more understated to reflect our growing maturity and wisdom.

From: Julie Lawson

What a fun party plan. Do you have a short list?

From: Allie Rainsbury

The only idea I have at the moment is to meet at the Warrington, play drinking games and challenge Chris to down a shot from each bottle on the top shelf.

From: Julie Lawson

That does almost define understated.

From: Allie Rainsbury

Yes, well, biting sarcasm aside, I suppose you do have a point.

Hence my need for further suggestions.

From: Julie Lawson

Maybe look at Vinopolis? It's a wine-tasting place that's big enough to host a party. Plus, it would be something fun and new for people to do apart from just drink – while still keeping alcohol very much the main thrust of the evening ☺

From: Allie Rainsbury

That's a great idea! I'll ring them now and check availability.

Well done you (and by 'well done' I do of course mean that you are to claim no part, creative or logistic, in the planning of the birthday on the evening itself :P)

I will be far too thrilled at the surprise of wine tasting to think such ill-tempered thoughts.

From: Allie Rainsbury

I thought as much.

From: David Marshall
To: Allie Rainsbury

Hi, how was your weekend? I was going to text you on Sunday but wasn't sure if you would want to hear from me x

Tuesday

From: Scott Cooper
To: Allie Rainsbury

Hi Allison,

Apologies for the email, but I haven't had a chance to set-up a face-to-face catch up. I'm writing out of courtesy, to let you know that I intend on taking a more customer-facing role with various accounts across the coming months.

As a key client of ours I am keen to get my relationship with Waterstone's up and running as soon as possible. Please can you organise a meeting with my equivalent along with yourself and your counterpart by way of introduction?

If you email my assistant then she should be able to provide you with a couple of dates. Any questions, please let me know.

Best regards, Scott.

From: Allie Rainsbury

Absolutely. I'll arrange it.

Should I be suited or clad in a wetsuit for this one?

Kind regards, Allie.

From: Scott Cooper

Is that intended to be humorous or the beginning of legal proceedings?

From: Allie Rainsbury

It depends. Do I have a case?

From: Scott Cooper

It's not water-tight, no.

From: Chris Trail
To: Allie Rainsbury

Vinopolis? How exciting! I really don't want a huge deal though; it's not even a big birthday.

From: Allie Rainsbury

Every birthday is big. But it only took a day to organise. Plus the wine-tasting course is your birthday present.

From: Chris Trail

Well then, it's a great birthday present. I'm really touched x

From: Allie Rainsbury

And it wasn't my idea in all honesty.

Also, there are only eleven people coming (including you and me).

From: Chris Trail

Are you trying to do yourself out of a thank you?

It still sounds amazing, whoever thought of it, and, as organiser, you get the praise!

A smaller group is better anyway; there won't be any hangers-on or wannabes – they can be really grating with all their fawning and compliments ☺

I shall be a wine connoisseur by the evening's end!

From: Allie Rainsbury

As long as you're drunk by the evening's end then my mission will have been accomplished.

From: Chris Trail

In that case, I think you can sleep soundly x

From: David Marshall
To: Allie Rainsbury

Really? You're still keeping silent? x

Wednesday

From: David Marshall
To: Allie Rainsbury

Why didn't you reply to my text last night? Please let me know what you're thinking.

From: Allie Rainsbury

I'm thinking that I'm not sure what I'm thinking.

From: David Marshall

Should I be giving up on us here?

It's obvious you don't want to talk and, since I'm not quite sure what I've done to deserve this hostility, I don't see how we can make any progress.

From: Allie Rainsbury

Is that honestly how you view things? You think of you and I as a collective; as an 'us'?

From: David Marshall

I was beginning to. I thought you felt the same.

From: Allie Rainsbury

I did! I do! I mean... I don't understand how you can say that you see us as a couple on the one hand but seem so dismissive of things that matter to me on the other.

I don't understand why, a week and a half after spending an amazing weekend together, we haven't spent any more time alone.

From: David Marshall

Are you free for a drink tomorrow?

From: Allie Rainsbury

No, it's my friend's birthday. I didn't ask if you wanted to come because I assumed it would be a no.

Besides, it's for close friends only, and, since you don't know any of them, it would be awkward.

From: David Marshall

That's really unfair.

From: Allie Rainsbury

I don't see how.

From: David Marshall

What do you want from me here?!

From: Allie Rainsbury

I want a boyfriend! I want somebody who wants to spend time with me. I think I deserve that.

From: David Marshall

And I see you as a potential girlfriend!

I don't think that we want different things, I just think we're on different timescales.

Look, can we at least start by agreeing that we both like each other? Even allowing for the current tension that's circling ☺

From: Allie Rainsbury

Yes, I like you. You know I do.

That's the problem – I think I've made that very clear, but I'm still unsure how you really feel about me.

From: David Marshall

Well, you shouldn't be. I like you too. An awful lot.

I do believe in taking things slowly, but I realise that can be frustrating.

From: Allie Rainsbury

I don't mind taking our time over things. I'm pretty sure that's what we've been doing for the past couple of months.

I know that you think I'm being pushy, but I'm just scared of being quite vulnerable in all this.

From: David Marshall

I understand.

And you're not being pushy, you're really not.

I'm sorry for making you feel so upset.

From: Allie Rainsbury

So where do we go from here?

From: David Marshall

How about this for a route forward?

For me to be more aware of how you're feeling and for you to be more aware of how much I like you ☺

From: Allie Rainsbury

Well. That's a start...

And we maybe start seeing a bit more of each other?

And make more of an effort to meet each other's friends?

From: David Marshall

We'll take Julie and George to dinner next week. Ask them today and we'll reserve a table somewhere.

Monday would be ideal, but any other day is fine if they or you would prefer it.

From: Allie Rainsbury

Really? OK then. I'll ask them and let you know.

From: David Marshall

Sounds good.

Now, I really must get on with some work; I'll text you later. Perhaps I'll even get a response to this one :P x

From: Allie Rainsbury

You shall, you definitely shall ☺

And I'm sorry too. I don't mean to be cross or angry. It's because I like you an awful lot as well x

Thursday

From: Chris Trail
To: Allie Rainsbury

Have you made it in?

I woke up in a blur and still can't remember how I got home!

From: Allie Rainsbury

I'm in, but keeping my head down and feeling slightly nauseated.

Did you have fun?

From: Chris Trail

I think I had a great time! ☺

Note to self for next time we try being sommeliers: spit wine out after tasting, do not swallow in vast quantities.

Thank you again, lovely, it was a really fun evening!

From: Allie Rainsbury

Glad you enjoyed it.

Another birthday done and dusted, old man :P

From: Chris Trail

So that's why my memory's going! And here was I blaming the alcohol.

Plans for the day?

From: Allie Rainsbury

My plan is to get through today in one piece. I have a meeting in an hour that I shall contribute nothing towards bar sit quietly shaking in the corner.

After that I will clock-watch desperately until the stroke of 5.30 upon which I'll walk unsteadily yet briskly to the bus stop, pray for a good journey home and fling myself under the duvet around the same time the front door is closing.

From: Chris Trail

Wow. Have you been reading my diary? We have identical days ahead :P

From: Allie Rainsbury

Then I shall leave you to your misery.

Even the effort of typing is now starting to make me feel ill :S

From: Chris Trail

Ha, you are pathetic ☺ Enjoy your wallowing.

Oh, and although this is well down your priority list, I've booked us in for that guitar lesson next week. Wednesday evening at 7 p.m. You promised...

From: Allie Rainsbury

The thought of loud noise is too much to bear.

From: Chris Trail

You're coming x

From: Allie Rainsbury

Only if I pull through :P

Friday

From: Allie Rainsbury
To: Julie Lawson

Hi, are you back in the land of the living?

From: Julie Lawson

Barely. I have a lot on today and I'm hanging on for the weekend. Which is strange logic to use as I have an even busier weekend playing chauffeur for the kids!

How are you holding up?

From: Allie Rainsbury

I can't complain. Or at least, I did complain, but I moaned a fair bit yesterday and feel that I've now used up my share.

From: Julie Lawson

How equitable of you. I have no such qualms and plan on grumbling to anyone and everyone during the course of the day.

I'm confident that this tactic will cause at least two people to eventually throw up their hands in despair and do some of the work I have hanging over me.

From: Allie Rainsbury

Ingenious!

Demented, obviously. But ingenious.

From: Julie Lawson

Thank you! I shall practise my evil laugh in preparation.

From: Allie Rainsbury

Before you do, can you let me know if you and George are free on Monday evening please? David has finally made himself available and we'd like to take you to dinner.

From: Julie Lawson

Ah, so David's checked his diary and discovered a window, has he?

From: Allie Rainsbury

Something like that. We had a long talk a couple of days ago and both put our points across. The upshot being that he apologised and I got my own way ☺

From: Julie Lawson

I have taught you all I can, I know that now.

From: Allie Rainsbury

He needed to be sorry. He owed me that much.

Anyway... You'll come?

From: Julie Lawson

Of course we will. But why don't you both come over to ours for dinner? As much as I appreciate the offer of an evening out, it's quite short notice to try and find a babysitter. It will be much easier for us to cook instead.

From: Allie Rainsbury

That sounds just as good!

From: Julie Lawson

Agreed then. Monday evening.

Although if David cancels this time he'll be in real danger of becoming *persona non grata*.

From: Allie Rainsbury

Don't worry – if he cancels this time he'll be *persona non* testicles.

From: Julie Lawson

Ha! So what exactly did you talk through the other day?

Wait... Tell me over the weekend instead. I have a meeting to moan in now.

From: Allie Rainsbury

Good luck delegating :P x

CHAPTER 15

Monday 11 April

From: Allie Rainsbury
To: David Marshall

Nervous? ☺

From: David Marshall

Do I need to be? I'm looking forward to it. I've heard so much about them that I feel part of the family!

From: Allie Rainsbury

Ha, well I've told them quite a bit about you too, so you'll all be well informed.

And, no, of course you don't need to be nervous, they're very relaxed and welcoming people!

From: David Marshall

I trust you faxed them my most recent resumé as well? :P

I'm sure it will be a fun evening. Although, worst case scenario, I'll bring a couple of bottles of red along and we can drink through any awkward silences.

From: Allie Rainsbury

You really don't know Julie if you think there'll be any silences.

I've asked her to go easy, but I can't guarantee that you won't be bombarded with questions anyway.

From: David Marshall

As long as she turns off the spotlight when she asks them then that's OK.

Stop worrying! I'll be fine – if you like them so much, then I'm sure I will too.

From: Allie Rainsbury

You're right, of course. I just really want the evening to go well x

From: David Marshall

It will be a great success and we'll all go home best friends. ☺

Now stop making yourself so nervous and let me get some work done please!

From: Allie Rainsbury

Sorry. I shall email Julie instead and see how she's getting on.

From: David Marshall

Fine. Enjoy your girly chat and perhaps calm yourself down with a cup of tea (caffeine free if possible).

From: Allie Rainsbury

Good luck with your work!

Should we leave together or meet at Putney Bridge? x

From: David Marshall

Putney Bridge sounds good, see you there x

From: Allie Rainsbury

Bye for now, see you soon!

Eek! ☺ x

Tuesday

From: Allie Rainsbury
To: Julie Lawson

So, what did you think?

From: Julie Lawson

What a fun evening! Did he have a good time? Did you?

From: Allie Rainsbury

I had a lovely time, thank you. And so did he – he told me on the walk back home.

But you didn't answer my question. What do you think of him now you know him better?! Did George like him too?

From: Julie Lawson

I thought he was very charming. He seems very confident which is always a good thing (in moderation anyway) and he was a very interesting guy.

I think George thought roughly the same, although the poor love was so tired from his early start yesterday that he'd fallen asleep five minutes after you both left. It did get him out of the washing up though ☺

From: Allie Rainsbury

So... You liked him? He said he liked both of you very much.

From: Julie Lawson

Well, that's nice to know! Yes, of course we liked him. He's not hard to like over dinner. He has a lot to say for himself and is entertaining, opinionated and charismatic. There, gushing enough for you?

From: Allie Rainsbury

I think so, yes ☺

Opinionated is a good thing, isn't it? You don't want someone to just sit there and be passive all night.

Are there any 'buts' to temper such high praise?

From: Julie Lawson

No! Not really anyway.

The main thing is that you like him and (more importantly) that he likes you.

From: Allie Rainsbury

But...

From: Julie Lawson

:P! But nothing!

If I was absolutely forced into saying anything that could be vaguely construed to be in the same vicinity of a negative comment, I might venture to say that I wouldn't have necessarily picked him to be your type.

But he clearly is, so what do I know?

From: Allie Rainsbury

Why would you think that? What wouldn't make him my type?

From: Julie Lawson

Um... And this is all still really reaching, remember... Maybe he comes across as a little brash sometimes. Is that the word I'm looking for?

Anyway, in the absence of a better one it will have to do. I always thought you went for the strong, silent sort.

From: Allie Rainsbury

Interesting. I don't think 'brash' is the right word, no, but he is confident in himself. I suppose you don't get to be as successful as David without having self-belief. But I like that!

Maybe I have gone for quieter men in the past, but they've not exactly panned out that great, have they?

From: Julie Lawson

Well, then there you go. It seems you're very smitten.

And, in fairness I must say this too – up close and personal, he is one gorgeous-looking guy! ☺

From: Allie Rainsbury

Ha, I trust you didn't tell George that.

From: Julie Lawson

George was the one who first mentioned it.

From: Allie Rainsbury

Aw, that's sweet. I'm so glad you both liked him anyway. It's a big relief to know that my best friend gets on with my boyfriend. My gorgeous-looking boyfriend no less...

From: Julie Lawson

Absolutely! Although among all these questions I've forgotten to ask you the most important one.

From: Allie Rainsbury

Which would be?

From: Julie Lawson

The crucial question that determines whether or not David's ever viewed positively again.

From: Allie Rainsbury

Yes...?

From: Julie Lawson

Did he like my roast chicken?

From: Allie Rainsbury

You're an idiot!

Yes – he loved it :P x

From: Julie Lawson

He's in the club x

Wednesday

From: Allie Rainsbury
To: David Marshall

Thank you for the text messages last night. Wish you'd been over at mine at the time ;)

From: David Marshall

Slightly tired this morning, I couldn't get to sleep for a long while afterwards.

From: Allie Rainsbury

I hope the thoughts keeping you awake were pleasant ones?

From: David Marshall

Very much so ;)

From: Allie Rainsbury

Sounds like we had very similar daydreams :P

Care to come over tomorrow evening and we can compare in person?

From: David Marshall

I'd love to, but suspect that I'll get even less sleep then than I did last night!

I have an important meeting first thing on Friday so plan to use Thursday as a quiet night in, working a bit and generally composing myself for the morning ordeal.

How about the day after? Friday evening? I'll be completely refreshed and ready for anything ;) x

From: Allie Rainsbury

Careful there, I'll hold you to that x

From: David Marshall

Hold away. It's in the diary.

Should I assume I'm staying over? ;)

From: Allie Rainsbury

You had better not stay anywhere else, that's for sure :P

We can go for a walk down by the river on Saturday if you like. Depending on the weather anyway x

From: David Marshall

Maybe... let's play that one by ear. I'm meant to be playing tennis on Saturday early afternoon – unless you want me to cancel?

From: Allie Rainsbury

No, of course not! Go play your tennis game, I don't expect you to put your life on hold!

Friday sounds perfect, I'll see you then x

From: Chris Trail
To: Allie Rainsbury

Are you still definitely coming this evening?

From: Allie Rainsbury

Since I promised you that I would, I suppose that gives me little room for manoeuvre!

From: Chris Trail

Really?

From: Allie Rainsbury

What can I say? You've worn me down ☺

From: Chris Trail

Fantastic! We're being taught by a guy called Pablo; apparently he used to be in a band that had a single that nearly reached the top 100!

From: Allie Rainsbury

No way! That makes him rock royalty.

From: Chris Trail

Don't dull this with your sarcasm, Raspbury.

We're becoming guitar legends this evening.

From: Allie Rainsbury

Uh-huh... and has Pablo been informed of our beginners' status and general musical inability?

From: Chris Trail

He has been warned yet still remains gracious enough to spare us his time.

From: Allie Rainsbury

For thirty pounds an hour...

From: Chris Trail

This will be awesome!

I'll pass by yours around quarter to and we'll walk up to the studio.

From: Allie Rainsbury

You're such a special friend... Very, very special...

Thursday

From: Allie Rainsbury
To: Julie Lawson

When I say the name Pablo, what image comes to mind? A swarthy, sultry Spaniard or a short, squat Caucasian from Bristol?

From: Julie Lawson

Ha! Was he a good teacher at least?

From: Allie Rainsbury

He was OK in fairness. He'd have been better if he hadn't spent the first half hour showing off and playing the damn thing himself!

But he did eventually show us how to play a couple of chords. It was fun, all in all.

From: Julie Lawson

So is this another of Chris's impulse hobbies you've been converted to?

From: Allie Rainsbury

I don't think I'd go that far. I suspect this will follow the same path as the cookery class and be a one-off life experience!

Chris seemed pretty into it though – he went and booked up another lesson.

From: Julie Lawson

Good on you both. Although I'd love to have seen Chris's face when he met Pablo, he must have been so disappointed. He was hoping to stumble across a strong Latin lover and instead gets a tiny white man from the West Country! ☺

From: Allie Rainsbury

He's not gay! And anyway, that wouldn't have been the reason for a guitar lesson even if he was.

From: Julie Lawson

You really do bite every time don't you? :P

From: Allie Rainsbury

If you didn't wind me up about it then I wouldn't have to!

Anyway! Changing the subject...

I need a big favour please.

From: Julie Lawson

I'm not taking your place at guitar lessons if that's what you're asking. It's bad enough I have to listen to Cale and Elly playing the piano without listening to Chris stumble along on his guitar.

From: Allie Rainsbury

No, nothing like that. In fact, much easier, much simpler and there's no noise involved.

I'm wanting to surprise David this evening and make him dinner. He's had a busy week so far with work and I thought this would help him de-stress ahead of a meeting he has tomorrow.

From: Julie Lawson

Aw, that's a nice thought. What are you going to cook?

From: Allie Rainsbury

Nothing fancy (obviously), just steak and chips. Maybe get in a bottle of wine, buy a dessert. Cheat a little!

From: Julie Lawson

Lucky guy.

What's the favour?

From: Allie Rainsbury

I don't know his address...

From: Julie Lawson

I don't understand?

From: Allie Rainsbury

Well, he'll be at his flat, which I know is in Finchley – but I can't remember exactly where.

If I ask him now it will ruin the surprise so... I thought you might be able to sneakily look it up on your personnel database ☺

From: Julie Lawson

Allie! Is that a good idea? Why not just tell him you're coming? What if he's out having a pint? You'll be standing outside in the cold with only a bottle of red wine for company. It will be just like your Uni days all over again.

From: Allie Rainsbury

Ha, ha - very clever :P

He won't be out because he's already told me he's relaxing and preparing for tomorrow.

If I turn up unannounced it will seem spontaneous and sweet as opposed to needy and demanding of attention. I've thought all of this through!

Please...?!

From: Julie Lawson

This is not a good idea. Take it from me – no guy likes being surprised like that.

Plus, I could get into serious trouble. I can't just go handing out personal information to everyone!

From: Allie Rainsbury

How am I everyone?

I need this one favour, Julie... And he'll love the surprise, I promise.

From: Julie Lawson

For this to be considered successful, he'd better get down on one knee and marry the damn surprise.

Promise me you'll at least double-check that he's around tonight first?

From: Allie Rainsbury

I will, I will.

From: Julie Lawson
To: Allie Rainsbury

12a Hurlington Place, N6 4PN. Against my better judgement...

From: Allie Rainsbury

Thank you, thank you! You're the greatest ☺

From: Julie Lawson

Thank me after, crazy girl!

From: Allie Rainsbury

I shall do, I promise!

Here's to a magical evening xx

Friday

From: David Marshall
To: Allie Rainsbury

Where did you go? Please pick up your phone!!

From: Julie Lawson
To: Allie Rainsbury

How was it, lover girl? ☺

From: David Marshall
To: Allie Rainsbury

Allie? You can't keep giving me the silent treatment when you're not happy about something. Please talk to me!

From: Julie Lawson
To: Allie Rainsbury

?? Are you not in today?

From: David Marshall
To: Allie Rainsbury

I'll call you over the weekend. We need to talk.

CHAPTER 16

Monday 18 April

From: Julie Lawson
To: Allie Rainsbury

Hey, how was your weekend? Did you spend it with David?

You haven't lost your phone again, have you? I texted you twice on Saturday and haven't had a reply yet.

From: David Marshall
To: Allie Rainsbury

I feel terrible.

I nearly came to visit you this weekend but decided against it in the end.

From: Julie Lawson
To: Allie Rainsbury

Where are you? I've just sent you another text as well. I'm getting worried and want a reply.

From: David Marshall
To: Allie Rainsbury

How did you even get my address? I don't understand why you just turned up like that out of the blue! It was a really nice surprise but it obviously wasn't something I was expecting and it looks like you've completely misread things.

From: Julie Lawson
To: Allie Rainsbury

I'm giving you until tomorrow to call me or else. It's only through speaking to your boss that I know you're alive!

What's going on? Please talk to me, I want to help x

From: David Marshall
To: Allie Rainsbury

Allie, she means absolutely nothing to me.

Surely you must realise that?

Tuesday

From: Allie Rainsbury
To: Julie Lawson

Did you know?

From: Julie Lawson

There you are! Are you OK? Did I know what? Where have you been?

From: Allie Rainsbury

Did you know that David lives with another woman?

From: Julie Lawson

What?! No! What woman? Are you serious?

From: Allie Rainsbury

I don't know who she is. His wife? His fiancée? His real girlfriend with whom he spends the majority of his time?

Yes, I'm serious.

No, I'm not joking. This is far from being a joke.

From: Julie Lawson

I don't know what to say. I don't believe it.

It can't be his wife surely? I thought they split up years ago?

From: Allie Rainsbury

And I thought he was single, but since it turns out that I was wrong about that, I don't think we should rule out the possibility.

From: Julie Lawson

This is nuts. What a bastard!

Did you find all of this out on Thursday? Why didn't you tell me sooner?

From: Allie Rainsbury

I found out on Thursday, yes. I went all the way to Finchley and rang his doorbell. This glamorous blonde woman opened the door.

I honestly thought I'd got the wrong address.

From: Julie Lawson

Oh. My. God. What did you say?

From: Allie Rainsbury

I don't think I said anything at first. I remember looking at the door number, and looking back to her. I must have done that at least five times. And then he appeared behind her. Walking down the hall looking concerned. No doubt wondering if I was there selling something or bothering her. It was only when he came up right behind her shoulder that he saw me. Horror spread across his face just before recognition did.

From: Julie Lawson

Total bloody bastard!

What did you say then?

From: Allie Rainsbury

Total bloody bastard, as it happens. Not loudly, I think I was too stunned to do anything more than whisper. And then I walked off.

I heard his voice shout my name a couple of times, but I didn't stop. I spent the next hour walking around aimlessly, then got on the tube and went home.

From: Julie Lawson

Unbelievable!

You didn't call him to ask what the hell was going on? What a bastard!

From: Allie Rainsbury

No, I didn't call him. I couldn't face it Jules.

I can't believe how stupid I've been. I've felt horrible all weekend. I feel used, naïve, gullible, idiotic and completely worthless.

And I still don't understand what's happened. I just know that I'm miserable because of it.

Now don't you dare be miserable for him. He's not worth it.

You go and put your coat on – we're going out for a long lunch to talk this through properly. I can tell you how amazing you are and how bastardy he is!

From: Allie Rainsbury

It's 10.30! We can't go for lunch yet. Plus, I have a lot of emails to get through. Two days off has left me with a lot of outstanding work.

I'll be fine, I just need to accept that this was always going to happen. When it comes to men I'm cursed. That's all.

From: Julie Lawson

I'm coming up to get you. We're going for coffee, then lunch.

Then potentially shooting David.

From: Allie Rainsbury

Stay there! I'm fine, I'm fine.

From: Julie Lawson

I'm on my way x

Wednesday

From: Ann Rainsbury
To: Allie Rainsbury

Hi darling,

We haven't heard from you in the past couple of weeks and couldn't reach you this weekend, so I'm just checking that everything's OK.

Is it particularly busy in the office at the moment? I wouldn't have thought people buy more books than usual at Easter time but maybe they do. Is that how it works? I know you've told me before that you sell Christmas books in Easter and vice versa. Or something like that. I get very confused when it comes to your job – but then you always have been far more intelligent than I ever was!

Anyway, this was just to let you know that I've packed for Teignmouth. I'm getting very excited and am looking forward to the trip, especially since you'll be keeping us company down there. Your father is less enthused, but I think that's because he has to do all the driving.

We're heading off tomorrow and should arrive in Devon around dinner time, depending on traffic around Stonehenge. I've never really understood the attraction of those rocks. I suppose they're very old and very heavy. But then so is your uncle and you don't see thousands of people queuing up to see him, do you?

There's a South Western train at 21 minutes past every hour, running from Kings Cross through to Teignmouth on Friday. The last train leaves at 8.21 p.m. so be sure to get there before then, won't you? The journey time is just over three-and-a-half hours and I'll get your father to pick you up from the station when you arrive. Do you want to travel back with us? We can sing some songs from the back like we used to when you were small. Do you remember? Oh, I really am looking forward to seeing you.

Remember to let us know when you're en route.

With much love, Mum xx

From: Allie Rainsbury
To: Julie Lawson

The long weekend can't come soon enough. I really don't feel like being here.

From: Julie Lawson

Why don't you tell Garry you're not feeling well and go home? With what's just happened you can't possibly concentrate on work anyway.

From: Allie Rainsbury

Maybe. Although at least I can be distracted by people here; at home I know that all I'll end up doing is replaying things in my mind.

From: Julie Lawson

I've got a good mind to walk straight into David's office and tell him exactly what I think of him. I'm surprised you haven't already yourself.

From: Allie Rainsbury

No! Don't do that! Please, promise me you won't do that, Julie.

I don't want to give him the satisfaction.

I don't want to talk to him or about him. I don't even want to think of him! OK?

From: Julie Lawson

I won't. I promise. It just makes me so angry that he's done this to you, that's all.

Don't bottle things up though, OK – I'm always here if you need to chat x

From: Allie Rainsbury

Agreed.

Now cheer me up please and tell me something fun!

From: Julie Lawson

Hmm… Have you heard the story of a naughty little boy called Cale, whose teacher called yesterday to inform me that he'd locked a classmate in a cupboard?

From: Allie Rainsbury

No! It sounds like a classic though ☺

From: Julie Lawson

Come meet me in the café and I'll tell you all about it.

Thursday

From: David Marshall
To: Allie Rainsbury

Dear Allie,

I'm writing this to properly explain things as you seem determined to not give me the chance to do so.

Firstly, and most importantly, I am not in a relationship with the woman who opened my door to you. But, in the distant past, I did use to be.

To begin with Hannah was a good friend, but matters progressed and we found ourselves drawn to each other. Long story short, a couple of years later we moved in together. Things went OK for the first few months, but to be honest cracks started to appear relatively early on. Like a lot of couples though, we tried to keep forcing something that wasn't there any longer and we stumbled along ignoring the growing number of arguments while excusing our increasing distance between one another on work; new interests; anything that served to extend the charade and postpone the storm that was brewing.

The inevitable happened last January. I told her I didn't love her any more and we agreed that we should start seeing other people. From my perspective, any romantic feelings had left so long ago that the whole break up, when it did happen, was very amicable. In retrospect, whether this was a blessing or not I don't know because, as you've no doubt guessed, by that stage we'd bought a flat together.

Why had we bought? Partly because of the seriousness of the relationship I suppose, but mostly it was because we both wanted to get on the property ladder and it seemed like a good time and opportunity to do so.

Over a year later we haven't sold the place. Neither of us has moved onto other relationships and we still get on as friends – when you combine that with the fact that financially it doesn't make any sense to sell at the moment, it just seemed logical to continue as things were (although obviously both bedrooms are now being used). I didn't tell you initially because I thought it might scare you off – you must admit, it does all sound pretty intense, doesn't it? After a few weeks, as I got to know you better and started to like you more and more I felt that the chance to mention it had passed and that, if I brought it up at that stage, then you'd be suspicious of why I hadn't told you before and wonder what else I was hiding.

I knew that when I broke up with Hannah it was more my choice than hers and recognised that there may be feelings other than friendship still there for her. She's been a great friend to me for so long that I've been incredibly sensitive to that. Perhaps my biggest crime here is that I've cared too much about protecting her and have tried to ensure that she doesn't get hurt. That, again as you've probably guessed, is why it's been difficult to take your calls and invite you over before now – it would have told her definitively that it was all over between us.

While this has been true for a long, long time for me, I wasn't sure how she'd take it. In hindsight I should have been more up front with her sooner over my feelings for you and not tried to make everyone happy.

I've been so scared of this happening as I knew you'd be furious if you found out and that it could jeopardise things between us. What's made it all the more frustrating is that over the past couple of months I've talked to Hannah about our current situation becoming untenable. I've been talking with several estate agents about letting the property out and moving into a place by myself. I was even thinking about moving south of the river, Putney way...

I really like you, Allie. I think we have something special and I hope that the above will go some way to explaining things in a way that can make you see sense and recognise that, while I may have made mistakes, I'm an honest and thoughtful guy.

I hope you have a great Easter break and use some of that time to consider what I've said here. To put yourself in my shoes and ask, in all practicality, what I could have done differently?

I, in turn, shall have a horrible Easter and shall no doubt spend most of it knowing that I've been the victim of a big misunderstanding and that it might well have cost me a wonderful, beautiful person.

I fervently hope that it doesn't.

With love, David xx

Friday
Bank Holiday

CHAPTER 17

Monday 25 April
Bank Holiday

Tuesday

From: Peter Rainsbury
To: Allie Rainsbury

Allie,

Let me start on a positive note. Over the years, as parents, we have been incredibly proud of you. I don't know if we've told you it often enough, but your mother and I have always been impressed at how thoughtful, polite and friendly you are to everyone you come across. It's how we brought you up; they're the values we believe in, and we were so immensely glad to have a daughter who personified them. You put a smile on the face of everyone you meet including, and especially, your mother's. You are, very simply, the light of her life. Perhaps you don't quite see or fully understand her excitement at the thought of seeing you. Or even, for that matter, getting a phone call – with the two of you laughing over jokes and subjects that I can't even pretend to be a part of.

Hopefully this might help describe some of the disappointment that she, and indeed I, felt at you not coming down to Devon for Easter, after confirming only a week ago that you would – quite aside from the fact that your aunt and uncle went to the effort of preparing a bedroom for you, of buying in extra food and were themselves looking forward to seeing you.

I do not believe that as parents we are particularly demanding ones. We have never tried to push you in any particular direction in life; we never consciously judged you on the decisions you've made. The one thing we have requested is for you to display manners, thoughtfulness and respect. I don't think that that is too much to ask. It's something that you completely ignored this weekend. I cannot remember a time when I have been more disappointed with you.

You are of course far too old to discipline and perhaps now far too self-involved to care. I'm so cross and insulted by your actions (or lack thereof) that I feel it best you don't try and call us for a while. I can only imagine that the conversation, on my part at least, would be terse, tense and angry.

Whether silence is punishment or not I don't know; perhaps you'll view it as a blessing.

Dad.

From: Allie Rainsbury
To: Ann Rainsbury; Peter Rainsbury

Dear Mum and Dad,

I really am so sorry about this weekend. I felt terrible all week and was bed-ridden most of the time. I feel really bad about it and was so looking forward to seeing you all, but I would have made for horrible company (you know what a bad patient I am ☺).

Please don't be cross. I'll phone you this evening and we can arrange a date for me to come visit you very soon, OK?

With much love, Allie xxx

From: David Marshall
To: Allie Rainsbury

Hello! How was your Easter?

Have you come back refreshed and rejuvenated? ☺

Are you free this week at all? x

Wednesday

From: Julie Lawson
To: Allie Rainsbury

Guess who I had to suffer through a meeting with.

From: Allie Rainsbury

How come? You didn't do anything I hope...

From: Julie Lawson

I resisted the urge to throw my coffee all over him and contented myself by giving him a death stare.

From: Allie Rainsbury

Good, thank you. I really don't want this to be brought into work and definitely don't want you to get involved.

From: Julie Lawson

I'm still in favour of emailing the whole company and telling everyone what a rat he is.

But it's your call I suppose.

From: Allie Rainsbury

That would certainly fuel gossip! Although it wouldn't be very fair on him.

From: Julie Lawson

Why wouldn't that be fair on David? I can understand it not being fair on you!

From: Allie Rainsbury

I had a very protracted email from him just before Easter explaining the situation. Apparently this woman is just a flatmate. They used to have a thing but it was all a long time ago.

I don't know – maybe he's just been stupid by not telling me the whole story, rather than doing anything terribly wrong.

From: Julie Lawson

Are you kidding? He's been living with another woman and didn't tell you about it! I'd say that's pretty much as terribly wrong as you can get!

From: Allie Rainsbury

It wasn't like that though, Jules. There were lots of reasons why he didn't say anything, and to be honest, they all kind of made sense.

I know you'll think I'm being crazy here but I think he kept silent to try and protect my feelings rather than trying to be duplicitous.

From: Julie Lawson

You're right. I do think you're being crazy. I don't think you should even be thinking on these lines!

He wanted the best of both worlds and, for a few months, was able to have just that. He's only trying to weasel his way out now because you caught him red handed.

From: Allie Rainsbury

Maybe... I don't know. I just need a bit of time to think everything through.

If what you say is true then I still don't understand why he's so determined to chat to me now. If I really was just a bit of fun on the side then why would he want to talk at all?

From: Julie Lawson

Who knows? Maybe he just enjoys the drama and the challenge. Maybe he's getting a kick out of all of this!

I don't know why, but I do know that you shouldn't even be trying to answer that question at the moment.

From: Allie Rainsbury

That's easy to say but less easy to do. My head's spinning and I can't think straight.

Why did he do it? Did he even do anything?

I wish I wasn't thinking these questions, but I can't help it. I can't think about much else.

From: Julie Lawson

I know it's tough; it's incredibly difficult for you. I'm not sure what I can offer that would make things any easier. Maybe an evening round at ours? A bit of time away from your own company?

From: Allie Rainsbury

That's sweet, Jules, thank you. Another time maybe, I'm not really feeling up to an evening out just yet. I'll figure it out soon enough I'm sure.

From: Julie Lawson

Hang in there, kid.

Be strong – don't get lonely and call him x

Thursday

From: Allie Rainsbury
To: Ann Rainsbury; Peter Rainsbury

Dear Mum and Dad,

Where are you? I called you on Tuesday evening and yesterday with no success. I hope you're not still cross over Easter. I really am sorry but, as mentioned already, I'd been running a temperature for several days (flu is very difficult to avoid when it starts spreading around a cramped office!).

Are you around this weekend for a chat? It would be nice to catch up.

Miss you both. With love, Allie xxx

From: David Marshall
To: Allie Rainsbury

I suppose I should admit defeat then...

I don't want to hassle you with unwanted emails or phone calls, so you'll no doubt be pleased to know that this is the last of them.

I'm sorry that you couldn't take my explanation for what it was: a simple retelling of an innocent misunderstanding. I'm sorry too that you're so determined to stay silent and not talk this through – I think what we have is worth that; clearly you feel very differently.

I think that's part of what hurts so much in all this. I feel that I'm the one who has put my heart on the line and had it trodden on while you've been able to move on without a care in the world. Did you ever really care for me or was it all just a bit of fun for you?

I suppose I'll never find out now. For the record you should know that, on my part at least, it was something potentially very special.

Good luck in everything, Allie, you're an amazing person and you deserve the very best. I'm just sorry that you're not giving me the chance to offer you that.

Love, David.

From: Allie Rainsbury

How can you say that it's only a bit of fun for me when for weeks I've been the person asking for more?

And do you really think I've been fine this past week? If you honestly think that then you don't know me at all.

From: David Marshall

A reply! Forgive me while I deal with the shock...! ☺

How are you?

And if you still care about us then why haven't you replied to any of my messages?

From: Allie Rainsbury

I haven't replied because I'm still recovering from the bombshell that you live with a woman who (you say) is your ex-girlfriend.

I would have thought that was obvious.

From: David Marshall

I suppose I deserve that.

But I have tried to explain, several times. There's nothing going on between Hannah and me – there hasn't been for a while.

I understand that it must have been a nasty surprise, but it's been a couple of weeks now. How long are you planning to punish me for being well intentioned? That's essentially what it boils down to.

From: Allie Rainsbury

Can you really not get how hurtful it was for me to see her in your flat? I need you to acknowledge that, David.

I need you to understand why I've been totally thrown by this, and why I am still wondering whether it's a good idea to even email you, let alone anything else.

From: David Marshall

I do get it. It must have been a terrible shock, I know that. But I've admitted that already. I've apologised already, despite not having done much wrong!

I don't know how many more times I can say I'm sorry before we can agree to move on?

From: Allie Rainsbury

I don't know the answer to that. I do know that I'm still angry and sad and not in place to just forget about this though.

If you've been keeping that from me then how can I trust that you're not keeping other secrets? How can I be expected to trust you? Can you answer me that?

From: David Marshall

That's crazy! Of course you can trust me!

I've already told you; the only reason I didn't tell you anything was to protect your own feelings. It's only because I like you so much that I got myself into this situation in the first place. It's really unfair for you to hold this over me now when all I've tried to do is be considerate of you.

Allie, you can trust me. You can trust that I like you a lot, you can trust that I'm falling for you, and you can trust that, if you give us a chance, we could have something that grows into more.

But, ultimately, that is up to you. Will you give us that chance? Will you fight for what we might have?

From: Allie Rainsbury

I don't know. Right now, I just don't know.

I need more time to think, David.

From: David Marshall

Do you still even like me?

From: Allie Rainsbury

Yes. I wish that I didn't at the moment, but I do.

I need some space to sort my head out though. Please respect that.

From: David Marshall

Of course! I understand; I'll wait for you.

You're worth it x

Friday

From: Julie Lawson
To: Allie Rainsbury

Good morning! I have an invitation for you ☺

From: Allie Rainsbury

?...

From: Julie Lawson

I was chatting with George last night and we're both in agreement — we think it would be a good idea for you to come to Egypt with us.

You can get some sun, some relaxing beach time, a few drinks. Get a chance to properly clear your mind.

What do you think?

From: Allie Rainsbury

A pity holiday?!

Hmm… I'm not sure – it's very kind of you both, but I'd be intruding on what sounds like a lovely family trip you've got planned.

A sweet offer but I think I'll leave you all to it.

From: Julie Lawson

Nonsense – you are family!

And it's not a pity invite – if anything it's a selfish one: I'll have my best friend with me and George will feel less guilty about leaving me to spend the day scuba diving! The kids won't move from the pool all fortnight, and would rather have you there than not anyway.

You're coming!

From: Allie Rainsbury

I'm really not sure. Think I'll just be extra baggage at the moment. I'm likely to spend most of the time moaning about the unfairness of life, crying behind my sunglasses and generally being a dark cloud on the horizon.

From: Julie Lawson

Well then, you'll be a welcome bit of shade… It's going to be mid-thirty degrees out there.

Please come! I wouldn't be inviting you if we weren't sure.

Imagine it – lounging by the side of the pool with a good book… Maybe a flirtatious glance at the lifeguard… Definitely a piña colada or two… And a knock-out tan to walk back into the office with in a couple of weeks, showing you-know-who just what he's missed out on!

From: Allie Rainsbury

That does sound appealing, I must admit. And I suppose a complete change of scene would do me good.

From: Julie Lawson

It sounds like you're out of excuses then!

So you'll come? I'll even sort out all the booking details, so you don't need to worry about that.

From: Allie Rainsbury

George honestly doesn't mind?

From: Julie Lawson

Of course he doesn't! You can give him some pointers on wake-boarding ☺

All I need from you is a passport number and a smile.

From: Allie Rainsbury

Jules, you're the best friend in the world! I'll come, but feel free to change your mind at any stage.

From: Julie Lawson

Just remember to bring your passport tomorrow and start thinking which bikinis to pack.

From: Allie Rainsbury

I shall do! Thank you again. I've just found my smile for the first time in days.

From: Julie Lawson

Glad to hear it.

Who knows, we might even be able to sell you for a camel ☺

From: David Marshall
To: Allie Rainsbury

Just to say that I hope you have a good bank-holiday weekend.

If you happen to be around this evening I was going to ask you for a drink, but I'm guessing you're busy?

From: Allie Rainsbury

Not busy, just tired. I'm going to have a quiet one tonight, and this whole weekend for that matter.

Perhaps next week, depending on how I feel.

From: David Marshall

I'll hold you to that!

You go relax and enjoy yourself. I'll be thinking of you x

CHAPTER 18

Monday 2 May

Bank Holiday

Tuesday

From: David Marshall
To: Allie Rainsbury

Good morning, my favourite person! ☺ Any stories from the weekend?

Do you feel like having that drink this evening? I believe it was promised!

From: Allie Rainsbury

No stories I'm afraid.

I can't do this evening. Perhaps tomorrow we can meet up briefly after work.

From: David Marshall

Great! Shall I come over to yours? We can go to the Duke's Head and enjoy the river view – I know how much you like that.

From: Allie Rainsbury

Well, it's definitely best I don't come to yours again, isn't it.

Let's just meet in The Firestation. I can't stay for long anyway so it's silly going far.

From: David Marshall

Why can't you stay for long? I thought we could spend the evening together.

I'm happy to come Putney way. I could even stay over if you wanted? ;)

From: Allie Rainsbury

I don't think that's a good idea to be honest. Like I told you last week, I'm not really sure how I feel about things at the moment; you staying over definitely wouldn't help.

From: David Marshall

OK... That's disappointing though – I've been looking forward to seeing you for ages!

From: Allie Rainsbury

David, I did ask you last week not to expect too much too fast. You need to respect this, otherwise there's no point in even meeting up at all. I can't say that any more clearly.

From: David Marshall

I do respect it. I'm just disappointed, that's all! I miss you.

Tomorrow evening then; and perhaps we can meet up over the weekend if that goes well ☺

From: Allie Rainsbury

I'm on holiday for two weeks from this weekend.

Let's just take each day as it comes for now and not think beyond that.

I'm just not in a position to do anything else at this stage. Sorry.

From: David Marshall

What? You're away for two whole weeks?!

Why didn't you tell me? Where are you going?

So I get to see you for an hour tomorrow and that's it?

How can I possibly get you to understand how much I'm suffering here if you won't even see me properly?

From: Allie Rainsbury

David, I can't get into this now. Let's meet after work tomorrow and chat through things then.

I need to go and do some work now and I'd imagine you, as usual, have a lot to be getting on with as well.

From: David Marshall

I just hope you're not using me.

I know you're confused and mixed up, but I don't think anyone's as fragile as I am right now.

From: Allie Rainsbury
To: Ann Rainsbury; Peter Rainsbury

Dear Mum and Dad,

I feel like I'm six years old again and in trouble for eating those Christmas biscuits you'd hidden in the larder! Please pick up the phone – you've made your point, lesson learnt. I'll try not to get ill the next time an important holiday comes up! ☺

Dad, if you stay cross with me for too long then you won't be able to tell me about all the flowers that are no doubt beginning to bloom in the garden.

Your contrite and loving daughter, Allie xxx

From: Ann Rainsbury
To: Allie Rainsbury

Hello darling!

I have to be quick as your father has insisted we have no contact at all with you for a couple of weeks. Between you and me I think he's blowing it all a bit out of proportion but he really was very cross! You are silly, you should have told us earlier that you weren't feeling well! I think it was just the shock and embarrassment of having to explain to your aunt and uncle at the last minute that got him so riled up. Anyway, give it another few days and the whole episode will have blown over, you know what he's like.

All is well, it was a very enjoyable few days in Devon. Back home now though and keeping busy with a few bits and pieces. I must go in case I'm caught in the act! I feel quite the spy ☺

You make sure you look after yourself, eat lots of fruit and take a scarf with you when you go out.

Love you lots, Mum xxx

From: Allie Rainsbury

Thanks Mum!

I'm actually off to Egypt for a couple of weeks this Saturday so that should definitely burn the final vestiges of cold out of me!

I'll give Dad his stewing time and call you both when I'm back – even he can't make a mood last that long ☺

Love, Allie x

Wednesday

From: David Marshall
To: Allie Rainsbury

Did you get my text last night? I was watching *The Constant Gardener* and thought of you every time Rachel Weisz came on screen! Today can't go quickly enough ;)

From: Allie Rainsbury

Hello. Yes, I got it thanks.

I'm not so sure that it's a good idea to meet up this evening. Perhaps it's too soon and we should leave it until after I get back.

From: David Marshall

What? No!!

You can't do that to me, Allie – this evening is all I've been holding onto for the past few days.

From: Allie Rainsbury

But that's exactly the point. I can tell that you're putting all your hopes and energies into this evening and I'm worried that you're expecting something to happen that just won't.

I don't want to be responsible for making you even unhappier.

From: David Marshall

Nothing you can say or do will make me unhappier than not seeing you at all.

This is crazy. All we're doing is going for a drink. I'm not even going to see you for ages after that anyway!

Am I really that much of an effort?

From: Allie Rainsbury

I get the impression that you're a bit... all over the place emotionally at the moment. I'm not sure that it's a good idea to confront those emotions just yet, which is what we'll end up doing if we meet up.

From: David Marshall

Allie, if you don't want to hear from me again I wish you'd told me that weeks ago.

I had got my hopes up that you might still be interested but I guess not. I suppose it's my own fault for caring so much.

From: Allie Rainsbury

I'm not saying that! I just don't want to rush things, especially when we're both feeling uncertain and afraid over lots of things.

Why are you so anxious to meet up? Surely we've both said everything that needs saying at this stage anyway?

From: David Marshall

Things might have been said, but they've not necessarily been fully understood or heard.

I'd like to meet up because, as I've told you many times before (or tried to at least!) I miss seeing you, talking with you and kissing you.

Despite knowing that you're not in a place where you can countenance the latter, I would hope – if you have any ambition left for us working through this – that you could bear to consider the first couple of sentiments.

One drink. No flood of emotions. No pressure and no expectations, I promise.

From: Allie Rainsbury

You don't give up easily do you?

From: David Marshall

Not when it comes to you, no.

From: Allie Rainsbury

And one drink means just that? I can't stay any longer.

From: David Marshall

If needs be, I shall even down my pint ☺

From: Allie Rainsbury

Ha! Well, that might be overdoing it.

From: David Marshall

So we're still on?

From: Allie Rainsbury

OK. Despite reservations. I'll see you in the Firestation at 6 p.m.

Thursday

From: Julie Lawson
To: Allie Rainsbury

All packed? ☺

From: Allie Rainsbury

Just about. Very excited! How many dresses are you taking?

I met up with David last night by the way.

From: Julie Lawson

Really? Why did you do that? Are you OK?

From: Allie Rainsbury

He was really persistent and I felt that I at least owed him the chance to explain things a bit further.

It was a nice evening in the end.

From: Julie Lawson

Hmm. Well, you know what I think you owe him, but I suppose that's not important.

What did you talk about?

From: Allie Rainsbury

Lots of things.

But, yes, the 'incident' was discussed, if that's what you're asking ☺

From: Julie Lawson

That's what he's calling it now, huh?

Well? Was any new light shed on this 'incident' or was it more of the same?

From: Allie Rainsbury

You're even tougher than I am (and I was pretty tough on him). He told me more detail behind how they came to be living together, why they had split up and how he was looking to move on.

I suppose it was more of the same in that sense (if you want to be cynical :P) but I did begin to feel reassured that he was genuinely sorry and that I'd jumped to a couple of hasty conclusions.

From: Julie Lawson

I think cynicism is a valuable ally most of the time.

So, what are you concluding now?

From: Allie Rainsbury

Nothing. I'm not concluding anything until I'm back from holiday and I've had a chance to properly unwind and clear my head!

But at least now I can do that having spoken to him face-to-face and better understood what he wants and where he's coming from.

From: Julie Lawson

That's sensible I think. You definitely shouldn't be making him any promises before you've thought long and hard about the whole thing.

You mustn't forget that you're a very special person who (despite my frequent jokes to the contrary) doesn't need to settle.

Hopefully this break will help to get you thinking rationally again – so no more meeting up with him before then, OK?

From: Allie Rainsbury

No, that was it, I'm done! But I don't want you thinking badly of David. And you need to promise me that you'll respect my decision when it comes to him too – I know you're looking out for my best interests but I need to figure out what I want by myself. Agreed?

Anyway, this is all very pre-emptive; nothing else should matter right now except tips on tanning and which ingredients make up the best afternoon cocktail ☺

From: Julie Lawson

Sounds suspiciously like you've decided things already. But – OK, I won't push any further right now. I do retain the right to quiz you further over a Vanilla Daiquiri or two though (obviously the best cocktail).

To be shelved. But not dismissed :P

From: Allie Rainsbury

Ha, it's beginning to sound as if this holiday is just a ruse to get me alone for interrogation!

From: Julie Lawson

So you've finally stumbled across the plan.

Is torture legal in Egypt?.

From: Allie Rainsbury

For the promise of thirty degrees every day, I'll take my chances!

From: Julie Lawson

That's my girl!

Right, one final push of work needed before I kiss this place goodbye for a fortnight. I'll see you at ours tomorrow evening.

Holidaaaayyyy! x

From: Allie Rainsbury

Hurrah!! See you then, Cleopatra! x

Friday

From: David Marshall
To: Allie Rainsbury

So I know I've been banned from speaking (☺) but I wanted to wish you a great trip!

From: Allie Rainsbury

Thank you! Only have a couple of hours here as I've got the afternoon off.

I must admit, I'm not exactly doing much work this morning; excitement is definitely kicking in!

How are you?

From: David Marshall

A bit sad that I won't get to see my favourite girl for a couple of weeks.

From: Allie Rainsbury

Aww... well, I'm sure you'll be kept busy while I'm away, and two weeks isn't that long either, is it?

From: David Marshall

Hmm... am I allowed to say that every day seems long when you're not around?

From: Allie Rainsbury

Only if you want me to throw up under my desk. :P

From: David Marshall

That's a no then.

I suppose I'll see you when you get back.

From: Allie Rainsbury

Stop being so sensitive, I'm teasing!

I'm in a good mood that's all – who wouldn't be with a fortnight at a luxury resort ahead of them?

From: David Marshall

True. It does make it especially hard for me though. I'm glad that you're happy, but I don't have a holiday to cheer me up – just the opposite in fact. I now have two weeks of not seeing you to look forward to, after just having managed to do so again.

From: Allie Rainsbury

That must be difficult for you, I'm sure – although I won't offer to switch places ☺

I promise we'll meet up when I get back. Does that help at all?

From: David Marshall

It does somewhat, yes. If you promise that we'll see each other every night for a week that would really cure me though...

From: Allie Rainsbury

Ha! That's a pretty steep demand. Hmm... Twice.

From: David Marshall

Twice and one stay over. Canterbury underwear to be worn.

From: Allie Rainsbury

Cheeky!

We shall see ;) x

From: David Marshall

I'm starting to feel a bit better now. It's incredible what alternative medicine can do.

From: Allie Rainsbury

Glad you're on the mend :P

Right then – I need to sign off.

Don't miss me too much x

From: David Marshall

I can't promise that.

Don't steal any of the Sphinx by the way, I'm told that's viewed poorly by the locals xx

---

CHAPTER 19

Monday 9 May
Holiday

Tuesday
Holiday

Wednesday
Holiday

Thursday

From: David Marshall
To: Allie Rainsbury

Hi there!

Are you picking up emails at all? x

Out of office reply: Hi, I am now on holiday until Monday 23 May. In Egypt.

At time of writing it's 32 degrees there and raining in London. I hope this note brightens up your day ☺

Please contact Garry Blackman if your call is urgent. Thanks, Allie.

Friday

Holiday

CHAPTER 20

Monday 16 May

Holiday

Tuesday

Holiday

Wednesday

From: Chris Trail
To: Allie Rainsbury

How are the pyramids? I tried calling you but got a foreign-sounding message. Have you been married off to an Egyptian prince yet?

From: Allie Rainsbury

Sorry, my phone isn't responding well to continental signals.

No royal wedding here I'm afraid, but the resort is fantastic, the sun is out and the drinks are flowing!

From: Chris Trail

Is it the ineptitude of the phone or its owner?

Sounds fantastic – can't wait to hear all about it. Are you back soon?

From: Allie Rainsbury

Ignoring the insult but returning the bottle of Egyptian wine I'd bought for you :P

Flying back tomorrow evening; I'll call you when I'm home x

From: Chris Trail

You pack that wine carefully now x

Thursday

From: Peter Rainsbury
To: Allie Rainsbury

Allie,

Can you call me as soon as possible?

Mum's been in an accident.

Love, Dad

Friday

Holiday

CHAPTER 21

Monday 23 May

From: Julie Lawson
To: Allie Rainsbury

How is she? Any update?

Let me know if there's anything I can do x

From: Allie Rainsbury

Thanks, Julie. I'm just on the way to the hospital now.

Dad is sleeping (on instruction – he hadn't sat down for over 48 hours) and coming up later.

I'll call you when I know more.

Don't worry, you just look after yourself as well as them.

We're here if you need us x

Tuesday

From: Allie Rainsbury
To: Julie Lawson

Still no update. She's not woken up and the doctors can't seem to give any sort of estimate as to when or if she will.

Dad's looking ashen and is pretty comatose himself.

From: Julie Lawson

Thanks for letting me know.

It must be so worrying and frustrating, but all you can do is what you already are: to be there for both of them.

Is there anything I can do here? Do you need me to organise compassionate leave?

From: Allie Rainsbury

I don't think so, no. Garry's actually been great about everything and given me the rest of the week off.

Beyond that he's said he'll be as flexible as I need him to be. He almost hinted at innuendo but then decided, even for him, that it would have been tactless.

From: Julie Lawson

A good decision. Ridiculous man... at least he's being understanding (for him anyway!).

From: Allie Rainsbury

Who'd have thought it?

OK, I'm going to go back and sit with her for a bit. I don't know if she can hear me but it might help.

From: Julie Lawson

I'm sure it will x

Wednesday

From: David Marshall
To: Allie Rainsbury

Hey! Aren't you back this week?

Am I not owed another look at a certain negligee? ;)

From: Chris Trail
To: Allie Rainsbury

Good to chat with you last night. You and your family are in my prayers.

I meant what I said – if I can help in any way then please don't hesitate to ask.

Love to you all x

From: Allie Rainsbury

Thanks, Chris – now shush and stop making me cry ☺ x

Thursday

From: Allie Rainsbury
To: David Marshall

Hi, I actually got back last Friday but I've been in Oxford since then. My mother was involved in a car accident and has been placed in intensive care.

From: David Marshall

Wow. I wasn't expecting that. Is she OK?

It's been a good couple of weeks; work has revolved around the autumn retail presentations but hasn't been too arduous (yet!) and I played squash and/or tennis most evenings when I wasn't kept late in the office.

Plus generally counted the days until you got back of course!

From: Allie Rainsbury

You mis-counted by quite a bit then, didn't you...

No, she's not OK. She's in a coma; the doctors aren't sure whether she's going to wake up or not.

I'm relieved that you're in such good spirits though.

From: David Marshall

That's a bit harsh. I didn't want to smother you when you first got back.

And I'm only in good spirits because I might get to see you soon. But I suppose that's going to have to be delayed again with what's going on with your mum.

From: Allie Rainsbury

Yes. It might have to wait!

Maybe I haven't fully communicated the severity of the crash, but she's in a critical condition, David.

So she's slightly higher on my priority list than organising a drink with you.

From: David Marshall

OK, no need to be so sharp! Sorry, I understand she's your concern, obviously. Don't forget about me, that's all I mean.

Look, I'm sure your mum will be fine. If she's anything like her daughter then she'll be strong enough to pull through.

I'll leave you alone for now since you sound understandably distracted.

Let me know when you're back in London x

Friday

From: Julie Lawson
To: Allie Rainsbury

Just checking in. How are you holding up?

From: Allie Rainsbury

Tired. Grouchy. An absolute state to look at.

But, on the plus side, I'm getting used to hospital food.

From: Julie Lawson

You need to try and rest if you can, hun. As tough as it is to say, there's nothing you can do beyond what you already are, but you'll make yourself ill too if you don't get some sleep.

That goes for your dad too, by the way.

From: Allie Rainsbury

You're right. Dad's told me to go back to London after the bank holiday this Monday. I suppose I should really, but I don't want Mum to think I'm abandoning her.

And I'm worried about leaving Dad as well of course. Although he does have my aunt up with him now which helps. She's been great so far through all this.

From: Julie Lawson

I think coming back for a bit could be a good idea. Your nerves must be totally frayed sitting in a hospital all day waiting for an update that may not come.

From: Allie Rainsbury

I do feel slightly jumpy. Although that could just be the caffeine I've gone through this week!

From: Julie Lawson

Come back, get a change of scene. Use work as a distraction.

Visit in doses, but you can't make a campsite at the hospital – it's not healthy for anyone.

Come back; you're two hours away if you're needed.

From: Allie Rainsbury

I know, I know. It's just hard to pull myself away, that's all.

I'll stay here until Sunday and come back that evening I think. If I have any hope of making it through a work week then I'll need to sleep through most of Monday anyway.

Was Egypt really just a week ago?

From: Julie Lawson

I'll pop in on Saturday and put some food in your fridge so you can properly hibernate for the day.

At least you'll still have some of your tan left to show off ☺

From: Allie Rainsbury

I'm running out of ways to say thank you, Jules.

Thank you again x

Don't be silly. You go give your dad a talking to about getting some sleep himself and I'll see you in work on Tuesday.

Love to you all x

CHAPTER 22

Monday 30 May

Spring Bank Holiday

Tuesday

From: David Marshall
To: Allie Rainsbury

Do my eyes deceive me, or did I spy a particularly cute behind walk past my office this morning? ☺

From: Allie Rainsbury

Hello. Yes, I'm back.

For now anyway. Feeling very tired and thoroughly drained.

Yours was one of the first emails I read of over a thousand that I had, eagerly awaiting my return.

From: David Marshall

Great! Finally ☺

How's your mother, is she all better yet?

I didn't call over the weekend as I figured you'd be wanting some space.

From: Allie Rainsbury

You ask as if she's got a mild cold. She's in a coma! She could well not recover – ever. So no, David, she's not all better yet.

A call would have been nice, if for no other reason than to know that you were thinking of me.

From: David Marshall

I'm only trying to be positive here. I know that it's serious! Just feel you have enough negativity without me adding to it.

And I was thinking of you; I was thinking that you'd want to be left alone and I didn't want to intrude on any reflective time you might have been having.

How am I meant to win exactly? If I had called, you'd have as likely as not accused me of hassling you!

From: Allie Rainsbury

I don't want to argue. It just feels that you're not really taking in the enormity of the situation, that's all.

I'm sorry. I'm just exhausted and that's probably making me much more sensitive and snappy than I mean to be.

From: David Marshall

That's all right, you're forgiven! ☺

It's completely understandable that you're shattered. How are you, in yourself?

From: Allie Rainsbury

A bit emotional but OK.

It's a strange sensation to carry around really; a sort of permanent sense of numbness. I'm not sure if that's lack of sleep or a state of shock – probably an element of both.

From: David Marshall

That does sound odd.

And, have you come to any conclusions over us yet? Once you've had a couple of nights' sleep, it would be nice to get you sleepless again ;)

From: Allie Rainsbury

I haven't thought about us at all, no. With everything that's gone on I haven't even had a chance to think about it.

From: David Marshall

What about when you were in Egypt? Surely you thought things through out there?

From: Allie Rainsbury

Egypt seems like a lifetime away. David, I don't feel like getting into this now, I'm sorry.

From: David Marshall

What does that mean for us then?

From: Allie Rainsbury

It means please be patient. I feel pretty empty at the moment and need you to think as a friend first and a boyfriend second.

From: David Marshall

OK... although I feel I am being pretty patient already.

Of course I'll be here as your friend. But I suppose I'm slightly confused as to why the boyfriend bit needs to be secondary? Can't I be both? ☺

From: Allie Rainsbury

Yes, of course. That's sort of what I mean... I think. I don't know!

I'm so tired that I can't really think straight! I just want you to be thoughtful and make a few allowances for me at the moment. If you can do that then you won't go far wrong.

Does that sound better, or clearer at least?

From: David Marshall

Message received! Thoughtfulness is the name of the day.

I'll leave you to it for now then; good luck sorting through all your emails and welcome back; I'm sorry it's not under nicer circumstances for you x

From: Allie Rainsbury

Thank you x

Maybe we can meet up for dinner next week ... if I can and if you want to of course.

From: David Marshall

Yes, let's do that. As a friend and boyfriend I'll even cook you a meal. Hopefully that will help relieve some of your tiredness x

From: Allie Rainsbury

Some big brownie points for you right there x

From: David Marshall

Let me know when you're free.

No worries if you need to cancel; like I say, completely understand that you've got other things on your mind x

From: Allie Rainsbury

Now you're just showing off :P

Wednesday

From: Scott Cooper
To: Allie Rainsbury

Hi Allison,

I was hoping you'd have some time tomorrow to run through a few questions I have in preparation for our Waterstone's meeting.

Thanks, Scott

From: Allie Rainsbury

Hi, yes, I'm free in the afternoon if you like. Although I should warn you that I'm likely to be even more disorganised than normal.

From: Scott Cooper

I shall try and be detailed enough for the both of us then.

Shall we say 3 p.m. in the cafeteria?

From: Allie Rainsbury

Sounds fine.

From: Scott Cooper

Also... I heard about what's happened recently. I'm very sorry. If I can help at all during what must be a difficult time then please let me know.

From: Allie Rainsbury

Thank you. That's very kind.

I suppose I shouldn't be surprised that office gossip has already spread that story by now.

From: Scott Cooper

I'm sorry, I didn't mean to pry.

And it's no problem at all, it was an offer meant in all sincerity.

From: Allie Rainsbury

That's OK. Without wanting to shout about it from the rooftops, it's better people know – at least then I don't have to explain why I look and feel how I do.

Thanks again.

From: Scott Cooper

Anytime.

You've no doubt got a strong network of friends and family to talk to, but if you do need to chat about things, I'll listen.

From: Allie Rainsbury

Are you looking for a confessional?

From: Scott Cooper

No, not at all. I've found in the past that those who know you most also feel best placed to offer advice. And I suspect that you're swimming in advice by now.

I can't give you advice, I don't know you and I wouldn't presume to; I can just listen.

From: Allie Rainsbury

Mum was driving back from a shopping trip. She's been driving for over thirty years and had never had an accident. Less than a mile from home a local lad accelerated over a cross-section when he should have stopped.

He hit her with such a force that she broke three ribs, fractured her left leg in two places and lost consciousness, dropping into a coma that she hasn't come out of.

I hadn't seen her in over three months. She lives two hours away and I haven't even bothered to go up there. She wanted to see me at Easter and I stayed at home instead. And did absolutely nothing.

All she wanted, all she asked for, was my company for a single day – even that was too much. And now I might never get the chance to tell her what a wonderful person she is. I want to tell her that she's the sweetest, most caring, kindest mother I could ever have hoped to have. And she can't hear me say that.

I've been so incredibly selfish, so preoccupied with other things, that the people who should matter most haven't mattered at all. I didn't want to spend Easter with my family because I thought I might be bored. And now all I want, with all my heart, is to have that time back. To have one more day of how things used to be.

From: Scott Cooper

I'm sure she knows how much you love her.

Sometimes time goes so quickly that it can feel like a week has passed by in a blink.

But little things that seem trivial in retrospect are just as much a part of life as the big decisions. You can't look back and judge yourself then against your situation now.

From: Allie Rainsbury

You said you wouldn't give advice. And you don't need to spare my feelings.

If Mum does pull through this, if I can talk to her even just one more time, I'll never lose sight again of what should be important. Of what means most to me.

From: Scott Cooper

I don't doubt that she's incredibly proud of you, and of your determination now.

I do doubt she would want you berating yourself unfairly though.

From: Allie Rainsbury

It's so easy to say, much harder to do.

I'm going to go now before I get upset.

Thursday

From: Scott Cooper
To: Allie Rainsbury

Still fine for this afternoon?

From: Allie Rainsbury

Yes, all OK. I've pulled together some consumer and Sales data from the last few months along with revenue targets for the rest of the year.

Anything else that immediately springs to mind?

From: Scott Cooper

No, that should cover it.

Just remember to bring your coat too – I'm taking you out of the office and we're going to the pub. Drinking isn't compulsory but by the sounds of that data it might help.

From: Allie Rainsbury

Well, that's enlivened things!

This is still a work meeting though, isn't it? It was good to open up a bit yesterday, however unexpected the opportunity, but I don't need a shoulder to cry on. To be honest I'm finding work a nice refuge from other thoughts.

From: Scott Cooper

And I'd hate for my new suit to be bawled on. It's just work. But a couple of drinks never hurt.

From: Allie Rainsbury

All right, you're on.

Will I get to find out a bit more about the enigma that is Scott Cooper? ☺

From: Scott Cooper

If we're not talking about you then we're sure as hell not talking about me!

Besides, I'm not enigmatic, just dull. I think the data talk will be more interesting anyway.

From: Allie Rainsbury

Mysterious and modest?

Maybe a pint or two will loosen your tongue.

From: Scott Cooper

Don't make me regret this rare outburst of impulse.

Friday

From: Julie Lawson
To: Allie Rainsbury

Are you up in Oxford again?

From: Allie Rainsbury

Not yet no. I'm leaving early today to head up this afternoon, why?

From: Julie Lawson

I passed by your desk yesterday afternoon and you weren't there. I just assumed you'd gone for the week.

From: Allie Rainsbury

Ah, I see. No, not quite yet. I was at the Firestation actually.

From: Julie Lawson

That certainly beats being at your desk. What were you doing there?

From: Allie Rainsbury

I was enjoying a glass of white wine. I went for a drink with Scott.

From: Julie Lawson

Who's Scott?

From: Allie Rainsbury

Scott Cooper, our CFO.

From: Julie Lawson

What? Why? It wasn't just the two of you, was it?

From: Allie Rainsbury

Ha! As uninterested as usual! :P

He (like everyone else it appears) had heard about my mum's accident and asked if I'd rather get out of the office for a change of scene. It was very thoughtful of him, but very business focused all the same.

From: Julie Lawson

That's nice of him. What did you talk about though? It wasn't all business chat, surely?

From: Allie Rainsbury

Pretty much, but yes, we talked about what I've been going through too and I suppose I told him more than most.

From: Julie Lawson

You sneaky little thing! I didn't even know you knew him. I thought he was your enemy for life after that away day?

From: Allie Rainsbury

Perhaps I was too hasty. He's easy to talk to and I actually found myself pouring my heart out. Probably too much.

But he does have very kind eyes ☺

From: Julie Lawson

Uh-huh... and I'm rolling mine as I write this.

From: Allie Rainsbury

Well, don't! Besides the fact that it was utterly innocent, I also happen to have a boyfriend. David? Remember him?

From: Julie Lawson

With a vengeance. But I wouldn't count him as a proper boyfriend though.

From: Allie Rainsbury

What do you mean?

From: Julie Lawson

For a start, you've hardly seen each other for the past month.

No, that's true, but then I haven't had a chance to, with everything that's happened.

You might not like to hear it, Jules, but I haven't given up on him yet.

And, at the risk of using my emotional state as collateral, I'm too vulnerable right now for you to lecture me on those thoughts :P

From: Julie Lawson

OK. I'll hold my tongue and my fire.

If you get the chance, call me over the weekend and give me the latest, please.

Love as ever to your dad. And your mum too, of course x

Ps. Allie and Scott Cooper, who'd have thought it?! ☺

From: Allie Rainsbury

Hush with your wind up!

Any gossip on Monday and I'll know its origins :P

CHAPTER 23

Monday 6 June

From: David Marshall
To: Allie Rainsbury

Hey! Was wondering if you fancied coming over tonight and I can cook you that dinner I promised.

From: Allie Rainsbury

I've been in Oxford all weekend with my mum – still no change unfortunately. Can we rain check on this evening please? I've had very little sleep the past couple of days so I think I'll just have a quiet one tonight.

From: David Marshall

But you can have a quiet one at mine. Put a film on and enjoy the culinary delights of Chez David.

From: Allie Rainsbury

Hmm, I'll definitely hold you to that offer at some point!

As tempting as it sounds though I'll pass for now. I desperately need a good night's rest in my own little flat.

From: David Marshall

Well, that's being a touch dull. I'm hurt that I can't better your current offer of a lonely night doing nothing! But fair enough ☺

Let me know if you change your mind and I won't have to throw out the extra groceries I bought.

From: Allie Rainsbury

You had everything bought in already? Now I do feel guilty.

But I'm going to stay strong all the same and decline your generous invitation. Another time though, I promise x

From: David Marshall

I'll believe it when I see it x

From: Chris Trail
To: Allie Rainsbury

Hey there, gorgeous girl! We've let this slip slightly over recent weeks, but I am putting jogging firmly back on the agenda.

The added bonus for us now is that we'll have a good base fitness level to take it even further forward.

From: Allie Rainsbury

An optimistic summary of our heath status.

From: Chris Trail

Five miles.

It will hurt.

But it will be glorious.

From: Allie Rainsbury

It will be disastrous.

Anyway, as positive as you know I like to be over your suggestions, I'm really tired today and want nothing more than a lazy night in.

So there :P

From: Chris Trail

If you come, I'll tell you who I'm doing all this running for.

From: Allie Rainsbury

What?!

You're getting body beautiful to impress someone? Who is it?!

From: Chris Trail

If you come then maybe you'll find out :P

From: Allie Rainsbury

Chris!! How exciting! Tell me.

From: Chris Trail

Five miles first.

From: Allie Rainsbury

Damn you! This is blackmail!

From: Chris Trail

Undeniably so.

From: Allie Rainsbury

Five miles then. But if I break down before the end and lie gasping in a puddle then you have to tell me anyway.

From: Chris Trail

I shall sing like a canary.

See you at yours, lovely ☺

From: Allie Rainsbury

You will be greeted by a frosty yet intrigued glare.

Tuesday

From: David Marshall
To: Allie Rainsbury

I don't understand why you're not fun anymore.

From: Allie Rainsbury

? Did you mean to send this to me?

From: David Marshall .

I was thinking about things after our email chat yesterday. I thought last week we agreed to meet up and spend some time together, yet then when I ask you to come over you say no, despite not having any other plans.

How can that be fair?

From: Allie Rainsbury

David, are you honestly asking me this?!

From: David Marshall

I'm just trying to understand you.

What are you thinking at the moment? Where do you see you and me going?

From: Allie Rainsbury

I'm not thinking anything much at the moment! For some strange reason I'm putting lots of decisions on hold, in order to prioritise others.

From: David Marshall

So it's nothing I've said or done? Because I keep turning stuff round in my mind and I can't see where I've gone wrong.

From: Allie Rainsbury

Why does it have to involve you at all? It's nothing to do with you!

And, I swear, if I have to explain one more time why I'm slightly tired and down at the moment, I'll scream.

From: David Marshall

I understand. I keep saying that. But you keep pushing me away, so what else am I meant to think?

From: Allie Rainsbury

You're not meant to think. You're meant to wait! You're meant to be patient, tolerant and accepting. If you can't do those things then there's nothing much I can offer you right now.

From: David Marshall

That doesn't exactly sound reassuring.

It might be difficult to hear, but life does go on you know.

From: Allie Rainsbury

Get over yourself, David, for God's sake!

And don't you dare preach to me about something like that.

From: David Marshall

I just mean that there are other people who also care for you and still need attention.

You're treating me like a teenager, Allie, and I won't stand for it.

From: Allie Rainsbury

And you're acting like a child, so I guess that makes us even.

From: David Marshall

Unbelievable!

I'll wait, and I'll wait in silence, since every time I talk you insult me anyway.

Wednesday

From: Julie Lawson
To: Allie Rainsbury

How you doing?

From: Allie Rainsbury

Ugh. In a word. I'm shattered (again) and grouchy (again). I must make for terrible company these days.

From: Julie Lawson

Never! Even at your most miserable you can still make me laugh; however unintentionally that may be ☺

Should I ask for an update?

From: Allie Rainsbury

Still no change. Although Dad looks as if he's aged years in the past few weeks.

It's just a matter of not thinking the worst, but it's terribly difficult to banish your fears completely.

And to top it off I put David in his place yesterday too; a bit unfairly perhaps. So I'm feeling bad about that as well.

From: Julie Lawson

You must try to stay positive, for your dad, as much as anyone else. She's in the best possible place and she's getting all the care and expertise that could possibly help.

From: Allie Rainsbury

I just don't like feeling helpless, that's all.

From: Julie Lawson

Well, it sounds as if you're taking charge of those things that you can control. You showed David the door finally? ☺

From: Allie Rainsbury

No, I didn't say that! We had an argument, that's all. And I said a couple of things that he probably didn't deserve.

From: Julie Lawson

Such as?

From: Allie Rainsbury

Things that I feel I'm repeating really. He just doesn't seem to be able to take in what I'm going through at the moment. Maybe he feels a bit insecure about the fact that I don't have as much spare time right now as I did a month or so ago.

I wish he could be a bit less self-involved, but at the same time I know that that very self-involvement is borne from a desire to see me and since that's all I've wanted from him in the first place, it must be very confusing for him to hear me criticise him for it now.

From: Julie Lawson

Self-concern and David seem to go hand-in-hand, in my opinion. But I know you still like him, so I won't warn you off again. What was the upshot?

From: Allie Rainsbury

I don't know. He presumably spent yesterday evening in a mood as he didn't reply to a text message I sent him.

I'm not sure. Hopefully it's a storm that will blow over; the last thing I need are any more rain clouds.

From: Julie Lawson

Hey! I told you to stay positive, remember! ☺

From: Allie Rainsbury

Ha! I'm trying, Jules, really I am.

From: Julie Lawson

Would a cup of tea and a chocolate brownie help your mood?

From: Allie Rainsbury

Hmm, potentially. I suppose we could run the experiment and find out ☺

From: Julie Lawson

Agreed! See you in the café in a few minutes.

I can tell you all about Elly and Cale's recent adventures and why I think summer holidays should be shorter for kids.

From: Allie Rainsbury

I'm already intrigued...

Thursday

From: Scott Cooper
To: Allie Rainsbury

Hi Allison, thanks for your time last week.

It was really useful to catch up and properly get to grips with Waterstone's as an account and as a customer.

Ahead of our meeting next week I wanted to pull off a couple more statistics to ensure we're completely covered; but other than that I'm happy with the presentation you've crafted.

I'll email you the final version and have copies printed and bound.

Regards, Scott.

From: Allie Rainsbury

What a formal note ☺

Thanks for the update. Let me know if you need anything more from me.

From: Scott Cooper

I didn't want you to think I was being inappropriate, especially since our last meeting was in a pub.

From: Allie Rainsbury

I don't think that at all.

And for future reference, I'll always be happy for our meetings to held in the local.

From: Scott Cooper

Good, I'm glad. So you're still OK to go on Wednesday?

From: Allie Rainsbury

Absolutely, ready and raring.

From: Scott Cooper

I genuinely don't mind doing this one alone if you don't feel like it.

From: Allie Rainsbury

That's kind, but I don't need any special treatment. I'm assuming you'll be running through the financial side though?

From: Scott Cooper

Yep. The ball's in my court for that part.

You just talk about the fluffy trade marketing stuff and that should be fine...

From: Allie Rainsbury

Finally I understand why some people see you as disparaging and aloof (which, if I remember correctly, you mentioned you had already garnered a reputation for?)!

Luckily I know it's just a bad attempt at humour.

From: Scott Cooper

My humour is like fine wine. Subtle and better over time.

From: Allie Rainsbury

And too much of it gives everyone a headache?

From: Scott Cooper

Ha! Touché. Very clever.

From: Allie Rainsbury

You sound surprised?

From: Scott Cooper

At the away day, before hypothermia set in, I remember handing you a towel and you saying, 'A dry blanket for a wet blanket, just what I need'.

No, I'm not surprised.

From: Allie Rainsbury

Ha! I can't believe you remember that!

From: Scott Cooper

Well, I think that's what you said anyway. To be honest your teeth were chattering so much it could have been complete gibberish.

See you on Wednesday then. I'm driving up to their offices if you'd like a lift?

From: Allie Rainsbury

Very aloof. Incredibly disparaging :P

A lift would be great, thanks!

Friday

From: David Marshall
To: Allie Rainsbury

Hi Allie, how's your mum?

From: Allie Rainsbury

No news, thanks for asking.

From: David Marshall

I wanted to apologise and, if this is the end of things, to at least leave it on a pleasant note.

From: Allie Rainsbury

How do you mean?

From: David Marshall

I mean that, because I like you so much I have been very selfish. I've concentrated too often on wanting to see you and not enough on asking how you are first.

I suppose I thought that if we did meet up, I'd be able to ask you properly how you're coping along with other details behind your mother's current state.

So I'm sorry – I should have been less demanding.

From: Allie Rainsbury

Thank you. I really appreciate you saying that, David.

All this time I've never felt that you've fully sympathised with how stressful things are for me right now.

I do get how difficult the situation must be for you too, and I know that you want to spend time with me. Believe me, under almost any other conditions I'd want the same.

But I can't commit to that at the moment, simply because I have to be completely focused on being there for my mum. No matter what. Irrespective of how much I like someone. And, hopefully you know by now, I do like you very much.

236

From: David Marshall

Which is exactly why I wanted to say sorry and clear the air between us.

If things were different then maybe you'd want me in your life, but, as it stands, I think I have to finally admit that I no longer have a girlfriend (and she was so beautiful too ;) x).

From: Allie Rainsbury

That's not really what I'm saying...

From: David Marshall

No?... Sorry, I'm confused (again! ☺)

From: Allie Rainsbury

I just mean that I won't always be able to be there for you at the drop of a hat.

I might have to be in Oxford at the hospital, I might have to spend all night talking to and counselling my father, I might just be tired and depressed some nights and need my own space and time to think.

But I've never said I don't want you as a boyfriend.

From: David Marshall

You still want to be with me?

From: Allie Rainsbury

Yes! Of course I do. I just can't put us first all the time, however frustrating that must be for you.

From: David Marshall

No, that's fine! I'm not remotely frustrated!

In fact, right now, I'm experiencing more a mix of relief and excitement than anything else.

So... Do I get to see you at some point?

From: Allie Rainsbury

Absolutely, yes! ☺

I'm with Mum all weekend but back in London on Monday. How about we meet up then?

From: David Marshall

It's a date! Where do you want to go? I could come to Putney if you'd like?

From: Allie Rainsbury

Yes, let's do that.

From: David Marshall

This could very well be the first time I've ever wished away a weekend!! I'll bring an overnight bag too, just in case ;)

From: Allie Rainsbury

Let's see how it goes – I do think we still need to take things slow.

But I am greatly looking forward to seeing you x

From: David Marshall

Slow – check! I can cope with that. (I'll pack a change of clothes though, all the same.)

Ps. I hope things go well for you this weekend – I'll be thinking of you and your parents x

---

CHAPTER 24

Monday 13 June

From: Julie Lawson
To: Allie Rainsbury

You sounded knackered last night. Did you sleep OK?

Come round for dinner this evening and enjoy a proper meal for once – you need a change from hospital food and ready meals.

From: Allie Rainsbury

Incredibly, I feel surprisingly refreshed for the start of the week. I was so tired that sleep took over pretty quickly anyway.

Will have to refuse your kind offer – I have a date this evening ☺

From: Julie Lawson

With David?

From: Allie Rainsbury

I can almost hear the disapproving cluck from here! Yes, with David. I'm actually really looking forward to it.

From: Julie Lawson

Well, that's a good start at least. Hopefully you'll have a lovely time.

From: Allie Rainsbury

Really?

From: Julie Lawson

Of course really! As I've told you many times before, if you're happy then I'm happy!

I have, or rather have had, reservations about David, but you both seem determined to try and work through your problems, so maybe there is something there worth pursuing.

From: Allie Rainsbury

How strange to see such enthusiasm from you. What are you after?! :P

From: Julie Lawson

Ha! Purely the satisfaction of seeing my best friend happy.

From: Allie Rainsbury

Hmm, OK then... slightly sycophantic but acceptable.

From: Julie Lawson

Just, be careful. That's all I'll add!

From: Allie Rainsbury

I knew it! ☺

From: Julie Lawson

Hush! I do hope it all works out.

I hope you have a good time tonight and for many nights to come.

But just look after yourself, that's all. And in fairness I'd give you the same advice no matter who you were going out with.

From: Allie Rainsbury

Aw, I know. I'm only teasing.

David and I have spoken an awful lot over the past few weeks. We've discussed what we're both looking for in a relationship, what we can offer and where we can potentially go. I think he is finally listening to my answers on all of these questions and I'm pretty sure I know how he feels.

So I'm excited. Cautious and careful, absolutely. But excited nonetheless.

From: Julie Lawson

What can I say? You're all grown up and sensible.

From: Allie Rainsbury

It had to happen at some stage ☺

From: Julie Lawson

True. As long as you're not too mature to call time on our occasional girly nights out.

From: Allie Rainsbury

Never! They will always have a place on our social calendar!

From: Julie Lawson

In that case, I fully embrace this new thoughtful you ☺

Good luck tonight kiddo x

Tuesday

From: Julie Lawson
To: Allie Rainsbury

I must have deleted your email by mistake, please can you resend?

From: Allie Rainsbury

Which email?

From: Julie Lawson

The one telling me how yesterday's date went with David?

I haven't seen it yet...

From: Allie Rainsbury

Ha! Sorry, I'm a bit frantic today. I'm swotting up on final details for the meeting in Reading tomorrow.

From: Julie Lawson

Ooh, is this the one with Scott Cooper? Now I don't know which question to ask you first!!

Date details I think, then excitement factor over Scott ☺

From: Allie Rainsbury

Your world sounds fun, I must visit it some time :P

The date went well! David was as attentive as he had been when we first met. It made me glad that we haven't given up on each other.

From: Julie Lawson

That sounds promising!

Was he attentive emotionally or physically? ;)

From: Allie Rainsbury

He stayed over, so I suppose he covered both ☺

I'll let your imagination take over from there!

From: Julie Lawson

Wow. Taking things slowly has been shelved for a different plan then?

From: Allie Rainsbury

It felt right, Jules. I didn't want him to go, so just thought I should stop pretending otherwise.

If there's one thing that recent weeks have taught me it's that you never know when you'll get a second chance to do or say something.

Since I have the opportunity, I may as well take it.

From: Julie Lawson

How wonderfully pragmatic!

And all the great love stories have used 'you may as well take it' as their tag line :P

From: Allie Rainsbury

I'm not in a love story either. I need to wake up to real life with all its bumps and bruises ☺

David's a nice guy. He's incredibly bright, good looking and funny and he likes me. I should stop fretting every time a hiccup occurs.

From: Julie Lawson

As long as you're sure your hiccups don't outnumber your laughs.

From: Allie Rainsbury

I'm sure they won't. I really am.

Now leave me be; I need to finish my preparations!

From: Julie Lawson

Ah yes, the Scott factor.

From: Allie Rainsbury

Apply factor zero. There is no Scott factor!

Stop winding me up; he's a nice guy but nothing beyond that. And what's more, nor would I want there to be.

From: Julie Lawson

OK! Sorry.

I hope the meeting goes well anyway.

Are you presenting anything?

From: Allie Rainsbury

Yes, unfortunately! And you know how flustered I get with public speaking. Many deep breaths will be needed.

From: Julie Lawson

Imagine the audience naked, that always helps.

Hmm, the head buyer is a rather leathery 60-year-old woman. I'll stick to my breathing exercises I think.

From: Julie Lawson

Or turn your gaze to our CFO ;P

From: Allie Rainsbury

You're rotten to the core x

Wednesday

From: David Marshall
To: Allie Rainsbury

Hello gorgeous, fancy meeting up after work? My evening's become free and I can't think of anyone I'd rather see ;)

From: Allie Rainsbury

Out of the office reply: I'm away from my desk today but picking up emails intermittently.

Kind regards, Allie.

From: David Marshall

Your out of office has jogged my memory; you're at your big meeting this afternoon, aren't you?

Hope it goes OK!

From: Allie Rainsbury
To: David Marshall

Hi, just stepped out of it now. It went well thanks!

I'm actually going to head on up to Oxford now and spend some time at the hospital; it seems silly not to since I'm halfway there already.

How about we meet up on Friday instead?

From: David Marshall

Sounds good. Have a good evening! x

Thursday

From: Peter Rainsbury
To: Allie Rainsbury

Dear Allie,

I hope you weren't too tired after your journey back last night. It really was very thoughtful of you to come all that way for just a couple of hours.

I'm writing this while sitting in an Internet café at the hospital, after a kind (and I must say, rather pretty) young nurse helped me log on. There's no change and no more news obviously, but I wanted to drop you a note since you mentioned how frantic you have been feeling recently.

You must remember, there's only a limited amount that any of us can do at this stage. You have your own life to lead and, while I (and your mum) always love to see you, I absolutely do not expect you to visit us every weekend much less weekday evenings as well. You'll find yourself exhausted, unable to concentrate at work and you'll risk impacting everything you have worked so hard for over the years.

I'm sorry we argued before the accident. I was in a foul mood and feel I went horribly overboard. Obviously, both of us as parents are proud of you. I shouldn't have ever hinted otherwise, darling, because that's just not true. I hope and trust that you know that.

Anyway... Enough mushy stuff. Go and enjoy your weekend for once, that's a parental order. Maybe go out with Scott for some of it? He seemed a very polite, well-presented young man. I suspect your mother would approve and be terribly excited at the same time.

That's all for now, we'll chat soon I'm sure. With love, Dad x

From: Allie Rainsbury

Hi Dad!

I never thought a day would arrive when you could be found in an Internet cafe!

I'm so proud of you as well and I love you both more than anything. I fear you're reading too much into the Scott situation (who's just a work colleague). Probably best not to get too fond of him.

I don't come up because I have to, I visit because I want to and, to ensure traditional disregard for parental instruction is carried out, shall see you on Saturday as usual ☺

Your loving daughter, Allie xx

From: Allie Rainsbury
To: Julie Lawson

Well, that was one of my more interesting evenings...

From: Julie Lawson

Nocturnal activity with David?

From: Allie Rainsbury

Technically, I suppose you could say it was nocturnal activity with another man.

From: Julie Lawson

What?! WHAT?! If there was anything bigger than cap locks, I'd use it for this sentence. Tell me!

From: Allie Rainsbury

Ha! I should warn you, before you have a hernia, it's all very innocent.

From: Julie Lawson

Isn't it always...

Talk!!

From: Allie Rainsbury

After the meeting finished in Reading yesterday (which went well in the end, they were quite impressed with our organisational proficiency – the irony!) I suddenly thought that, as we weren't far from Oxford, I'd pop on a train and visit the hospital for the evening.

Since Scott had driven us up, I asked if he'd mind taking me to Reading station.

From: Julie Lawson

Yes. YES?!

From: Allie Rainsbury

He drove me all the way to Oxford instead. We were on the motorway before I even registered what he was doing, and despite all my protests to the contrary he insisted, after stopping to pick up flowers, on dropping me at the door of John Radcliffe.

From: Julie Lawson

Who's John Radcliffe for goodness sake?!

From: Allie Rainsbury

The name of the hospital. Calm yourself.

Anyway, I invited him in. I don't know why really. It seemed the polite thing to do. I didn't really think that he might say yes!

From: Julie Lawson

But he said yes.

From: Allie Rainsbury

He did. He came in and he met my father, saw Mum and then went and waited in the cafeteria while I caught up with them in private.

Afterwards he gave me a lift back to Putney.

From: Julie Lawson

Well, that's... hmm...

What's the right word to use here?

From: Allie Rainsbury

Sweet?

From: Julie Lawson

Thoughtful? Generous? (Romantic?)

What did your dad say?

From: Allie Rainsbury

He's now got the wrong end of the stick. Which isn't entirely his fault I suppose – it's not as if you introduce people by adding on the post-script, 'By the way, we're not together'.

From: Julie Lawson

What did David say?

From: Allie Rainsbury

I haven't told him. I mean, I said I was spending the evening in Oxford, but I thought it best to leave out the extra detail.

He hasn't even met my parents yet.

From: Julie Lawson

Wow.

From: Allie Rainsbury

I know!

From: Julie Lawson

But really... Wow! That is a good, good story! ☺

So what are you going to do?

From: Allie Rainsbury

I don't know. It probably doesn't mean anything, and what's more I shouldn't want it to either.

I'm going home, that's what I'm going to do. I'm having a glass of wine and I'm doing some serious self-analysis!

From: Julie Lawson

How exciting! And how typical – the one night of the week I can't get away; otherwise I'd bring a glass and keep you company.

From: Allie Rainsbury

Not to worry. It's probably for the best. We'd be hypothesising until the early hours otherwise.

From: Julie Lawson

Tell me tomorrow about any conclusions you reach.

From: Allie Rainsbury

But of course. Where would I be without my advice council after all? :P x

From: Julie Lawson

Don't you forget it ☺

Run a bath and try not to stress (council's last advice for the day) x

Friday

From: Julie Lawson
To: Allie Rainsbury

So? Where did your thoughts lead you?

From: Allie Rainsbury

Along a pathway of self-scolding mostly.

I spent a little bit of time basking in the glow of attention from another guy before realising that actually Scott hasn't shown the slightest interest in me romantically.

It was a nice thing that he did, but then, since he seems like a nice man, it wouldn't exactly be out of character, would it?

From: Julie Lawson

Perhaps. Although, I'm not sure I've ever met a guy nice enough to drive me a hundred miles on a whim.

From: Allie Rainsbury

True, but then since any other conclusion is purely self-aggrandisement, it's the one I've decided to stick to.

Especially because I feel guilty about not telling David. I mean, thinking about it, isn't this along the lines of what David did to me – not telling me things for fear I'd misinterpret them?

From: Julie Lawson

Hold on a minute! That's totally unfair. You can't paint yourself with the same brush at all, no! One, you've never been romantically involved with Scott as David had been with that woman. Two, you don't jointly own Scott's car, like David does with his flat. Three, I have numerous other reasons I could list if you're not convinced by one and two.

From: Allie Rainsbury

Well, OK... I don't necessarily mean a literal comparison.

I just don't think it's a very healthy or honest road to start going down. I like Scott; he can be overly proper, rather reserved and some people could think he has a large rod up his backside. But he's got a good heart, he's actually great fun to talk to and we definitely have the same sense of humour.

That's as far as it goes though, and as such, I should be happy to tell David about it.

From: Julie Lawson

Maybe the fact that you didn't feel able to tells you more about the state of your relationship with David than your friendship with Scott.

From: Allie Rainsbury

I considered that as well, but it's difficult to compare the two. After all, I care more about what David thinks because of our very involvement with each other.

From: Julie Lawson

So because you're more emotionally invested with David, you're less able to tell him the truth?

From: Allie Rainsbury

Something like that, without such a heavy dose of cynicism.

Trust is the most difficult emotion to gain.

From: Julie Lawson

Did you order in Chinese and get that in a cracker? ☺

From: Allie Rainsbury

For instance I can always trust that you'll make fun of my dilemmas :P

From: Julie Lawson

Ha! I'm sorry. And you've obviously put a lot of thought into this.

Your conclusion basically is that you should tell David about Scott meeting your parents?

From: Allie Rainsbury

No!

But starting from now, I'll be upfront about everything.

From: Julie Lawson

Ha! You do make me laugh ☺

From: Allie Rainsbury

What? Shush! It's much ado about nothing anyhow.

From: Julie Lawson

We shall see...

From: Allie Rainsbury

We certainly shall.

Thanks for your input, it's been as valuable as ever :P

I'll call you over the weekend x

From: Julie Lawson

!

From: Scott Cooper
To: Allie Rainsbury

Hi Allie, thanks for your help and input at the meeting on Wednesday. I walked away with greater insight and understanding of the customer than I had before.

On a separate note, it was a pleasure to meet your father, however sombre the circumstances. He was very engaging, intelligent and dignified. Please thank him again; I hope my presence wasn't awkward or intrusive for either of you.

More than ever, my thoughts are with you and your mother – if I can ever be of help then feel free to ask.

Enjoy your weekend, Scott.

CHAPTER 25

Monday 20 June

From: Julie Lawson
To: Allie Rainsbury

Tea and croissant are sitting in front of me and my one-hour departmental meeting has been postponed – it's going to be a good week!

So did any more plot twists occur over the weekend?

From: Allie Rainsbury

No further updates to report I'm afraid.

Saw David on Friday, although only briefly as I had to be up early to get to the hospital.

From: Julie Lawson

No shocking developments? No mystery third man appearing on the scene? Bah, what use are you?

I'll just have to read *Hello!* instead :P

From: Allie Rainsbury

I've never felt closer to you than I have right now.

From: Julie Lawson

☺!

How's your mum? Any progress?

From: Allie Rainsbury

No, none at all. I must sound like a broken record.

The doctors are able to pick up lots of data that show healthy brain activity, but that doesn't change anything really.

From: Julie Lawson

No, but hold on to the positives. And talk to people about it too, it's never good to bottle frustrations up too much.

Do you chat to David about her ever?

From: Allie Rainsbury

Quite a bit, yes. Although he doesn't seem particularly comfortable when I do. I don't think he knows what to say. In fact (and here's your 'development' story :P) I invited him up to the hospital with me when I saw him on Friday.

From: Julie Lawson

What did he say?

From: Allie Rainsbury

He said no. Or rather, he said that hospitals freaked him out; then that he wasn't sure if he could; and finally he remembered that he had something on. Which is a roundabout way of saying no.

From: Julie Lawson

A typically male way of saying no as well!

Were you OK with that? Did it come about because of Scott's visit?

From: Allie Rainsbury

I suppose I was a bit disappointed.

I didn't really think that I would mind either way but, to be honest, I quite enjoyed having the company when Scott was with me. It lightened the mood and gave Dad someone and something different. I guess I hoped that David could lift the atmosphere too.

From: Julie Lawson

You would hope.

From: Allie Rainsbury

But, then I realised that was really unfair of me. I've just spent weeks lecturing him on the importance of taking things slowly and then I ask him to come and meet my parents! I wouldn't be surprised if he thought it was a test, the poor man!

Anyway, the visit was fine in the end, so that's the most important thing.

From: Julie Lawson

True. Very compassionate of you, but I suppose there's a point in there.

To be honest, it was probably a good thing he didn't go anyhow.

From: Allie Rainsbury

Why's that?

From: Julie Lawson

Well, it might have backfired and totally flustered your father. You haven't introduced him to a man in years and then you suddenly bring up two guys in a week? He'd worry! ☺

From: Allie Rainsbury

Ha! I hadn't even thought about it like that. For the best, definitely.

From: Julie Lawson

Lunch later? 1 p.m. in the cafeteria?

From: Allie Rainsbury

See you there – no more croissants between now and then :P

Tuesday

From: David Marshall
To: Allie Rainsbury

Hey sexy, fancy hooking up this evening? I've no plans and am imagining things we could do ;)

From: Allie Rainsbury

Yes, we could meet up later I suppose.

From: David Marshall

Are you sure? You don't sound overly keen.

From: Allie Rainsbury

No, sorry – absolutely, let's. I'm not sure if I feel like going out though; perhaps just a film and a quiet night on the couch...

From: David Marshall

That sounds perfect. You bring the film; I'll bring the popcorn (unless the film is *The Notebook* in which case I have right of veto).

From: Allie Rainsbury

Ha, OK!

Do you want to come over to mine or for me to come to yours?

From: David Marshall

I'll come to you; if you're tired then I don't want you trekking halfway across London.

Plus, I have a change of clothes in the office already.

From: Allie Rainsbury

? Why on earth would you keep any spare clothes here?

From: David Marshall

For exactly this sort of occasion!

From: Allie Rainsbury

You're weird :P

From: David Marshall

I just think ahead, that's all.

You can thank me later ;)

From: Allie Rainsbury

We'll see ☺

See you this evening and we'll cuddle up to *Dirty Dancing* x

From: David Marshall

No! Abort, abort!!

See you there gorgeous x

From: Allie Rainsbury
To: Scott Cooper

Hi Scott,

Hope you had a good weekend. I just wanted to thank you again for last week. It wasn't invasive at all; I wouldn't have invited you into the hospital if I'd felt like that!

Anyway, it was fun to have you there. I know my father enjoyed it. He asked after you on Saturday so you obviously made an impression (which is no mean achievement at the moment).

Best wishes, Allie.

Wednesday

From: Allie Rainsbury
To: Julie Lawson

With everything else that's been happening, I completely forgot to pass on this piece of gossip: Chris is in love!

From: Julie Lawson

What?! No way. Since when? Who is he?

From: Allie Rainsbury

Who is *she*!

I don't know though – he wouldn't tell me much.

From: Julie Lawson

He told you he was in love with a woman though?

From: Allie Rainsbury

Well, no, not explicitly.

But he's not gay!

From: Julie Lawson

That's ridiculous. How long have you known? I can't believe you forgot to tell me!

From: Allie Rainsbury

A couple of weeks? He was very cloak-and-dagger about it. He didn't even crack after two pints and a Baileys, which is well beyond his usual level for divulging everything.

From: Julie Lawson

Hmm, true, his usual level is the drop of a hat.

Curiouser and curiouser... I'll email him now I think, it's been too long.

From: Allie Rainsbury

Well, go softly – don't charge in with your usual bull-in-a-china-shop approach! He sounded very nervous about things.

From: Julie Lawson

I will be the epitome of sensitivity! I always am!

From: Allie Rainsbury

Just tread a bit carefully, OK?

From: Julie Lawson

OK, OK… Jeez – you'd think bringing up two kids would earn me some respect.

From: Allie Rainsbury

I know your kids though :P

From: Julie Lawson

Low blow! If I only had a comeback for it.

I'll be careful, don't worry!

From: Allie Rainsbury

And report back with findings…!

From: Julie Lawson

Yes, Sergeant!

Over and out x

Thursday

From: David Marshall
To: Allie Rainsbury

I'm guessing you're out of London again this weekend?

From: Allie Rainsbury

Yes, I'm afraid so. The usual trip to my parents. Why do you ask?

From: David Marshall

No real reason – I just wondered.

If you'd been around then perhaps we could have got together, but I suppose I'll have to ask someone else instead ☺

From: Allie Rainsbury

Do you not have any tennis or squash games planned for once? No biking trips anywhere?

From: David Marshall

Not this time, no.

Anyway, I have you to ride now don't I ;)

From: Allie Rainsbury

??

I'm not sure I like that joke.

From: David Marshall

Ah, I'm just teasing! Don't stress, gorgeous.

From: Allie Rainsbury

I'm not stressing. I just don't appreciate the humour, that's all.

From: David Marshall

Are you being serious? It was a joke!

From: Allie Rainsbury

I'm being completely serious. It wasn't funny and it wasn't very pleasant.

From: David Marshall

What's rattled your cage today? Of course I was joking!

In case that wasn't abundantly clear though, I'm sorry. I didn't realise you were in such an obviously bad mood.

From: Allie Rainsbury

Whatever, David. I don't want to make this into a big deal and frankly I can't be bothered to argue. It would occasionally be nice though if you were less consumed with stupid innuendo and slightly more mature.

From: David Marshall

I was trying to lighten the atmosphere, for God's sake! And this is what I get for it!

From: Allie Rainsbury

You could better help by simply asking how I am or talking to me normally, instead of constantly insinuating how much you want to jump me all the time.

From: David Marshall

Well, apologies again for finding my girlfriend so attractive.

Clearly this is another deadly sin.

From: Allie Rainsbury

Let's stop here for the moment. You're winding me up too much and I'll just end up saying something I regret.

I'll call you later.

From: David Marshall

It's just a good thing I didn't joke about ball games as well.

Fine, speak later. Hopefully you'll be in a better mood by then.

Friday

From: Scott Cooper
To: Allie Rainsbury

Hi, how's your week going?

From: Allie Rainsbury

I'm fine, thank you. And you?

From: Scott Cooper

I'm in Gloucestershire. Have been all week. Meeting with other group CFOs.

From: Allie Rainsbury

Oh. That sounds...

From: Scott Cooper

Incredibly dull, yes.

Look, this thing carries on until Monday morning, but my PA's cleared my diary for the whole day so I'll have some spare time.

From: Allie Rainsbury

Nice! Are you writing just to brag or is there a message behind it? ☺

From: Scott Cooper

I'll be driving back through Oxford. I wondered if your father would want an extra visitor. You mentioned he enjoyed the company last time.

From: Allie Rainsbury

Oh! Wow! Well, that's a very kind offer, Scott, but I couldn't possibly ask you to do that.

From: Scott Cooper

Why not?

From: Allie Rainsbury

I'm sure the last thing you feel like doing is spending a free afternoon in a hospital.

From: Scott Cooper

If I didn't want to, I wouldn't have brought it up.

Should I not have asked?

From: Allie Rainsbury

No! No, not at all. It's really thoughtful of you. It's just that... Well, also, I hardly know you, do I?

From: Scott Cooper

And my being there would make you uncomfortable?

From: Allie Rainsbury

No! I don't mean that. It's just not the sort of thing you ask someone to do, is it?!

From: Scott Cooper

You haven't asked. I'm offering.

From: Allie Rainsbury

Well... I can't really think of a reply to that.

From: Scott Cooper

So you wouldn't be offended if I dropped by and took him a coffee?

From: Allie Rainsbury

No. I wouldn't be offended. I just think that... You shouldn't feel you have to do something like this.

From: Scott Cooper

If you can mention to him that I'll be there about 2 p.m.

From: Allie Rainsbury

OK...

I mean, is this OK?

From: Scott Cooper

Of course it is. It's done.

From: Allie Rainsbury

I feel a bit thrown by the gesture I think...

From: Scott Cooper

Right. Well, maybe work on that.

I have to go.

From: Allie Rainsbury

Scott, this is so lovely of you. It's the sweetest thing.

From: Scott Cooper

It's not a big deal. If it was, I wouldn't be doing it.

Enjoy your weekend.

From: Allie Rainsbury

Thank you.

I'm still unsure whether I should accept.

I am certain though that this is the kindest offer you could possibly have made x

CHAPTER 26

Monday 27 June

From: David Marshall
To: Allie Rainsbury

Hey you, I'm so glad you called me over the weekend. I was feeling terrible. I don't like it when you think badly of me.

It was a silly, thoughtless joke to make and I'm so sorry for upsetting you.

From: Allie Rainsbury

Since I said that you were forgiven on Sunday, I can't very well still be cross now, can I? ☺

From: David Marshall

Thought it was worth doubling checking! ☺

So how's your week shaping up? Mine's really hectic, but I should be able to find a spare evening or two for my favourite girl.

From: Allie Rainsbury

I'm pretty busy as well.

Plus it was quite a stressful weekend as Mum's state of coma went beyond the five-week mark – medically considered an unwelcome time threshold to cross into. I suppose the layman would describe it as ominous.

Dad was understandably more down than usual, which was difficult to cope with.

From: David Marshall

I'm sorry to hear that.

You should have told me when you called. I always want to hear about these kind of things.

From: Allie Rainsbury

I was just tired and probably a little emotional. But I'm sorry, I should have said. Sometimes I feel like talking about it and other times I want to shut everything out completely. It must be awfully difficult for you, I do appreciate that.

From: David Marshall

It hasn't been easy at times, I must admit. But I cope, and I don't want you worrying about me either! I'll be fine.

From: Allie Rainsbury

Because I'm happy to talk about things that are on your mind too. I don't mean for it always to be me, me, me...

From: David Marshall

I know, but I do try not to be a burden for you. You have enough on your plate.

I'm glad we talked though, and I'm glad to be back in your good books!

From: Allie Rainsbury

I don't think of you as a burden, silly!

How about we try and meet up on Thursday? If you're free and you've got time this week.

From: David Marshall

Sounds good.

I'll get my head down now. Hopefully I'll just about get through my work load by then!

Hope your dad feels better x

Tuesday

From: Peter Rainsbury
To: Allie Rainsbury

Dear Allie,

I hope your week is going well. This café is starting to turn into a regular spot for me!

I actually have a quiet day here for once. Between you and your aunt visiting at the weekend and then Scott turning up yesterday, I've done more entertaining than I do at home across a normal year!

Scott was full of praise for you over lunch, as a colleague and as a person – apparently you're quite the golden girl at the office. I had already guessed that of course, but it's never a bad thing to hear first-hand! Like your mother, you're far too modest for your own good.

Anyway, it was awfully good of him to pass by again; I really do find him a very endearing chap. Terribly bright of course, and more than happy to talk about gardening and golf (which is always a winner with me!). He was very happy to talk about you too so it was a fun few hours spent. And, no, don't worry, I didn't tell him any embarrassing childhood stories. Although I can't vouch for your mother, if the situation should arise. I'm very impressed with him, and very pleased for you.

I've given up trying to get you to take a weekend for yourself, but I sincerely hope you do for this one coming. I hope you spend it with your new 'friend'.

Take care sweetheart, love Dad x

From: Allie Rainsbury
To: Julie Lawson

OK, this is getting out of hand.

I've just had an email from my father saying how much fun he had chatting with Scott yesterday.

From: Julie Lawson

Huh? What do you mean?

You were in the office, weren't you?

From: Allie Rainsbury

Yes, *I* was...

Long story short, Scott offered to visit on his own as he passed through Oxford. And since I know that Dad needs all the company he can get at the moment...

From: Julie Lawson

Allie...!!

From: Allie Rainsbury

I know, I know! I should have declined right?

From: Julie Lawson

Of course you should have declined!

From: Allie Rainsbury

But it was such a sweet thing to offer!

What do I do? Do I need to even do anything? I suppose, really, nothing much has happened.

So he visited my father and bought him lunch. Friends can do that, right?

From: Julie Lawson

And your father is currently under the impression that you're going out with him?

From: Allie Rainsbury

Probably. He's from that sort of generation, isn't he?

From: Julie Lawson

Ah yes, the infamous 'suspect daughter of dating the guy who goes way above and beyond the call of duty, visits parents, buys them lunch and speaks fondly of aforementioned daughter' generation. Those people are so closeted, aren't they? :P

From: Allie Rainsbury

Not helpful.

From: Julie Lawson

Does Scott even know you're seeing anyone?

From: Allie Rainsbury

I don't know. I haven't told him.

From: Julie Lawson

You need to. He's clearly interested, Allie – you need to be fair on the man.

From: Allie Rainsbury

Do you really think so? If he was so interested why wouldn't he say anything?

From: Julie Lawson

Who knows? Maybe he's shy. Maybe he's hoping he doesn't have to. But one thing's for certain – he is definitely, definitely keen. And if you're with someone else, you need to tell him sooner rather than later.

From: Allie Rainsbury

I'm still not convinced he wants to be anything more than friends.

From: Julie Lawson

You're wrong. He does.

But why do you care either way? I thought you were making a go of things with David?

From: Allie Rainsbury

I am. I am! I don't care, you're right!

From: Julie Lawson

Well then, if you're so confident that he's just looking for friendship, and if you just want friendship too, what's the big deal telling him about the relationship you are in?

From: Allie Rainsbury

True. Yes, that's true.

From: Julie Lawson

So you'll tell him?

From: Allie Rainsbury

Yes, I'll tell him, I'll tell him.

Tomorrow.

From: Julie Lawson

If you don't, then look down when you get a chance – the hole that you're digging is getting bigger every day :P

Wednesday

From: Scott Cooper
To: Allie Rainsbury

How are you?

From: Allie Rainsbury

I'm well, thanks. Still enjoying all the compliments that my father said you paid me.

From: Scott Cooper

I don't recall doing that. He must have misunderstood.

From: Allie Rainsbury

Ah. That must have been it, yes! :P

Thank you again. I shouldn't have allowed you to visit but Dad had a lovely afternoon, and that's completely down to you.

From: Scott Cooper

You have to stop thanking me. It wasn't any effort and besides, I don't take praise well.

From: Allie Rainsbury

THANK YOU!

OK – I'm done now! ☺

From: Scott Cooper

Good, relieved to hear it.

From: Allie Rainsbury

So, look, I'm not quite sure how to ask this...

From: Scott Cooper

Structure it in the form of a question and go from there.

From: Allie Rainsbury

Ha. Yes, OK.

It's just, I'm sure you'll think I'm incredibly arrogant for doing so, and no doubt I'm reading too much into things as usual...

From: Scott Cooper

No doubt.

From: Allie Rainsbury

You do know I'm seeing someone, don't you?

From: Scott Cooper

Yes.

From: Allie Rainsbury

OK...

From: Scott Cooper

That's all?

From: Allie Rainsbury

Well, yes. It's just, I thought you might be interested in me, that's all.

I didn't want you to get the wrong impression or anything.

From: Scott Cooper

OK, thanks for clarifying.

From: Allie Rainsbury

Right. Well. No problem.

It's a good thing to get completely clear though, don't you think?

Anyway, I'll change the subject now before I make you feel awkward. Do you have a busy afternoon ahead?

From: Scott Cooper

Very. Must go, catch up soon.

From: Allie Rainsbury

Yes, definitely! I'd like that.

Call me when you're next free OK?

From: Allie Rainsbury
To: David Marshall

Want to grab those spare clothes and come over this evening?

From: David Marshall

I thought we were meeting tomorrow?

From: Allie Rainsbury

I could do with some company tonight. Can you come?

From: David Marshall

You don't need to ask me twice ;)

I'll see you at yours!

Thursday

From: Allie Rainsbury
To: Julie Lawson

As so often has been the case in the past, you were wrong :P

From: Julie Lawson

You've spoken to him?

From: Allie Rainsbury

I asked him outright and he said that he wasn't interested.

From: Julie Lawson

He's lying.

From: Allie Rainsbury

I don't think so. But it doesn't matter anyway. Plus, David came over last night and we had a nice evening in together. So it's all sorted – I have a clear conscience and Scott is clear where we stand.

From: Julie Lawson

And you're happy with that?

From: Allie Rainsbury

Very happy.

Scott's been incredibly thoughtful over the past couple of weeks, but I don't owe him anything more than a thank you for that.

From: Julie Lawson

You don't owe him anything at all. It just depends on what you want to offer...

From: Allie Rainsbury

I want the same thing he does – friendship! And we have that. And I have David. And everything is as it should be.

From: Julie Lawson

Sounds like you've got it all figured out then.

From: Allie Rainsbury

The me of a year ago would never have been this emphatic! I'd have confused things in my mind by not confronting them and eventually would have found myself in a tremendous emotional muddle.

From: Julie Lawson

The word hero is often overused. But in this case, Allie, you are truly one of the great British heroes :P

From: Allie Rainsbury

You're just jealous of my new-found assuredness!

From: Julie Lawson

Uh-huh...

So what would you have done if Scott had told you that he was interested?

From: Allie Rainsbury

Well, I'm not sure...

I was panicking that he might – what on earth would I have said?

From: Julie Lawson

How decisive... ☺

From: Allie Rainsbury

I'm certain what I think of you right now :P

Ha! You wouldn't be the first!

Chat later x

Friday

Dear Allie,

I wanted to write this to you in case I'm not brave or composed enough to broach it in person: I think we need to consider what we should do if your mum doesn't wake up.

I know that this is incredibly tough but I also know that, as a person who was always so full of life, she wouldn't want to just be left comatose in perpetuity.

The doctors tell me (and have no doubt informed you of much the same) that there have been a few previous cases where years have gone by before a patient eventually regains consciousness. Clearly however, they awake to a quality of life that they hadn't previously known or that their loved ones had necessarily been prepared for. In all cases, movement has been restricted and there has been severe mental degeneration.

I'm not looking for an answer at this stage or indeed even yet forming a question, but I think we need to consider whether this is something your mum would have wanted for us and more importantly for herself.

The alternative is obviously a terminal one. Again, as much as I hate to write this, based on the doctors' opinion, we might need to consider this option. And, if it's a consideration that we decide to pursue, at what point we should agree that 'enough is enough'.

I don't want you to feel that I'm giving up or that I'm succumbing to any negativity. I absolutely still believe that we'll have your mother back and fighting fit. But in case this doesn't materialise, I want us to be cognitive of her dignity and wishes.

OK, no more of that for now. I'm sorry for not discussing this face to face, but I fear I'd start to break down somewhat and no one wants to see that sight!

Are we seeing you this weekend? (A silly question no doubt.) Perhaps Scott will be making an appearance as well?

As always, with my love, Dad x

CHAPTER 27

Monday 4 July

From: Allie Rainsbury
To: Ann Rainsbury

Dear Mum,

I was thinking last night about the things we'll have to do when you wake up. I've jotted them down here; we can talk them through when you're better. So far I have:

1. Visit Teignmouth (I think I owe you a visit or two there!)

2. Go to America. Maybe a weekend shopping in New York, maybe a longer holiday on the West Coast? (Maybe both ☺)

3. Spa weekends – no more needs to be said here!

4. Rummy evenings (I can't imagine you'll put up much resistance to this one)

5. Days out around Britain (you always mentioned how much more of England you wanted to see. Well, let's go and look!)

Not an exhaustive collection by any means, but enough to get started and keep us busy for a while. And hopefully something for you to look forward to as well.

I miss you so much, Mum. You keep fighting and I'll chat with you soon.

All my love, Allie xxx

Tuesday

From: Scott Cooper
To: Allie Rainsbury

Let me know if you want/need to catch up at some point this week.
Scott

From: Allie Rainsbury

Hello, I wasn't too sure I'd hear from you again.

From: Scott Cooper

Why?

I'm free on either Thursday or Friday if you like.

From: Allie Rainsbury

Sure, definitely!

Can I let you know later though? I might have to meet up with my boyfriend instead.

From: Scott Cooper

No problem.

From: Allie Rainsbury

I don't mean 'I might have to' see David in a reluctant sense... just that I should check with him first if he wants to get together.

That's not to say I'm trying to brush you off though. Sorry!

Is that OK?

From: Scott Cooper

Stop panicking.

Let me know if you can – another time if not.

From: Allie Rainsbury

Absolutely! I'd really like that. I'll let you know as soon as possible.

From: Allie Rainsbury
To: David Marshall

Are you free on Thursday?

From: David Marshall

Yep, you bet! What did you have in mind? ;)

From: Allie Rainsbury

Nothing special; just wondered if you were around.

Are you sure you're not playing tennis or anything?

From: David Marshall

Ha! No, I'm certain. All yours...

From: Allie Rainsbury

OK. Because it's fine if you wanted to. I know how much you like your exercise!

From: David Marshall

I'm not playing tennis!

Let's go out, definitely! x

From: Allie Rainsbury

Great... x

Wednesday

From: Julie Lawson
To: Allie Rainsbury

George has kindly volunteered to oversee the kids this evening! I haven't figured out what he's playing at yet – no doubt it will mean returning the favour with interest at some stage in the near future.

But for now, I'm choosing not to worry about that.

Girls' night out?

From: Allie Rainsbury

Ah, what a thoughtful husband, doing something so sweet for his callous wife :P

Um, as happy as I am that you have your free pass, I might be really boring and turn down the offer, Jules. I'm terribly tired again this week (as repetitive and annoying as that must be to hear). I'm already going out with David tomorrow, so was hoping for a quiet evening tonight.

From: Julie Lawson

Fair enough. A girls' night in then :P

From: Allie Rainsbury

A slumber party? I wouldn't want you giving up your once-in-a-blue-moon evening out to stay in and watch *Titanic*!

From: Julie Lawson

But that sounds far more appealing than discouraging unwanted attention in an over-crowded, over-noisy bar anyway.

Let's watch Leo!

From: Allie Rainsbury

You're sure? I feel bad asking you to be unsociable as well.

From: Julie Lawson

Who else would I rather socialise with?

At the moment my only other option would be Chris, and he'd only spend most of the time being cryptic and annoying over who this new beau of his is.

From: Allie Rainsbury

Ha! Still no headway with that?

From: Julie Lawson

None. I'm giving up and ignoring him until he sees sense and tells me everything!

From: Allie Rainsbury

Good luck with that strategy. There's no way you'll last.

From: Julie Lawson

I've been quiet before, I'll be quiet again! Although, not with you and not tonight. We can gossip about who Chris might be seeing and you can fill me in on the latest developments between you and David.

From: Allie Rainsbury

OK then, if you're sure! Maybe a *Grey's Anatomy* marathon as well, depending on how emotional I feel once Leo's drowned.

From: Julie Lawson

I still think he deserved what he got – if he'd taken turns with Kate on that mantelpiece instead of spending all his time bobbing in the water he would have been fine!

From: Allie Rainsbury

I bet you've ruined so many films for your family.

From: Julie Lawson

I just don't suffer fools, that's all. You're the exception that proves the rule. See you later ☺ x

Thursday

From: David Marshall
To: Allie Rainsbury

Want to see a film this evening? It's been such a busy week already that I don't think I could face another pub!

From: Allie Rainsbury

I didn't know you'd been in any yet?

From: David Marshall

You know me – work hard, play hard! ☺

From: Allie Rainsbury

Evidently.

What's all the drinking been in aid of?

From: David Marshall

No special reasons really. The first was a work night out for my team, the other with a few friends from home.

Nothing crazy, but not sure I can justify a third evening propping up the bar!

From: Allie Rainsbury

OK. You should have invited me to the latter one – I would have liked to have met your friends.

From: David Marshall

Yeah? I didn't think you'd be keen, to be honest.

From: Allie Rainsbury

Well next time, ask me and find out!

From: David Marshall

Understood!

So, this evening…?

From: Allie Rainsbury

Yes, the cinema's fine. I don't mind escaping from reality for a couple of hours these days!

Shall I come up to yours? I've taken a leaf out of your book and brought in an overnight bag today.

From: David Marshall

Or I can come to you, if you'd prefer?

From: Allie Rainsbury

No, I've stalled long enough about visiting again. I think it's time I braved another trip.

From: David Marshall

Ha… Yes, OK. You're sure it won't be weird for you or anything?

From: Allie Rainsbury

No, I'll be fine. I want to come. Enough water's flowed under the bridge by now.

From: David Marshall

Great! In many ways it might be good for you to meet Hannah anyway.

From: Allie Rainsbury

Hannah?

How do you mean?

From: David Marshall

Well, if you're coming over then you'll get to meet her obviously…

From: Allie Rainsbury

Hannah, as in your ex-girlfriend? She hasn't moved out yet?

From: David Marshall

No, she's moving out next week.

From: Allie Rainsbury

What is she still doing there? You told me that she was moving out!

From: David Marshall

She is – next week!

It's taken her a while to find a new place, but all the paperwork has been signed now and most things are packed up.

A few more days and I'll be pretty lonely! ☺

From: Allie Rainsbury

What does than mean? You'll be lonely?! Why haven't you told me she hasn't moved out yet?

From: David Marshall

Wait a minute! Are you mad again?

I haven't said anything because I didn't think it was a subject you'd want to listen to very much.

As usual, I was thinking of you!

From: Allie Rainsbury

I'm counting very slowly to ten right now...

When exactly is this woman leaving?

From: David Marshall

Next Thursday. Do you want to help carry the bags?

From: Allie Rainsbury

I cannot believe you wouldn't tell me that she's still been living with you these past two months.

From: David Marshall

And I was surprised you didn't ask. But when you didn't, I just assumed you wanted to forget about the whole thing. So I didn't mention it again.

From: Allie Rainsbury

For someone so obviously intelligent in certain areas of their life, you are monumentally stupid in others.

From: David Marshall

Why thank you, Allie. I can always rely on you to give my confidence that much-needed boost.

From: Allie Rainsbury

You don't need me to – you still have someone else who can do that for you.

From: David Marshall

Don't say that. That's so incredibly unfair.

By Thursday she'll be gone.

From: Allie Rainsbury

Fine. Whatever. Let's see how things sit next week. At the moment, you'll forgive me for thinking that she'll be there till next year, never mind next Thursday.

From: David Marshall

Ever the cynic! ☺

So should I come over to yours this evening instead?

From: Allie Rainsbury

No, let's postpone this evening. I don't much feel like it now.

From: David Marshall

I don't mind coming over!

From: Allie Rainsbury

No, don't come. I'd rather a quiet night in; by the sounds of things you could do with one too.

From: David Marshall

I'll call tonight and check in at least.

We'll arrange another time xx

Friday

From: David Marshall
To: Allie Rainsbury

Good morning, gorgeous! No reply to my phone calls last night. I trust I'm not in your bad books ☺

From: Allie Rainsbury

I was tired and really didn't feel like getting into another protracted conversation.

From: David Marshall

No, sure — I think we've had enough of those recently.

Are you better today though?

From: Allie Rainsbury

I'm looking forward to the weekend, put it that way.

It's just exhausting trying to keep my spirits up all the time.

From: David Marshall

I know what you mean. But there's not long to go now. By Thursday this will all be done with and you can relax. I'm looking forward to it too!

From: Allie Rainsbury

I wasn't referring to your living situation, David.

From: David Marshall

No, of course... Your mum as well, obviously! How's she doing?

From: Allie Rainsbury

No new news.

From: David Marshall

That must be frustrating.

Hopefully being able to visit me will cheer you up somewhat, even if only a little bit?

From: Allie Rainsbury

Yes. It's made my week.

From: David Marshall

Really?

I'm excited as well! Sincerely, you mean it?

From: Allie Rainsbury

Yes, David, I'm being entirely genuine.

Suddenly, I have quite forgotten about everything else!

From: David Marshall

I'll leave you to it – this is clearly a bad day.

I'll call you over the weekend.

From: Allie Rainsbury

Great! I'll either be in IKEA picking you out a new coffee table or at the hospital visiting my gravely ill mother.

I shall leave you in suspense.

From: David Marshall

Sarcasm is such a low form of wit, Allie.

CHAPTER 28

Monday 11 July

From: Scott Cooper
To: Allie Rainsbury

You looked a little vacant in that meeting just now. Are you OK?

From: Allie Rainsbury

Was it that obvious? I didn't get much sleep this weekend. Combine that with my natural disinclination to function properly on Monday mornings and it's a perfect recipe for mind-wandering.

From: Scott Cooper

Ah. That would explain you telling Garry you'd applied for a credit card when he asked how your account was performing.

From: Allie Rainsbury

I didn't say that, did I?

From: Scott Cooper

In so many words. At least it brought some humour to proceedings.

Come on, grab your coat – sounds like you need a strong cup of coffee.

From: Allie Rainsbury

He did give me a funny glare. I just thought it was his face though.

I must have looked like a complete idiot.

From: Scott Cooper

It factored low on an Allie scale. I wouldn't worry about it.

From: Allie Rainsbury

I'm falling apart here, aren't I?

From: Scott Cooper

Coffee. Downstairs. I'm buying.

And that's an order.

From: Allie Rainsbury

Right. See you there.

Now, you mean?

From: Scott Cooper

Absolutely right now.

Talking is optional. Caffeine, croissant and some rest time are all compulsory.

From: Allie Rainsbury

You're lovely. You know that?

From: Scott Cooper

Less typing, more action.

Tuesday

From: Allie Rainsbury
To: Julie Lawson; Scott Cooper; Chris Trail; David Marshall

She's awake!!

She's awake!!! I've just had a call from Dad!

She's just woken up now!

From: Julie Lawson
To: Allie Rainsbury

That's amazing news!

Call me as soon as you can! x

From: Scott Cooper
To: Allie Rainsbury

How is she responding?

Please keep me in the loop if you can.

Thoughts are with you all.

From: Chris Trail
To: Allie Rainsbury

Hurray and hurrah!!

Awesome news, sweetheart!

How's she holding up? Is she asking for you? x

From: David Marshall
To: Allie Rainsbury

Great...

Since when are you ccing Scott Cooper on personal emails?

Wednesday

From: Allie Rainsbury
To: Julie Lawson; Scott Cooper; Chris Trail; David Marshall

Hey everyone,

A quick update since you've all been so kind as to ask.

Mum woke up yesterday morning just after ten o'clock. Dad was in her room at the time when he noticed some movement. It started in her left foot and seemed to cause a chain reaction – that's how he described it anyway!

You know those scenes in films when a patient finally opens their eyes, sees their loved one looking down at them tenderly and says something incredibly emotional that reduces viewers to tears? It wasn't like that!

Dad started shouting wildly and in his haste to fetch a doctor, tripped over a chair. So any touching one-liners my mum may have opened with got lost beneath his swearing!

Anyway, that was yesterday. She was asleep by the time I arrived last evening and I was terrified that she'd slipped back into the coma again. I had to contain a powerful urge to try and shake her awake! Fortunately I part-resisted and was part-restrained by people far more sensible than I, and we left her to rest through the night.

I was at the hospital at 6 a.m. this morning and she woke up about 15 minutes after I arrived. There were a lot of tears, I'm not ashamed to say! She looked so tired and so frail and so gentle that it broke my heart and I was blubbing a fair while before I managed to say anything remotely comprehensible. If anything, she was the more lucid. We talked for about ten minutes, although I kept it short because she was still extremely sleepy. I'm going back in to visit her this afternoon; hopefully I'll be able to chat a little longer and cry a little less! But we'll see! ☺

Mentally, there doesn't appear to be any lasting damage (although it is early days obviously) – there are likely to be one or two bits of memory loss in the short term, but apparently that's to be expected. She's still very weak, as you'd also expect, although the intravenous drip she's been on has helped.

It is going to be a while before she's allowed to go home, despite the fact that she's desperate to do so already! The doctors still need to perform various tests and checks before they'll sanction a move away from the hospital. Basically, she needs a lot more fluid, nutrients and rest, but appears to be on the mend.

I'm going to grab a sandwich and maybe even a celebratory cupcake now!

Thank you all for your good wishes and your support – I'll be sure to pass it all on to Mum and Dad.

More updates to follow, love Allie xx

From: Scott Cooper
To: Allie Rainsbury

Fantastic.

Thanks for the update – yes, do please pass on my best wishes.

From: Chris Trail
To: Allie Rainsbury

Ha! Love the thought of your dad screaming blue murder as your mum is coming round! What a tranquil scene to awaken to! ☺

So happy, happy, happy for you!

Call me if you're not too tired and give both your parents a big hug from me in the meantime.

From: Julie Lawson
To: Allie Rainsbury

I don't blame you for being anxious about her going back to sleep. I'm surprised you're not constantly ringing a little bell in her ear to keep her from drifting off again!

Such good news. I'll call you this evening and you can give me a proper update then.

Love you xx

Thursday

From: Scott Cooper
To: Allie Rainsbury

Everything still OK?

From: Allie Rainsbury

Yes, yes! The sky seems bluer and the birds are definitely singing more loudly than usual! ☺

She sat up in bed this morning (which might not sound much, but is terribly exciting and a good progressive break-through). It's mostly a question of staying patient and allowing her to recover at her own pace. Now that she is back and alert, the temptation is to want to see her speaking, eating and generally doing the thoughtless day-to-day things we all take for granted. But, of course, it will be weeks, perhaps many months, before she's back to anything like before.

From: Scott Cooper

The weather is clearly nicer where you are...

Great news.

From: Allie Rainsbury

About the weather, or Mum's progress? :P

My father asked after you today as well by the way. He said to say hello and commented that (for the thousandth time!) you are a 'fine example of a young man'.

From: Scott Cooper

Well, he has good taste, clearly.

In all seriousness, how is he getting on? Your mother's been the focus of all the attention, quite rightly, but this must be a huge weight that's been lifted from his shoulders.

From: Allie Rainsbury

It's as if he's been to the best health clinic in the world, had everything bad and stressful flushed out of his system and come back completely refreshed and revitalised.

It's a strange paradox, but you often don't realise how much things have changed until they return to normal. He laughed yesterday,

I can't even tell you why, but the noise came as a shock. I haven't heard him do so in so long!

From: Scott Cooper

A nice shock to have I bet.

Are you up there for a while?

From: Allie Rainsbury

Definitely until the end of the week, yes. Garry has been so good throughout all of this, and the past week hasn't been any exception.

From: Scott Cooper

Glad to hear it. And to hear you're in such good spirits.

I won't take up any more of your time for now. Let me know if I can do anything for you though.

From: Allie Rainsbury

Scott, you've already done far too much. Thank you for being so incredible through this as well.

The one bright spot from the past couple of months is the new friend I've found in you.

From: Scott Cooper

There's your corny film line...

From: Allie Rainsbury

☺! Speak soon x

From: Allie Rainsbury
To: David Marshall

Are you picking up my emails?

Friday

From: Allie Rainsbury
To: David Marshall

Hi there. I can't seem to get hold of you at the moment.

From: David Marshall

No, I'm here, just busy.

How are you?

From: Allie Rainsbury

I'm all the better for Mum waking up this week, that's for sure!

Is everything all right? You seem a bit distant?

From: David Marshall

Does confused and hurt equate to distant? If so, then I suppose I am, yes.

From: Allie Rainsbury

What's up?

Is this about our argument last week?

From: David Marshall

No, why would it be? I said Hannah was going to move out yesterday and she did.

I'm upfront about these kind of things because I realise how much they impact on a relationship.

From: Allie Rainsbury

Right...

Sorry, David – where are you going with this exactly?

From: David Marshall

You copied Scott Cooper in on an incredibly personal email which raises a few questions, don't you think?

What's more, you still haven't even had the decency to reply to the one question I have asked: Why?

From: Allie Rainsbury

Scott is a friend. Just as Julie and Chris are friends! They've all been very supportive, both to me and to my family, over the past few months and I wanted to let them know the good news. It's that simple.

From: David Marshall

I didn't even know you spoke to the guy, let alone that you shared intimate secrets with him.

From: Allie Rainsbury

I didn't feel it an especially important thing to tell you. He asked if he could help and that was it.

Look, David, I've just had the best news of my life this week. I don't want to fall back down to earth yet with an argument as trivial as this, OK?

From: David Marshall

That's exactly your problem, Allie; you walk around with your head in the clouds all the time! A relationship isn't just about what you want, it's about what we want. And we should want to be honest about everything.

That's exactly why I'm so hurt by the fact that, after putting myself out there by telling you all about Hannah, I find that you're skulking around with Scott bloody Cooper!

Probably at work too, right under my nose.

From: Allie Rainsbury

This is nothing like the same as you and Hannah.

Jesus! I'm not getting into this!

And, since you value honesty so highly, I only emailed you now because I was disappointed with your muted response to news of my mother's recovery!

From: David Marshall

Perhaps I'd have been more thrilled if the story hadn't come gift wrapped in 'Your Girlfriend's Cheating on You'.

From: Allie Rainsbury

?! I'm absolutely not!

You get all this from a name being on an email?

From: David Marshall

It's what it implies, Allie. I'm pretty good at reading people.

From: Allie Rainsbury

This is ridiculous. As so often seems to be the way with your conversations.

I'm going now. I'll speak to you later when you're in a more sensible mood.

From: David Marshall

Don't bother. I won't pick up.

Call Scott instead and no doubt the two of you can while away the small hours somehow...

It's always the good guys who get hurt the most.

From: Allie Rainsbury

Then you should be impervious to pain.

Thanks for the flowers you didn't send, they were a nice touch.

CHAPTER 29

Monday 18 July

From: Allie Rainsbury
To: Julie Lawson

I've just remembered that it's the kids' birthdays tomorrow!
This officially makes me the worst godmother in the world. I feel terrible.

From: Julie Lawson

Good morning.

Under general circumstances you might qualify but this year you get a pass ☺

Don't worry about it, they get far too much stuff anyway!

From: Allie Rainsbury

Absolutely not! Of course I'm buying them presents. What do they want? All suggestions are welcome...

From: Julie Lawson

Well, they really don't need anything...

But it you feel compelled to, then perhaps get Elly a little purse or a handbag; nothing too ostentatious. And Cale – anything Lego, anything cars. You can't go wrong with those.

From: Allie Rainsbury

I'll pop out at lunchtime and pick them up a few things.

From: Julie Lawson

One thing. No more. They're spoilt enough as it is!

Come over tomorrow evening; I'm cooking a special birthday dinner and there'll be far too much of it.

And of course David's very welcome as well.

From: Allie Rainsbury

Ha! How much effort did that take to write? ☺

From: Julie Lawson

I've only partially chewed off my tongue.

From: Allie Rainsbury

I thought as much! Well, you're safe for the moment anyway :P He won't be coming but I'd love to.

From: Julie Lawson

Do I detect a trace of frustration with the lovely man?

From: Allie Rainsbury

Another day, another argument. Over incredibly stupid stuff.

I'll tell you about it later – repeating it now would only cause my blood to start boiling again.

From: Julie Lawson

Ooh... Sounds like a good one. Tell me later, I'm about to head into a meeting.

Also... and I'm only saying this because I know you'll feel bad if you don't...

From: Allie Rainsbury

Go on.

From: Julie Lawson

You might want to pick up a bottle of something for George – it was his birthday yesterday.

From: Allie Rainsbury

Arrrgh!! Worst godmother and worst friend ever!

I'm going to the shops now, my head bowed in shame and disgrace.

From: Julie Lawson

☺ x

Tuesday

From: Ann Rainsbury
To: Allie Rainsbury

Hello darling,

How are you? I'm writing this from my hospital bed which, as comfortable as it is, I shall be glad to be out of!

A doctor came and examined me again this morning and went through my latest test results. I nodded away as if I knew what he was talking about, even though most of it went straight over my head. All I could really gather is that everything seems rather positive, which is nice of course. It means that I can go home this weekend, albeit under strict instructions to rest and carrying a bucket-load of pills and other medicine. I really do think I could open a pharmacy, the number of prescriptions I have.

Anyway, your father has been telling me how often you've visited and what a superstar you have been. He also mentioned that you may have found yourself a nice young friend called Scott, whom I believe he's even met a couple of times! This all makes me very curious, and I'm ashamed to say slightly jealous. I'd like to meet him as well, please! Perhaps, if you were planning on coming this weekend you could extend an invitation to him too?

I may well not be up to much conversationally, but if he can brave that then I'd be terribly excited to meet him too! It's entirely up to you though, sweetheart, of course and I certainly don't mean to imply that I'm expecting you here either; far from it.

No doubt I'll speak to you later. Your father is waving hello too —
he's sitting in the corner, happily eating my breakfast and reading
my newspaper. You see? Things are already getting back to normal!

Much love, Mum xx

From: Allie Rainsbury

Dear Mum,

That's great news! Of course I'm coming up. I wouldn't miss your
homecoming for the world!!

As far as Scott is concerned — yes, Dad did meet him once or twice,
and he has been incredibly good and kind to me recently, however I
do need to emphasise that we are just friends.

I've actually been seeing another man, David, and he's great too.
Perhaps I could invite him up to Oxford instead?

So excited to see you, and see you home again.

With love Allie xx

From: Ann Rainsbury

Darling, your father is definitely saying it was a 'Scott' that he met.
He's never heard of anyone called David. Are you sure you're right?

From: Allie Rainsbury

Mum, of course I'm right! I'm the one dating them!

From: Ann Rainsbury

Both of them? Oh dear. Should you really be doing that?

Of course, I'm not one for being a prude and I do know that times
have changed an awful lot since I was last on the 'scene' as they
say, but that still doesn't seem quite right to me.

If I had to choose, I think I'd like to see Scott — I'd feel very awkward
having them both there at once.

From: Allie Rainsbury

I meant 'him' not 'them'! I was flustered — I did mean him!

From: Ann Rainsbury

Who? I'm terribly confused!

Anyway, I'm going to get some more rest now, darling. Have a think and let me know which friend you'd like to invite up. I'm sure they're both very nice.

Do be careful though, that's all I'll say xx

From: Allie Rainsbury
To: David Marshall

Hi, are you around this weekend?

My mum is coming home and would like to meet you!

Do you feel up to it? ☺ x

Wednesday

From: Allie Rainsbury
To: Julie Lawson

Thanks again for a lovely evening. I took a couple of very cute pictures of Elly and Cale – I'll send them to you later!

From: Julie Lawson

Thank you for coming and for all your presents! Far too generous though.

I dropped off two very tired, very cranky kids at the school gates this morning. A cute picture will be a nice reminder of their more angelic side!

From: Allie Rainsbury

They're cranky when they're tired? Aw... They're turning into their parents after all.

From: Julie Lawson

Ha! Tread carefully there – at least my parents don't think I'm having a threesome :P

From: Allie Rainsbury

Don't joke about that!

I still don't know what to do about it!

From: Julie Lawson

Have you heard back from David yet?

From: Allie Rainsbury

No. He's ignoring me. I even passed by his office earlier to see if I could catch him face to face, but it doesn't look is if he's in.

I'll pop up once more this afternoon and then give up trying.

From: Julie Lawson

It sounds as if he's being slightly childish in an effort to get your attention.

I wouldn't fall for it personally.

From: Allie Rainsbury

I'm not! Not really anyway.

Although I should have told him about Scott.

And I know that Mum will be really disappointed if I go up alone. Especially since she seems to think I'm dating half of London anyway!

From: Julie Lawson

Ha! That is funny. It sounds as if you've managed to utterly confuse them.

Maybe you should take George up with you, just to really make things interesting.

From: Allie Rainsbury

So having survived a coma, you reckon a heart attack should be her next challenge...

From: Julie Lawson

True! Plus George isn't the greatest actor, he goes red whenever he lies. I always know when a 'work from home' day has involved more TV watching than work doing!

From: Allie Rainsbury

Aw, poor George. He's such a lovely innocent.

So what am I going to do?

From: Julie Lawson

Apart from trying to find a boyfriend who actually wants to talk to you, you mean?

From: Allie Rainsbury

Hilarious...

From: Julie Lawson

Well, you can't really go up there alone, can you?

Your mum will either think you're too ashamed of her to bring someone back or that you've found yet another lover and have buried both Scott and David in your garden.

I can't see a whole lot of options for you here.

From: Allie Rainsbury

You are officially less than no help.

I'll keep trying David and hope he picks up my calls at some point.

From: Julie Lawson

Decisions, decisions ☺

Let me know how it all goes!

From: Allie Rainsbury

Keep George on stand-by :P

From: Allie Rainsbury
To: David Marshall

David, where are you?

Please can you return my calls or let me know what's going on. This weekend is a very big deal. It's something that means an awful lot to me, my mum and my whole family for that matter.

Just let me know either way, OK?

Thursday

From: Allie Rainsbury
To: David Marshall

I'm guessing it's a no.

Thanks very much. I'm bowled over by your commitment and generosity.

From: David Marshall

I wanted some space. And some time alone to think.

From: Allie Rainsbury

Think about what? Jesus! I've asked you enough times now.

Yes or no – it's not a bloody sacrifice is it?

From: David Marshall

I'm too hurt by you right now; I'd just make a bad impression.

You seem hostile and completely unapologetic for your actions.

Why don't you invite Scott instead? If he isn't already going, that is.

From: Allie Rainsbury

You take immaturity to new heights.

Maybe I'll do just that – Scott at least seems to be able to hold a civil conversation.

From: David Marshall

Unbelievable.

Fine, take him with you. I hope you're both very happy together.

From: Allie Rainsbury
To: Scott Cooper

I have a huge favour to ask you.

It's completely fine if you say no; in fact I honestly don't expect you to say yes, but I've managed to get myself into a bit of a muddle.

From: Scott Cooper

This sounds interesting...

From: Allie Rainsbury

Mum is going back home from hospital tomorrow. I'm taking the day off and accompanying her.

She's been hearing a lot about you from Dad, and has somehow come to the conclusion that you're... A special friend.

She really wants to meet you.

From: Scott Cooper

Right.

From: Allie Rainsbury

I've tried to explain that I'm actually seeing someone else, but that just served to make her very confused.

It's not helped by the fact that David and I are in the middle of an incredibly puerile argument and he's being somewhat reticent about accompanying me.

Would you be able to come along? Just as a friend obviously?

From: Scott Cooper

Wow. You don't often get an offer as generous as that. So, after exhausting all other options, you're turning to me for assistance?

From: Allie Rainsbury

Basically. Yes.

I'm not holding out much hope.

From: Scott Cooper

Will your parents know we're just friends by the time we get up there?

From: Allie Rainsbury

I'll do my best to reiterate that, yes!

And I shall certainly ensure that bedrooms are kept very separate.

From: Scott Cooper

OK, make sure you do, please – that would be a level too embarrassing otherwise.

From: Allie Rainsbury

Understood.

From: Scott Cooper

Let me make a couple of calls first, I'll see what I can do.

From: Allie Rainsbury

I don't want you cancelling any other plans though.

Maybe we should leave it. I'm sure my mum won't be that disappointed if I turn up alone.

From: Scott Cooper

I'll drop you a line in half an hour.

Friday
Holiday

CHAPTER 30

Monday 25 July

From: David Marshall
To: Allie Rainsbury

So I did some thinking this weekend.

From: Allie Rainsbury

Right.

From: David Marshall

I guess I've always had a bit of an issue with trust. I don't open up to many people but when I do I expect to know everything about them.

So you not telling me about Scott was a really big lapse on your part.

From: Allie Rainsbury

I can't do this any more, David.

From: David Marshall

Wait, what can't you do?

From: Allie Rainsbury

I can't keep having the same conversation with you.

The same arguments. The same frustrations. It's so tiring!

From: David Marshall

I don't understand. We're not arguing, we're talking.

From: Allie Rainsbury

Does this not just constantly feel like hard work? You never seem satisfied with what I can offer and I'm never sure what you really want. It's not a great basis, is it?

From: David Marshall

And yet here we still are. Still fighting.

From: Allie Rainsbury

That's exactly the problem! We're always fighting!

From: David Marshall

No, I mean we're still fighting for us.

I'm not ready to give up yet. And I don't have you down as a quitter either.

From: Allie Rainsbury

Why do you want us to keep going so much?

From: David Marshall

Because you're an incredible person.

You've been through so much recently and yet you've never tried to push your fears onto me. You're strong, you're determined, you're thoughtful and kind.

You're everything that I want.

From: Allie Rainsbury

I took Scott with me to Oxford this weekend.

From: David Marshall

Did anything happen?

From: Allie Rainsbury

No! I've told you – we're just friends. That's all we've ever been.

From: David Marshall

OK.

From: Allie Rainsbury

OK what?

From: David Marshall

Just OK. I choose to trust you.

I don't especially want to hear about it, but I believe what you're saying. I suppose all I want to know now is whether you can put as much faith in us as I have in you.

Do you want to walk away because of an argument, or dig a bit deeper and unearth our true potential?

From: Allie Rainsbury

I need to think.

From: David Marshall

Then I need to wait, don't I? ☺

From: Allie Rainsbury

I wish, I wish I knew where I stood with you.

Sometimes you say everything wrong, other times it's so charmingly right. I feel like a yo-yo in a game you're playing.

From: David Marshall

If I had you on a piece of string, I'd be reeling you back in about now ☺

From: Allie Rainsbury

I don't even know what that means.

From: David Marshall

It means come back to me, gorgeous, I miss you so much xx

Tuesday

From: Scott Cooper
To: Allie Rainsbury

After enjoying such a pleasant weekend, yesterday proved a real struggle.

Thank you again for the invitation. I had a good time. I trust your mother is still recovering well?

From: Allie Rainsbury

There's no need to thank me, Scott!

It was great fun, I'm just sorry you were subjected to so many questions!

From: Scott Cooper

Exhausted or not, she was certainly curious... I was interrogated less by the board when reviewing our yearly budget.

From: Allie Rainsbury

Well, you handled it very tactfully as ever.

You know, I have quite a bit of dirt on you now, don't I?

From: Scott Cooper

I trust that you'll keep it in confidence.

From: Allie Rainsbury

Hmm... everything save for the ballet lessons you took as a kid – that's far too precious a story!

From: Scott Cooper

If Billy Elliot taught me anything, it's that ballet is exceptionally good exercise and fantastic for defining core muscle groups.

Besides, I had no choice – I crumbled in front of my mother's will as much as I did yours.

From: Allie Rainsbury

Ah Scottina.

It's all right, it's all over now! You can skip away merrily ☺

From: Scott Cooper

You're walking a very thin line.

From: Allie Rainsbury

Are you going to teach me to pirouette along it :P

From: Scott Cooper

I'm going to change the subject, that's what I'm going to do.

Are you around for a drink this week? No childhood reminiscing to be involved!

From: Allie Rainsbury

I can't do this week unfortunately.

Maybe the following one though?

From: Scott Cooper

All right. Let me know when you're free and we'll try to arrange it.

From: Allie Rainsbury

Sure.

Scott. Can I ask you something?

From: Scott Cooper

Ridiculous question. Of course you can.

From: Allie Rainsbury

You're definitely not keen on me are you? As more than a friend I mean?

It's just that I do have a boyfriend, and as much as I like you, I wouldn't want you to think I was leading you on. Or for him to think that we were up to anything other than sharing harmless banter.

From: Scott Cooper

You've mentioned your boyfriend before. Several times in fact.

I'm very aware of his existence, you can rest assured.

From: Allie Rainsbury

OK.

From: Scott Cooper

Let me know if you want that drink.

From: Allie Rainsbury

Yes. OK.

I hope... If I wasn't with him, it would be different, you see?

From: Scott Cooper

Not on my part.

Work calls – chat later.

Wednesday

From: Allie Rainsbury
To: David Marshall

I'm going to send you an email in a minute that's quite lengthy.

Just to warn you!

From: David Marshall

OK. Will it make for good reading?

From: Allie Rainsbury

I'll leave it for you to decide that :P x

From: David Marshall

I consider myself forewarned! x

From: Allie Rainsbury
To: David Marshall

Dear David,

Thank you for been so patient over the last couple of days and for giving me the space and time that I asked for. Like you, I've spent a good while thinking. About you, about me and about us. But mostly about me ☺

I realise that I've been emotional, needy and self-involved over the past couple of months. My priorities and spare time have completely revolved around my parents. And I don't apologise for any of this. It's important, no, it's vital that you understand that. After my mum's crash, I made a promise to myself, and to my parents, that I'd never take them for granted again. I hope I've lived up to that promise so far, and I have no intention of letting it go.

That doesn't mean that I don't have anything to apologise for. Prioritising them came at the expense of marginalising you. I think I have a pretty healthy excuse – with the stress and constant worry – but looking back, it's also fair to say that my behaviour at times, irrespective of how understandable it may have been, did put pressure on you and on us. For several weeks tensions between us seemed to escalate at the same rate as my stress levels, which can't have just been coincidence!

So I'm sorry. I'm sorry for snapping at you when I had no cause to snap. I'm sorry for patronising you, for confusing you, for being so difficult and down. I'm sorry mostly that I wasn't completely open with you. That, despite the fact that this was never used for any underhand purposes, gave you a reason not to trust me, and made you question my commitment at a time when answers were in short supply.

But now you need to be sorry too. And you need to accept some responsibility for this relationship as well. For a long time I haven't known where we are as a couple. Indeed, on occasions, I haven't even been convinced we were a couple at all. A lot of this uncertainty has come from obvious events (I don't think we need to detail these again!) but a great deal has come through the little things. How you always seemed eager to take me to bed but less keen to talk through my fears. How you were always happy to work late but not able to spend time with me. How you always seemed to argue with me when I told you something rather than simply listen, take my point and maybe learn from it.

I think that most of the above – the arguments, the worries, the trust – began to beget the other. Thrown into the air they would have all formed a big circular storm, whose component parts fed each other and grew in intensity. This storm has been sitting over our heads for long enough. I'm proposing that we walk back into the sunshine for a while and see how the view looks from there.

If you can promise to work on your trust issues, I'll work on mine. If you can occasionally be more thoughtful and sensitive to my needs then I'll turn to you more often with them.

I think the fact that we've come through the worst few months of my life and are still talking is testament to us. If you can commit to me, then I'll commit to you. Agree to this and let's start again.

Love, Allie x

Ps. What do you think?

From: David Marshall

I think you're a wonderful person.

I think that I agree with everything you've said.

I think that we should go for a drink ☺ xx

Thursday

From: Julie Lawson
To: Allie Rainsbury

Of all the people in all the world to come across at Tesco's.

So we're back on speaking terms with David I see?

The plot thickens ☺

From: Allie Rainsbury

And so far away from the ready-meal aisle as well.

Yes, we're back talking!

I sent David a long email yesterday highlighting a few points that I felt had been holding both of us back for the last few months. He agreed with everything I wrote and we decided to start afresh so we went for a few drinks and an honest chat ☺

From: Julie Lawson

Hmm, interesting.

And were these points similar to the ones you've raised with him previously?

From: Allie Rainsbury

Meaning that you've heard this all before, seen it all before and doubt that this is anything other than another false dawn?

From: Julie Lawson

Don't be prickly. It's not becoming of you :P

But yes, I suppose those thoughts did cross my mind. They must have wandered over yours as well, since you've just summarised them so astutely.

From: Allie Rainsbury

I considered them, yes. But I considered other factors too.

And, in fairness to David, there have been times (that I haven't necessarily shared with you) when I've been hard work myself.

At least by beginning to excuse my own behaviour as justifiable then I can begin to understand his as well.

From: Julie Lawson

Well, that all sounds very sophisticated and terribly clever.

I've always been a simple girl who decides what she likes, who she likes and goes from there.

From: Allie Rainsbury

And I've always looked down on you for it. It's good you know your place :P

From: Julie Lawson

But... Despite scraping around all the way down here, I'm still very, very happy, which is all that matters really, if you're lucky enough to manage it.

From: Allie Rainsbury

I'm giving him a chance, Jules. I want your support on this. I've heard all the arguments against.

From: Julie Lawson

And you have it!

I'm just mulling through my thoughts, that's all.

From: Allie Rainsbury

Mull happier thoughts please x

From: Julie Lawson

David has a wonderful arse.

From: Allie Rainsbury

Ha! That will do to start with!

Perhaps we can try for dinner again, the four of us?

From: Julie Lawson

Absolutely.

Friday

From: Allie Rainsbury
To: David Marshall

Hey, lovely!

I know you can't make it to Oxford this weekend, but how about I come back early on Sunday and we can spend the afternoon together?

From: David Marshall

Sounds good. If the weather's nice let's go to Hampstead Heath and take a stroll. If it's bad we can snuggle on the sofa. Come on, rain! ☺

I'm sorry I can't make it to Oxford – if it had been anything other than the Summer Tournament I would have cancelled, but I've already committed to playing for the next few weeks.

We tennis players are an honourable lot.

From: Allie Rainsbury

That's OK – I know what a talented sportsman you are. I'm proud of it! I just wish you'd gone professional; you could have jumped in a private jet and flown up for the evening ;)

From: David Marshall

Ha, if only! That would certainly beat queuing on the M25.

I'm not sure tennis is anything to be proud of though, I've always been pretty coordinated. And there's no way I could have turned pro. If I'd practised a bit more, maybe. Part of the problem was that it all came a bit too easy.

From: Allie Rainsbury

I bet you could have done – I'm not buying all this modesty.

But try and keep the end of the month free, please. I want to take Mum and Dad back down to Devon, if she's up to it. Could be a nice little get away for us as well.

From: David Marshall

Absolutely, I wouldn't miss that.

If I'm knocked out of the competition early then I'll be free even sooner, but, to be honest, that's pretty unlikely.

From: Allie Rainsbury

Hurrah! I'm looking forward to it already.

You make sure you win that cup. It will be a nice little trophy to show off to my dad ☺

From: David Marshall

It wouldn't be so little actually.

From: Allie Rainsbury

Even better.

Big trophy or not though, I'm sure that he'll be very impressed by you.

From: David Marshall

I'm sure he will be too; stop worrying!

So you'll come over to mine on Sunday afternoon then?

From: Allie Rainsbury

Yes! I'll call you when I'm en route – hopefully with my umbrella up ;)

From: David Marshall

That should give me enough time to hide my other ex-girlfriends ☺

From: Allie Rainsbury

!!! That's so outrageously inappropriate it's actually quite funny. I'll let you off with that joke this one time :P x

From: David Marshall

At least now I know where the line is ☺

CHAPTER 31

Monday 1 August

From: Allie Rainsbury
To: Ann Rainsbury; Peter Rainsbury

Dear Mum and Dad,

Was your Sunday lunch fun yesterday? I hope having the neighbours over wasn't too exhausting. Mum, did you manage to eat much?

Anyway, to the real purpose of this Monday morning email. We briefly mentioned organising a trip down to Teignmouth on Saturday, but nothing really came of the conversation (I think it fizzled out when Dad was distracted by a weed growing near the rose bushes ☺).

I wanted to follow up on it though, as I'm very keen on the idea. I still have a couple of weeks' holiday to use and, since I missed the last visit at Easter, would really like to go down for a belated beach walk or two.

If we left on 20 August we can be there in plenty of time for your birthday, Mum, on the 23rd. What do you think? I'll call Auntie Jean today and check if they're able to have us all down there. It would be a very relaxing fortnight, and be nice to spend some proper time together.

Much love Allie xx

Ps. Mum, I'm looking into those spa weekends I promised you (sorry Dad, just for us girls!). I don't have dates yet but should get some details through this week and be able to book something up. Let the pampering begin!

From: David Marshall
To: Allie Rainsbury

Miss me yet? ;)

From: Allie Rainsbury

Maybe a little bit ☺

How's your day going?

From: David Marshall

Not great, I have a heavy meeting this afternoon that's been thrown at me from nowhere.

From: Allie Rainsbury

Oh dear, that's no fun.

If you get to see me tonight, would that help at all?

From: David Marshall

Depends what I get to see you in ;P

From: Allie Rainsbury

In not very much.

If you're lucky ;)

Come round to mine after you're done at work and I'll cook you dinner.

From: David Marshall

You'll cook me dinner?...!

From: Allie Rainsbury

Cook/order in... semantics.

From: David Marshall

Sounds great – see you there ☺

Although I'm not sure you've helped much. Now this afternoon is really going to drag.

From: Allie Rainsbury

At least you'll have something else to think about ;)

Tuesday

From: Allie Rainsbury
To: Scott Cooper

You've been a bit quiet the past week...

From: Scott Cooper

Not intentionally so.

From: Allie Rainsbury

Are you still keen to meet for a drink sometime? Maybe next Thursday evening if you're free?

From: Scott Cooper

That could work.

It sounds like your social calendar is run pretty tightly these days.

From: Allie Rainsbury

Busier than normal I suppose (disastrously I am now three episodes behind on *Desperate Housewives*).

I'm spending a lot of time with David at the moment. I felt that I owed him some attention, since he's been a little overlooked recently.

From: Scott Cooper

That would explain it then. Lucky David.

From: Allie Rainsbury

Hmm, he's probably thinking the opposite!

But you're OK though? I'm really looking forward to catching up with you.

From: Scott Cooper

I'm fine.

I'll see you later, if you're free.

From: Allie Rainsbury

Definitely.

You'd tell me if anything was wrong, wouldn't you, Scott?

I'm here if you need me to listen.

From: Scott Cooper

Well, I suppose I am having a bit of a problem with this girl.

She's been emailing me rather a lot and it's distracting me from my work.

From: Allie Rainsbury

Really?! Who? Do I know her?

From: Scott Cooper

Some account manager who insists on telling me about how much time she's spending with her boyfriend.

How do I politely tell her to leave me alone?

From: Allie Rainsbury

!! Fine – I'm going!

I hope your workload increases ten-fold during the reading of this email :P

From: Scott Cooper

It's OK – I think she's got the message now.

See you soon.

Wednesday

From: Allie Rainsbury
To: Chris Trail

Where are you?

From: Chris Trail

Helloooo! It's been a while. I'm still here though, don't worry ☺

How are things with you?

From: Allie Rainsbury

Life's good. But we haven't spoken in ages!

I'm getting Chris-withdrawal symptoms.

From: Chris Trail

Aww, we have been bad recently. I miss you too!

From: Allie Rainsbury

We've been terrible! Which, of course, is mostly your fault when you think about it.

From: Chris Trail

While I do realise it's abundantly obvious, remind me quite why that's the case.

From: Allie Rainsbury

You know I'm hopeless at staying in touch. You've always been brilliant at getting us together. That's your thing!

What's been keeping you so busy? Or should I say who? ☺

From: Chris Trail

I didn't know I had a thing. That's rather exciting!

All in good time, my dear...

From: Allie Rainsbury

Chris! You've been holding out for far too long. You told me nothing last time I saw you even though you promised you would!

From: Chris Trail

I suggested, I didn't promise. I didn't feel ready to share in the end.

From: Allie Rainsbury

But I'm your best friend!

From: Chris Trail

And as my best friend you should exhibit understanding and patience :P

Plus, while I remember, not ask Julie to dig away for information either.

From: Allie Rainsbury

But why all the suspense?

From: Chris Trail

Do you want a serious answer or a flippant one?

From: Allie Rainsbury

A serious response, please. All joking aside, are you OK?

From: Chris Trail

I have a couple of things to sort out first. Once I have done, you'll be the first to know.

And I'm fine, thank you, sweetheart. Honestly, I've never been better.

From: Allie Rainsbury

All right then. In that case I suppose that's all I need to hear. Although I'm putting my best pout on as I write this all the same.

From: Chris Trail

Ha! And you look so cute when you pout.

Now, very obviously steering the subject away from matters of the heart (unless you have any updates for me ☺) what are you doing this evening? Do you feel like one of our famous runs/stumbles along the river?

From: Allie Rainsbury

For once, I shan't even protest. You have yourself a jogging partner. I'll save any gossip for then, although there are very few juicy bits.

From: Chris Trail

See you later, hun, I'll swing by around 7ish x

Thursday

From: Allie Rainsbury
To: Julie Lawson

Chris is proving to be a very tough nut to crack.

From: Julie Lawson

You mean a very tough fruit, surely?

From: Allie Rainsbury

Clever :P

We went running yesterday and I got nothing out of him except some heavy breathing and a singular instruction.

From: Julie Lawson

Ooh, what was the instruction?

From: Allie Rainsbury

For you to stop probing him for gossip.

From: Julie Lawson

Ha! The nerve of the man.

I think we need to take him for a proper evening out and give him a grilling. We're two of his best friends, for goodness sake! Why would he be so cagey?

From: Allie Rainsbury

I've no idea. Maybe he's afraid we'd judge him.

From: Julie Lawson

How could we possibly judge him? I mean look at your love life over the years. It's been a complete train wreck.

From: Allie Rainsbury

:P!

I think we should hold off with our questions. He seemed a little stressed last night.

He actually started hyperventilating after 500 metres. Normally he can get to at least a mile before the paper bag comes out.

From: Julie Lawson

Fine – we'll back off and respect his privacy.

How weird does that phrase sound?

By the way, speaking of love lives, do your parents know what's going on with you now?

From: Allie Rainsbury

No, not yet. In fairness, I've only just figured that one out.

From: Julie Lawson

I wouldn't go that far :P

But you've put them straight on the whole 'David who' question?

From: Allie Rainsbury

I haven't mentioned any of it actually – it hasn't really cropped up in conversation since that last time. I think they're both a bit too intimidated to ask and I'm too wary of confusing them more.

From: Julie Lawson

An interesting approach to take.

From: Allie Rainsbury

I'll have a proper chat about everything when I next see them.

I need to start weaning them off their Scott crush for a start.

Honestly, why does it all always seem to be so complicated?

From: Julie Lawson

It's almost like you're the common denominator ☺

Are you up in Oxford this weekend again then?

From: Allie Rainsbury

Actually, I'm having a weekend off for once. I have various chores to do around an increasingly untidy flat and I'm seeing David on Sunday after his tennis competition.

From: Julie Lawson

Mine's similarly glamorous: taking Elly and Cale swimming on Saturday morning, then we have the in-laws coming round for lunch on Sunday.

I'll call you on Saturday though, maybe we can fit in a glass of wine in the afternoon x

From: Allie Rainsbury

That sounds like a plan!

Friday

From: David Marshall
To: Allie Rainsbury

Hey, gorgeous, thanks for such a good time last night.

I'm thinking the *Karma Sutra* might officially need updating ;)

From: Allie Rainsbury

My boss missed reading that email by about 30 seconds. You got very lucky!

From: David Marshall

I certainly did. Several times, if I remember correctly.

From: Allie Rainsbury

And still not satisfied by the sounds of things.

Make sure you run off your excess energy on the tennis court this weekend and then we can do something slightly cultured on Sunday afternoon ☺

From: David Marshall

Oh yeah, I forgot about that. You want to drag me around a museum, or a gallery or something, don't you?

Fantastic...

From: Allie Rainsbury

Hey! Don't be like that! I just thought it might make a nice change.

From: David Marshall

I'm joking – it will probably be fun! Culture first, debauchery second ;)

From: Allie Rainsbury

Go take a cold shower and do some work :P

I'll see you on Sunday x

From: Peter Rainsbury
To: Allie Rainsbury

Hi sweetheart,

Thanks for your voicemail yesterday. Sorry we missed you, we were in next door's garden enjoying the early evening sunshine and a jug of Pimms. A very pleasant way to spend a couple of hours.

Of course it's fine not to visit this weekend. We both feel you've been up and down from London far too much anyway – it's long overdue that you took some time to yourself. Are you planning to do anything in particular with it or just have a quiet couple of days?

A trip to Teignmouth sounds very appealing to me and your mother. Have you spoken to your aunt yet? I might give her a call this weekend to double check it's OK. She's spent a lot of time away from home recently with everything that's gone on, so might want some peace and quiet for a while. Unlikely, knowing her, but I'll ask just in case.

Also, I talked with Scott earlier this week to thank him for the flowers he sent your mum, which was very thoughtful of him as always. We had a little catch up and it turns out that he's going to come to Teignmouth too.

I don't really know what's going on between the pair of you and I certainly don't mean to pry but I didn't think him coming along could hurt. He said that he'd speak with you about it, but he sounded quite enthused – cause for encouragement perhaps? Your mother's telling me to leave it there, so I shall.

Enjoy your weekend, darling, we will speak to you next week. With love, Dad x

CHAPTER 32

Monday 8 August

From: Allie Rainsbury
To: Peter Rainsbury

Hi Dad (and Mum!),

What a nice surprise to start the week! Sorry for not writing back earlier but I only just read your email.

As you guessed correctly, I had a very relaxing weekend and switched off completely. I feel very refreshed for it though, which is fortunate as there's a busy week ahead with plenty of meetings and presentations to look forward to.

How about you? Did you do anything much? If the weather was as nice in Oxford as it was in London then I doubt you even left the garden. Anyway, don't get too used to the quiet – it was for one weekend only! I'll be back up to see you both this Friday.

Slightly confused by what you mean about Scott. I haven't invited him because we really are just friends (however fond of him you both seem to be!). I'm actually bringing David down with me. I know you haven't met him yet, but I have mentioned him a couple of times before, remember? I think you'll get on very well actually and Mum will definitely giggle at his sense of humour.

Anyway, hope that clears up the confusion! I'll call you later today and we'll organise something fun for this weekend.

With love, Allie xx

From: Peter Rainsbury

Hi sweetheart,

Your mother says I need to explain this straight away.

While talking to Scott, I may have mentioned the trip to Teignmouth at some point. So, in a round-about way, I suppose I might have invited him along.

I hope that's OK, especially now you're bringing someone else. Love Dad x

From: Allie Rainsbury

What? Please say you're joking?!

I was never bringing someone so how can I be bringing someone else?!

What exactly did you say?

From: Peter Rainsbury

I can't remember the exact details, darling. I just talked along the lines of it maybe being good to see him there. And that, in a way, he's viewed as one of the family.

I can see now how this might be awkward for you x

From: Allie Rainsbury

This isn't happening! This CANNOT be happening.

What did he say?

From: Peter Rainsbury

Darling, this is Mum, your dad's run off in a bit of a fright. Silly man.

Is it really such a big problem? I'm very much looking forward to meeting David, but if Scott's there as well and you're all just friends, then there's no harm done.

We may even have enough numbers for a little bridge competition.

From: Allie Rainsbury

That's great, Mum. I'll pack an extra deck of cards with my shotgun.

From: Peter Rainsbury

Don't be so melodramatic! An extra pack of cards is a good idea though. Does David play at all? This will be fun xx

From: Allie Rainsbury

OK... This is retrievable. I just need to calm down, think rationally and come up with a solution.

From: Peter Rainsbury

Yes, dear. I'm sure everything will be fine.

The more the merrier, I say!

From: Allie Rainsbury

I am not merry. Not merry at all!

Look, I've got to go to a meeting. I'll chat to you later.

Love you xx

From: Allie Rainsbury
To: Julie Lawson

Oh. My. God.

From: Julie Lawson

This sounds good.

From: Allie Rainsbury

Cafeteria in five minutes. I'm about to explode.

From: Julie Lawson

Wow. I'll get there early so I can watch the fireworks begin.

Tuesday

From: Allie Rainsbury
To: Scott Cooper

Next time you want to intrude into my life, I hope you'll have the decency to ask me first!

From: Scott Cooper

Sorry?

From: Allie Rainsbury

You'd better be. What the hell do you think you're doing?

From: Scott Cooper

Sorry meant pardon, it wasn't an apology. I still don't know what you're talking about.

From: Allie Rainsbury

You bloody well do, Scott! How dare you invite yourself onto a family holiday? It's beyond outrageous and, what's more, happens to be an occasion that David is coming to.

From: Scott Cooper

Bully for David.

From: Allie Rainsbury

Why are you being so obtuse?!

You can't come, Scott. I don't care how you've managed to weasel your way in. I'm telling you now: you're not invited.

From: Scott Cooper

For your information, Allie, I haven't weaseled my way in anywhere. Your father asked me to come. I said no and that since you hadn't mentioned anything to me, it was probably best I stay away. He was rather insistent however and I found myself in the ludicrous position of having to explain to *your* parents that we were just friends.

The whole phone call put me in a horribly awkward position. I have no idea what you've told your father about me, what you've said about David and I certainly have no idea why I'm the one who had to have this conversation.

You do realise I was even invited to stay in your aunt's house?

So before you start railing on about any intentions you misguidedly believe I may have, perhaps ask yourself why your father is still inviting me to family gatherings and is under the impression that I'm anything more than a passing acquaintance.

From: Allie Rainsbury

You didn't have to accept though, did you?

From: Scott Cooper

I didn't. I thanked him for his offer of hospitality and declined. But he wouldn't listen and anyway, Teignmouth sounds like a picturesque village and a nice escape. So I'm bringing someone along and we've booked into a local hotel. Quite frankly, I couldn't care less whether you're there or not.

From: Allie Rainsbury

Well… what hotel?

Who are you bringing?

From: Scott Cooper

Allie, how about we agree that, from now on, you stay out of my business and I'll stay out of yours.

Does that sound fair?

From: Allie Rainsbury

No! It doesn't sound fair at all!

Who is she and why haven't you told me you're going out with someone?

And what do you mean you don't care if I'm there or not?

From: Scott Cooper

I'm going to go now. I have neither the time nor the inclination for this sort of asinine chat.

From: Allie Rainsbury

Don't you go all noble on me! This puts me in an incredibly difficult position. I'm going to be feeling totally uncomfortable all fortnight!

From: Allie Rainsbury

Scott?!

At least tell me who you're bringing.

Wednesday

From: Julie Lawson
To: Allie Rainsbury

Still grumpy? ☺

From: Allie Rainsbury

I can't understand how he doesn't see how difficult he is making things for me!

From: Julie Lawson

Maybe he just wants some quiet time by the coast?

From: Allie Rainsbury

He could go anywhere in Britain for that. But nooooo...! He chooses the exact same place, at the exact same time and rubs it in my face for everyone to see.

From: Julie Lawson

OK... firstly, calm down; you're using hyperbole to create nonsense.

Secondly, why do you even care?

So Scott's there, so what? We like Scott, don't we?

From: Allie Rainsbury

I'll already be nervous enough because I'll need to make sure that David's fitting in and that everyone likes him. Which, let's face it, takes a lot of concentration.

And all the while Scott bloody Cooper will be cavorting about the town with this nameless little floozy! No doubt being hugely distracting and no less annoying.

From: Julie Lawson

Ah, I see.

From: Allie Rainsbury

What do you see?

From: Julie Lawson

You do like him!

From: Allie Rainsbury

Julie, I do not like him. At the moment, I can barely tolerate him!

And anyway, it doesn't matter. He obviously doesn't like me very much.

From: Julie Lawson

He's not in a position to like you, sweetie; you have a boyfriend...

From: Allie Rainsbury

Yes. Yes, I do.

As it turns out, that's a very good thing! Since stupid Scott has a girlfriend.

What a bastardy bastard he is. How could he not tell me?!

From: Julie Lawson

Had you put him under oath to share every detail about his private life then?

From: Allie Rainsbury

Well, this is a pretty big detail, isn't it?!

For a guy who was meant to have a bit of a crush on me, he's certainly moved on very quickly!

From: Julie Lawson

☺

Someone's eyes are looking pretty green today, I must say.

From: Allie Rainsbury

That has nothing to do with it.

It's the deceitfulness of the whole thing that vexes me so much.

From: Julie Lawson

Would it be easier if I just agreed with everything you're saying?

From: Allie Rainsbury

And another thing – who goes on holiday together for two weeks, after a month of going out? That's unheard of! Who does that?

From: Julie Lawson

Hmm, so you don't think they've been together all this time then?

From: Allie Rainsbury

Unbelievable.

Of course they have! No one moves that quickly. What a conniving, underhand, snivelling little wretch of a man!

From: Julie Lawson

And, breathe.

Well, thank goodness you're with David, hey?

From: Allie Rainsbury

Yes. Yes, that's exactly what I was thinking.

I'm just shocked at finding out how devious Scott has actually been.

From: Julie Lawson

For all you know, they could even have bought a house together :P

From: Allie Rainsbury

You're loving this aren't you?

From: Julie Lawson

It's like my own private soap opera ☺

From: Allie Rainsbury

I'm going to the canteen and I'm buying cake.

Thursday

From: Allie Rainsbury
To: David Marshall

You're still definitely coming to Teignmouth, right?

From: David Marshall

Yes. I couldn't think of a way out of it in the end ☺

From: Allie Rainsbury

OK. Well, this had better not serve as one but I wanted let you know that Scott Cooper will be there as well.

From: David Marshall

Come again? You've mis-spelt several words there I think.

From: Allie Rainsbury

I wish that was true. It's not ideal I know, and I'm sorry. But it's unavoidable.

From: David Marshall

Allie, this is many things. Awkward, certainly. Insulting, probably. But unavoidable, it is definitely not.

From: Allie Rainsbury

What do you want me to say to that? There's not much I'm able to do about it!

He'll be there of his own accord. Short of getting a petition together to ban him from the village there's not a great deal I *can* do.

From: David Marshall

That's something worth considering.

From: Allie Rainsbury

Please don't make this more difficult than it already is.

Look, he's going down with another girl and they're in a hotel up the road. It's not like he'll be staying with us.

From: David Marshall

Oh really? So the sly bugger has finally found someone to take on a dirty weekend away? That is interesting.

From: Allie Rainsbury

Don't call him that, David, it's not very nice.

And they'll be there for two weeks, not a weekend, so she must be pretty keen on him, whoever she is.

From: David Marshall

He's going to be there for the whole fortnight? Jesus! I'm not sure I can take that much of the guy.

From: Allie Rainsbury

You'll hardly have to see Scott at all. They'll be doing their own thing and we'll be doing ours. No doubt my parents will invite them around for lunch once or twice, but that will be it. Everything will be fine!

From: David Marshall

Why don't we visit for just a couple of days? We can go off somewhere by ourselves after that and get a bit of privacy. Away from prying eyes ;)

From: Allie Rainsbury

No! We're there for two weeks. I've already committed to spend that time with my parents. What's more I'm looking forward to being with them; and with you as well. I'm not changing it.

From: David Marshall

What is there to even do down there? I mean, it's just a sleepy little fishing village. How many beach walks can we take?!

From: Allie Rainsbury

David, we're going.

If you're that worried about filling the time then you can spend the first week getting to know my family while I draw up a list of local attractions for week two.

From: David Marshall

Wonderful. I'm so glad to be using up a large chunk of my holidays on such a riveting trip.

From: Allie Rainsbury

Good. I'm happy you're so thrilled. Now, if you could work ever so slightly on losing the sarcasm, then we might actually be able to enjoy ourselves.

From: David Marshall

Assuming we pack enough nitrous oxide.

From: Allie Rainsbury

I'll going to go now, darling, before I scream very loudly.

I will see you after work for dinner with Julie and George.

From: David Marshall

Absolutely, sugar plum. As it happens, I'd forgotten about dinner, but feel even luckier now I have that to look forward to as well.

Friday

From: Julie Lawson
To: Allie Rainsbury

Everything OK? You seemed a little fraught last night.

From: Allie Rainsbury

How could you tell?

From: Julie Lawson

You ordered two glasses of wine and promptly downed the first one.

From: Allie Rainsbury

Oh... Well, that actually helped.

It's been quite a tense week, that's all. The stress of planning a holiday almost outweighs the relaxation you get from it.

From: Julie Lawson

It can't have been an easy few days for you, that's for sure! I thought it best not to raise the subject over dinner though – I didn't want David choking on his food.

From: Allie Rainsbury

How unusually tactful of you :P But appreciated.

From: Julie Lawson

Still, that aside, he was definitely back to his normal confident best.

From: Allie Rainsbury

He was, wasn't he?! He can be very entertaining when he wants to be. I thought George began to bond with him a bit more as well, didn't you?

From: Julie Lawson

Yes, absolutely.

I'm not sure how much they have in common yet, but that doesn't really matter.

No, not at all. I mean, look at us – you, a harried mother of two and me, a carefree singleton. On the face of it, we should have nothing to talk about!

From: Julie Lawson

Ha! Is carefree really the word you would use to describe yourself at the moment?

From: Allie Rainsbury

Oh, if only I could!

Worried. Frazzled. Slightly stressed.

From: Julie Lawson

There you go, you see? You can understand motherhood perfectly! No wonder we're such good friends ☺

Roll on Saturday x

From: Allie Rainsbury

Yes please to the weekend!

Hurry up and get here! x

CHAPTER 33

Monday 15 August

From: David Marshall
To: Allie Rainsbury

How does it feel to be dating a tennis champion?

From: Allie Rainsbury

You won? Oh, well done you! I wish I'd been there to see it.

From: David Marshall

That's all right. I'm not sure how enjoyable it would have been. The final was so one-sided that it wasn't much of a contest. Not great for the spectators, but you can't afford to ease up at my kind of level.

From: Allie Rainsbury

Well, it sounds like it was a great achievement anyway. My boyfriend, the superstar!

From: David Marshall

Ha! Not really, but thank you.

How was your weekend?

From: Allie Rainsbury

Far less high flying, but just as rewarding.

Spent a lot of time planning things to do in Devon and making sure Mum has packed everything she needs. It's still quite an ordeal for her and I don't trust my dad to do the packing.

From: David Marshall

Nothing is as rewarding as holding up a winner's trophy.

But yours sounds nice as well I suppose. Are your folks excited about the holiday?

From: Allie Rainsbury

They're excited about meeting you mostly! At least, Mum certainly is. You'll have to be sure to be on your very best behaviour ☺

From: David Marshall

Don't worry. Parents always seem to love me.

From: Allie Rainsbury

Well, that's reassuring...

How many have you met then?!

From: David Marshall

A fair number over the years. I think they see me as this good-looking, sporty type, which most mothers want for their daughters. Throw in a good job and the fact that I'm polite and pretty easy to talk to... I guess that's why.

Not to say that I agree with all of that, by the way. I just reckon that's why I've got a good record with the older set.

From: Allie Rainsbury

Well, I couldn't disagree with that summary ☺

And I'm sure my parents' reaction will be just as positive as any you've had before. Just be your usual charming self and you won't go far wrong.

From: David Marshall

So no stories involving skimpy underwear and the night spent in that Canterbury hotel? ;)

From: Allie Rainsbury

No!! None of that, thank you!

If pressed, you can imply that you occasionally give me an affectionate peck on the cheek :P

From: David Marshall

Which cheeks? ;)

From: Allie Rainsbury

Enjoy the rest of your day, see you later! x

Tuesday

From: Julie Lawson
To: Allie Rainsbury

Now, you know I'm not someone to fan the flames...

From: Allie Rainsbury

You are a veritable vacuum of discretion.

From: Julie Lawson

But I've just walked out of a rather interesting, slightly tense meeting that included, among other attendees, a certain David Marshall and one Scott Cooper.

From: Allie Rainsbury

Do I really want to hear this?

From: Julie Lawson

It's hardly worth commenting on, so perhaps I shouldn't say anything...

I just thought you'd want to know, ahead of this coming fortnight.

From: Allie Rainsbury

Go on...

From: Julie Lawson

It was a bit of verbal jousting, nothing more. A public display of peacocking that went over most people's heads. Especially since, despite the occasional office rumour, not many people know about you and David, while no one at all knows you've even spoken to Scott in anything other than a work context.

From: Allie Rainsbury

What sort of things were they saying?

From: Julie Lawson

Maybe I'm blowing this out of proportion.

David mentioned that his budget was too tight for the Christmas period. Scott retorted quite sharply that the numbers were set, and there was no flexibility around them.

From: Allie Rainsbury

That doesn't sound too bad...

From: Julie Lawson

To which David countered that the situation seemed as illogical and out of touch as the finance department.

Then Scott said that if only David was as creative with his campaigns as he was with the truth then his budget would be plenty.

I think David was going to come back again there, but Garry stepped in and shifted the conversation away from them.

From: Allie Rainsbury

For goodness' sake!

They're acting as if they're ten-year-old boys who want their ears boxed.

From: Julie Lawson

It was quite funny.

What are you going to do?

From: Allie Rainsbury

Nothing. That's the best policy. The only policy!

I shall rise above it all and ignore any immature fractiousness that might be brewing.

From: Julie Lawson

Very sensible.

And perhaps wear a discrete video camera throughout the holiday? That way you can stream everything online and I won't miss out on any interesting developments.

From: Allie Rainsbury

Another great tip.

From: Julie Lawson

It's a good idea! You'll get more hits than Justin Bieber ☺

From: Allie Rainsbury

I see your musical tastes are as strong as your advice is as useless.

I'm just grateful the pair of them won't cross paths too often.

From: Julie Lawson

Well, let's just hope that stays true, lest they also cross swords when they do.

Wednesday

From: Allie Rainsbury
To: Scott Cooper

Look, I'm sorry if I over-reacted. It was just a shock.

From: Scott Cooper

Don't worry about it.

I should have told you myself but didn't get a chance.

From: Allie Rainsbury

Please don't think that I don't want to see you.

I would hate for things to be awkward between us when we do bump into each other down there.

From: Scott Cooper

They won't be. Not from my side anyway. Why would they be?

From: Allie Rainsbury

It's just I get the impression that you and David don't get on with one another.

From: Scott Cooper

I don't know him well enough for that to be true.

From: Allie Rainsbury

Right... But perhaps try and cut him the tiniest bit of slack over the next couple of weeks?

Imagine if you were in David's position...

From: Scott Cooper

Imagine that we are going out?

From: Allie Rainsbury

Yes. Well no, obviously, but yes.

All he knows about you is that you've met my parents and spent the weekend with my family in Oxford. He's probably, understandably, a bit wary as a result.

From: Scott Cooper

He has no cause to be.

From: Allie Rainsbury

Yes, thank you, as you keep saying. I get it! But maybe he doesn't.

From: Scott Cooper

Maybe he's too consumed by his own self-importance to listen to anyone else's explanations.

From: Allie Rainsbury

Scott...

From: Scott Cooper

It's just a theory.

From: Allie Rainsbury

For me, for my parents, and for the general atmosphere during this holiday, please make an effort to be nice.

From: Scott Cooper

I'll be perfectly civil. I'd like to think that I always try to be.

I'd also like to think that it's not something I'll have to confront particularly often. I'm going there under my own steam – the less I see of David the better.

From: Allie Rainsbury

I guess that's all the concession I'm going to get.

From: Scott Cooper

I'm not conceding anything.

From: Allie Rainsbury

Jesus, I'm not trying to negotiate a deal here, Scott!

Why are you trying to make this so hard?

From: Scott Cooper

I don't think I am. It might be tough for you, but I'm perfectly fine with the situation.

I trust that David will be adult and secure enough in your relationship not to feel threatened by the fact that a friend of his girlfriend is staying with someone else in the near vicinity.

From: Allie Rainsbury

Have a good journey down and I'll see you there – preferably with a smile on your face and a kind word on your lips.

Thursday

From: Allie Rainsbury
To: Peter Rainsbury

Hi Dad,

I know you mentioned that you'd be driving down with Mum, but just to reiterate that David and I will be taking his car tomorrow afternoon, so it wouldn't be an inconvenience at all if you wanted us to detour slightly and collect you both.

Let me know, it's a long trip after all and I don't want you getting tired.

Love, Allie xx

From: Peter Rainsbury

Hi sweetheart,

A kind offer but we'll head off by ourselves all the same. That way we can start the journey early tomorrow morning and get there by mid-afternoon. Besides, I'm not sure how keen your mum is to meet David from the back of a car.

Don't worry, I know how precious the cargo is that I'm ferrying! I'll drive very carefully.

Love Dad x

From: Allie Rainsbury

The ferryman is precious too ☺

We'll see you there, in time for supper!

Safe trip xx

From: Chris Trail
To: Allie Rainsbury

Time for a quick run before the big holiday tomorrow? Say no and you'll not see me for another two whole weeks.

From: Allie Rainsbury

You're on! A run would do me good this evening. I have many a frustration to sweat off.

From: Chris Trail

And you want to see my face.

From: Allie Rainsbury

Ah Chris, after a run, I always want to see your face – the comedic combination of redness and expressive discomfort never fails to make me laugh.

From: Chris Trail

I'll pass by your huge glass house later and pick you and some stones up :P x

From: Allie Rainsbury

☺

Friday

From: David Marshall
To: Allie Rainsbury

Hey, do I have time to squeeze in a quick squash game this evening?

From: Allie Rainsbury

No!? That was a joke right?

From: David Marshall

Um, sure...

From: Allie Rainsbury

Because I definitely reminded you last night that we were leaving a bit early, didn't I? I clearly said not to forget to bring your bags to the office so we can get away quickly.

From: David Marshall

That's fine, I've got them here.

I just asked on the off-chance.

I'll say no then.

From: Allie Rainsbury

Yes, please say no! We're leaving after lunch.

From: David Marshall

Right, OK... In that case I'd better crack on with some work.

If you happen to know anyone on your floor who'd fancy a squash game later then let me know and I'll put them in touch with my friend – he'll be playing by himself otherwise.

From: Allie Rainsbury

David, just... Please don't mention the word 'squash' to me again today. I've been stressed out enough as it is.

From: David Marshall

Wow, I've woken the beast...

What's got into you?

From: Allie Rainsbury

I just want to go, get down there and enjoy this holiday.

I have no intention of wandering around the office asking people what they're doing tonight.

From: David Marshall

Well, this will be a fun trip...

From: Allie Rainsbury

Give me strength.

I'll see you in the car park at 3 p.m., OK?

From: David Marshall

We don't have to go all the way to Oxford to pick up your parents, do we?

From: Allie Rainsbury

No. We don't.

From: David Marshall

That's good – it would have been a bit of a squash with them as well ☺

From: Julie Lawson
To: Allie Rainsbury

Just to wish you a lovely time.

I'll call you over the weekend so you can tell me how it's all going x

From: Allie Rainsbury

If I'm not on the 'Most Wanted' list for murder by that stage...

From: Julie Lawson

?!

From: Allie Rainsbury

Men, that's all!

Thanks for your well wishes – I'll call you from Devon!

Enjoy your weekend xx

CHAPTER 34

Monday 22 August
Holiday

Tuesday
Holiday

Wednesday
Holiday

Thursday
Holiday

Friday
Holiday

CHAPTER 35

Monday 29 August
Holiday

Tuesday
Holiday

Wednesday
Holiday

Thursday
Holiday

Friday
Holiday

CHAPTER 36

Monday 5 September

From: Julie Lawson
To: Allie Rainsbury

How was it getting up this morning?

From: Allie Rainsbury

'Ugh' is probably the adjective that best describes it.

From: Julie Lawson

☺! Any stories to share?

From: Allie Rainsbury

Well, I've come back more relaxed than when I first went away, that's for sure! It was really nice to spend some proper time with Mum and Dad.

The weather was hot for the first week and held up pretty well for the second, so we managed to get in our quota of beach walks and country air – it's amazing the difference that makes.

I don't know how psychological it is, but breathing seems far more fun on the coast than back here.

From: Julie Lawson

Very bracing! Although I hope you have better stories than just taking in the fresh air.

How did your mum get on?

From: Allie Rainsbury

She really enjoyed it. She took things easy and was fussed over, which was the main point of the trip after all. Obviously, she still had moments of tiredness, but that was always going to be the case. The most encouraging aspect was seeing her improving and getting stronger every day.

From: Julie Lawson

Aw, that's good news. I'm glad that she had such a nice time. Another month and she'll be back to fighting fitness.

And everything else passed by peacefully?

From: Allie Rainsbury

Pretty much.

The only real moment of tension came when my father invited Scott over for afternoon tea and suggested 'the boys' (I cringed too) play tennis at the local courts.

From: Julie Lawson

Ha! David must have loved that.

From: Allie Rainsbury

Not so much... Scott beat him.

From: Julie Lawson

I thought David was an all-singing, all-dancing tennis champion?

From: Allie Rainsbury

So did I! He certainly dressed the part. But, in fairness, Scott is really good – he won easily. David wasn't a particularly gracious loser.

341

From: Julie Lawson

Oh dear...!

What did David say afterwards?

From: Allie Rainsbury

He kept muttering about the racket tension or something. I didn't know what he was going on about and, to be honest, felt it best not to ask too many questions.

He was in a foul mood for the next couple of days though.

From: Julie Lawson

Aw, his sorely bruised ego ☺! At least you won't have to listen to as many tales of his sporting exploits now.

Did you see much of Scott? That couldn't have helped matters much?

From: Allie Rainsbury

Well, it did in a way. I think he realised that his victory on the tennis court meant that he wouldn't be an especially welcome presence off it. So any awkwardness that may have occurred never really materialised.

We saw him a couple of times in the village and once more for an evening dinner. That was it. For the rest of the holiday he kept away with the girl he'd taken down there...

From: Julie Lawson

Oh yeah! Of course!

Who's the girl? Is she cute? ☺

From: Allie Rainsbury

She's very pretty. She's very sweet. She's very sick too, poor thing.

She's his sister.

From: Julie Lawson

No way!!

So... no girlfriend? No nubile young lover frolicking about after all?!

From: Allie Rainsbury

Nope, just his younger sister. A chatty, friendly, lovely girl called Tess.

From: Julie Lawson

Wow... Well... wow. I did not see that coming!

You must feel... What's the word I'm looking for?

From: Allie Rainsbury

A little bit crap. I think that's the right description. I feel a bit crap about it all.

From: Julie Lawson

You said she's ill: What's the matter with her?

From: Allie Rainsbury

Tess was diagnosed with leukemia 12 months ago.

From: Julie Lawson

Jesus... How old is she?

From: Allie Rainsbury

She turned 29 in April.

From: Julie Lawson

Ah, I'm so sorry. That's terrible. How unfair.

The poor girl. Poor Scott.

From: Allie Rainsbury

Terrible is another appropriate word to use.

Crap, and terrible.

From: Julie Lawson

Can I have a happier story please?!

From: Allie Rainsbury

Sorry, it's not the most uplifting story I've ever told, is it? There are more mellow ones. I still need to tell you about David meeting my father ☺

Later over lunch?

You're on; see you in the canteen, hun!

Good to have you back x

Tuesday

From: Allie Rainsbury
To: Scott Cooper

How are you?

From: Scott Cooper

I'm thankful for my BlackBerry – and I never thought I'd write that sentence! Without it though, I'd have come back to a truly unmanageable workload.

From: Allie Rainsbury

You should have told me, Scott.

From: Scott Cooper

You had enough on your plate. I didn't think another sob story would have been particularly helpful.

From: Allie Rainsbury

But you're my friend! I want to know about what's happening in your life. And I certainly want to know about something like that.

I didn't even know you had a sister!

From: Scott Cooper

Well, now you do.

From: Allie Rainsbury

And I'm glad I do! She's lovely. And quite obviously thinks the world of you.

From: Scott Cooper

Tess thinks the world of chocolate. She tolerates me.

From: Allie Rainsbury

No, she adores you. And no wonder, from what she said that you've done for her.

From: Scott Cooper

Tess has a kind word to say about everyone. She even spoke highly of you, which perfectly demonstrates my point.

From: Allie Rainsbury

:P Stop being mean!

You can't pretend to be like that anymore – not now I have further proof (and a certain amount of inside information) of how caring you really are.

From: Scott Cooper

Lies. All lies, made up to try and sully my bad name.

From: Allie Rainsbury

You'd better start embracing the fact that you're a nice guy! Much more denial and I'll start dismissing it as a defence mechanism against everything's that happened to you recently.

From: Scott Cooper

Are you trying to corner me?

From: Allie Rainsbury

Everyone needs some help sometimes. Even you.

You were there for me when I wanted someone to talk to – let me do the same for you.

From: Scott Cooper

I'll bear that in mind.

From: Allie Rainsbury

Please do. I'm always here if you want to chat about anything. You don't have to push me away.

From: Scott Cooper

Well, there we shall definitely have to disagree. I have to keep you at a distance, Allie, I'm sorry.

From: Allie Rainsbury

Ridiculous! Now you're being stubborn without any reason. As your friend, I'm here to help or lend an ear or to do whatever you need.

You just have to open up a bit and realise there'll be days when you need some support.

From: Scott Cooper

I'll chat to you later.

Thanks for the advice.

From: Allie Rainsbury

I'll hassle you again soon ☺

Say hi to Tess from me please x

Wednesday

From: David Marshall
To: Allie Rainsbury

Good morning, gorgeous!

Free this evening?

From: Allie Rainsbury

I could be I guess. What did you have in mind?

From: David Marshall

I thought we could spend a bit of alone time together, now that all the family commitments are finally out of the way ☺

From: Allie Rainsbury

They weren't commitments, David. No one forced us to do anything.

From: David Marshall

Necessities then. Or whatever the right word is.

I just thought that maybe we could enjoy ourselves for a few weeks now? Surely we've got some credit in the bank after two weeks in Devon!

From: Allie Rainsbury

I did enjoy myself.

I dared to hope that you might have done as well, especially since you met my parents for the first time.

From: David Marshall

Ah, come on, sweetheart. Stop being so uptight! I didn't mean it like that and you know it.

From: Allie Rainsbury

I don't really know how else you could have meant it. I find it so frustrating that you're constantly being thoughtless! It's all the time!

From: David Marshall

Oh, for goodness' sake, it was a joke!

But you're right, I'm so incredibly thoughtless for travelling halfway across the country to spend two weeks with your family. How immensely selfish of me.

From: Allie Rainsbury

Why do we always seem to be arguing?

From: David Marshall

We don't. You do! You seem determined to pick up on tiny little insignificant things and blow them out of all proportion.

It's a testament to my patience and, oh yeah, MY THOUGHTFULNESS that I'm still putting up with it.

From: Allie Rainsbury

Perhaps we shouldn't meet up this evening after all.

From: David Marshall

Perhaps not. You're clearly in a mood about something yet again and I don't see why I should be hauled down because of it.

From: Allie Rainsbury

Fine. I'll see you later then. It's good that we've talked this through so maturely.

From: David Marshall

If only your humour was as strong as your sarcasm.

From: Allie Rainsbury

Enjoy your evening. I suggest you use the spare time to practise your tennis skills.

From: David Marshall

Oh really clever Allie...

That just shows you know nothing about sport.

From: David Marshall
To: Allie Rainsbury

Especially since you know I played badly! It wasn't representative of my true ability.

From: David Marshall
To: Allie Rainsbury

That was so insulting.

Thursday

From: Allie Rainsbury
To: Scott Cooper

I don't suppose you want to go for a drink after work this evening?

From: Scott Cooper

I can't this evening, sorry.

From: Allie Rainsbury

Another time maybe.

It's probably for the best anyway, I have an early morning meeting tomorrow.

Do you have any exciting plans instead?

From: Scott Cooper

Unfortunately not. Tess's having chemotherapy this afternoon and she generally feels pretty tired and washed out after it.

From: Allie Rainsbury

Oh. Right... Well, is there anything I can do? That sounds terribly vague, but if I can help at all then I'd be glad to.

From: Scott Cooper

You can prepare for your meeting tomorrow morning. That's down in my diary as well and I'd like it to be useful.

From: Allie Rainsbury

I'll take that as Scott-speak for 'I'm not ready to talk about things' :P

From: Scott Cooper

Perhaps. Or maybe I don't think you're the best person to be laying things on.

From: Allie Rainsbury

Try me.

From: Scott Cooper

I don't know what you want me to say, Allie.

From: Allie Rainsbury

Anything that's on your mind.

I know that when Mum was in her coma my biggest frustration was that I couldn't help her. I'd spend hours talking at her bedside, with no reason to think that she'd ever know I was there.

Speaking to friends about how I felt definitely helped me cope.

From: Scott Cooper

Frustration is a common emotion for people to carry in those sort of circumstances. You see someone you care about going through something terrible and the sense of helplessness... it's crushing.

But Tess is incredibly strong. If she's positive and brave enough to fight her illness, then what the hell right do I have to feel sorry for myself? There isn't time for that.

From: Allie Rainsbury

You are one harsh self-critic.

You don't feel sorry for yourself; you feel scared of the fact that someone you love suddenly faces an uncertain future. The only self-involved part is that you desperately want her to play an active part in your future too.

It's worry you feel, it's stress and concern. As tough as Tess is, however amazing and positive her character may be, she'll share those emotions too.

And I bet she'll want to talk them through with the person that she trusts most in the world. Namely: you.

From: Scott Cooper

Another friend of mine once compared the situation to being a football supporter.

You travel to the big game; you're in the terraces and shout loudly – you expend so much nervous energy that's ultimately useless because you can't impact the result anyway. And yet the players themselves, the people directly involved, don't appear to be nearly as nervous. They almost don't seem to care as much as you do.

And at the end of it all, the result could go either way. A bit of luck here, a quirk of fate there – it's a lottery. However much you scream and jump up and down.

From: Allie Rainsbury

That... Is a terrible analogy!

How typical of guys to boil everything down to football ☺

From: Scott Cooper

Which is why I bit my tongue before offering it to you when your mum was still ill!

From: Allie Rainsbury

That was probably for the best, yes. Thanks for telling me though. You know, this might even count as our first heartfelt exchange...

From: Scott Cooper

Really?

No wonder I feel so queasy.

From: Allie Rainsbury

:P!

When the sickness subsides and if you want another chat, then I'll still be here waiting x

From: Scott Cooper

That's kind.

We'll see... But thank you, that means a lot.

Friday

From: Julie Lawson
To: Allie Rainsbury

Fancy coming over for lunch this Sunday or are you Oxford-bound again?

From: Allie Rainsbury

Aw, you do miss me, don't you ☺

I'd love to – for once, I have no plans this weekend!

From: Julie Lawson

Fantastic! The weather's meant to be good, so I thought we could have a barbeque before we lose summer completely.

Especially since, after getting a cricket bat for his birthday, we can't get Cale out of the garden.

David, as always, is also invited.

From: Allie Rainsbury

Can I give you a maybe on David please? As nice as it was to spend two weeks together, he's been irritating me to no end this past week.

I'm offering him an olive branch tonight with an evening out in Putney, but I might leave Sunday as a bit of me time.

From: Julie Lawson

You certainly do seem to get irritated by him rather often! I'm not sure how good a sign that is.

From: Allie Rainsbury

To be honest, Jules, I don't know either. Everyone needs space though, don't they?

Besides, I'm not exactly the easiest person to get along with sometimes; I'm sure he won't protest too much at the thought of a day away from me.

From: Julie Lawson

That all sounds lovely. You're both clearly smitten with each other.

From: Allie Rainsbury

Hey! Just because we're not all part of the Brady Bunch doesn't mean I don't have a good thing going!

I'll leave being joined at the hip to you, and enjoy having the best of both worlds instead :P

From: Julie Lawson

As long as you are enjoying those worlds. Sometimes I think that you end up worrying about both of them.

Right, lecture over!

Bring a bottle of wine and some crayons please. We may well be dragged into helping Elly with her artwork.

From: Allie Rainsbury

As long as we're drawing stick people, otherwise I'll be slightly out of my depth.

See you on Sunday x

CHAPTER 37

Monday 12 September

From: Allie Rainsbury
To: Scott Cooper

Hello there! How was your weekend?

Your name cropped up in conversation yesterday and I realised that I wasn't sure if I should be saying anything about Tess or not.

From: Scott Cooper

How do you mean?

From: Allie Rainsbury

Well, is it a secret or do you mind me talking to people about it?

From: Scott Cooper

I'd rather you didn't take an advert out, put it that way.

From: Allie Rainsbury

OK... Because I told Julie, then thought I might have betrayed your confidence. In which case, I really am very sorry.

I should have thought before speaking.

From: Scott Cooper

But then you wouldn't be you.

From: Allie Rainsbury

Hmm... despite efforts to the contrary, I do tend to suffer from foot-in-mouth syndrome.

From: Scott Cooper

Give me a while and I'll try to think of an argument to counter that.

From: Allie Rainsbury

:P! So you're not cross?

From: Scott Cooper

No, I'm not cross. I already knew that you and Julie tell each other everything anyway.

From: Allie Rainsbury

Really? How did you know that? She hasn't been talking about me I hope!

From: Scott Cooper

Only indirectly. I passed her in the corridor the other day and she asked how my tennis elbow was...

From: Allie Rainsbury

Ah, OK...

I suppose I did mention that you were rather talented!

From: Scott Cooper

Then you're far too generous with your praise.

It was good fun though; it had been years since I picked up a racket.

From: Allie Rainsbury

Well, you'd never have known that to see you play.

It had definitely been years since Dad's shorts had seen the light of day though!

From: Scott Cooper

That would explain the 1980s tightness of them. I must have looked ridiculous!

From: Allie Rainsbury

You looked hot! I wasn't complaining ☺

From: Scott Cooper

Not decked out quite as professionally as David though.

From: Allie Rainsbury

All I remember was you looking a lot less sweaty, and just as cute!

From: Scott Cooper

Well, that seems like a good note to leave things on.

Meetings call. Speak to you soon.

Tuesday

From: Allie Rainsbury
To: Scott Cooper

Busy today? I have lots on but little inclination to get on with any of it.

From: Scott Cooper

You're every manager's dream...

Any reason for the attitude?

From: Allie Rainsbury

Not really. Well... I suppose, maybe.

From: Scott Cooper

Am I meant to understand that?

From: Allie Rainsbury

I had another argument with David last night. We were in a restaurant, having what should have been a romantic evening out, and he spent most of the meal on his BlackBerry. I mean, am I really such poor company that he can't even be bothered to strike up a conversation with me for an hour over dinner?

From: Scott Cooper

Why are you telling me this?

From: Allie Rainsbury

Because I want your advice!

I'm not exactly being too demanding, am I?

From: Scott Cooper

And you really want my opinion here?

From: Allie Rainsbury

Absolutely! ☺

From: Scott Cooper

I think you're acting like a whining child. If this is how you sounded last night then I don't blame him for ignoring you.

From: Allie Rainsbury

Excuse me?!!

From: Scott Cooper

Stop moaning! Especially when it happens over and over again. You've known David for long enough to know what sort of character he is. If you don't like him, stop going out with him!

From: Allie Rainsbury

Well, that's rather more harsh than I was expecting.

For the record, I do like him. I just don't always share those details with you!

From: Scott Cooper

To be honest, Allie, I don't know why you share any details with me, good or otherwise.

From: Allie Rainsbury

Right. Fine.

Sorry, I was under the mistaken impression that we were able to tell each other stuff.

From: Scott Cooper

Well, we're not. I told you that last week. I don't want you too close.

From: Allie Rainsbury

Why are you being so mean today?

From: Scott Cooper

But let me tell you this much: David's an idiot. He's a selfish ego-maniac, wrapped up with his image and how many girls he can get to glance his way.

He doesn't like you enough. As with every other woman he comes across, he treats you as a challenge. He'll flatter you with attention and compliments until you hand them back to him ten-fold, and then he'll turn his attention to another chase.

He's a liar, he's a cheat and he's not worth a hundred of you.

And I cannot believe that you continue to fall for it.

From: Allie Rainsbury

I think we should leave it there.

Wednesday

From: Allie Rainsbury
To: Scott Cooper

Dear Scott,

I'm sorry we spoke so harshly to each other yesterday. I don't want to do that, especially after everything you've done for me and with all that you continue to go through. I respect your opinion and want to hear your points of view but in this instance, for obvious reasons, I can't agree with what you say.

David isn't perfect, of course he's not. Who is? But he's been there for me, in his own way, throughout this year and I therefore refuse to hear you damning him so bleakly without speaking up for his character.

I know that you have my best interests at heart, but I must ask you to refrain from being so blunt with your thoughts over my boyfriend in future. In retrospect, I was too hasty to ask you for your insight, and for that I apologise. It's not a mistake I'll make again.

More than anything, I'd like us all to be friends. I know that David made a huge effort by even coming down to Devon in the first place, and by being polite, if admittedly restrained, across the whole holiday. I would ask for that same level of effort from you, or else it will start placing restrictions on our friendship. This isn't something that I want and it certainly isn't meant as an ultimatum, however, I would urge that you listen to the request. I value you as a person and as a friend very much, but I can't have you speaking so disparagingly about someone I care about.

I hope this isn't too stark; indeed it's meant to be conciliatory in tone. I trust it is read and digested as such.

Love, Allie x

From: Scott Cooper

Apologies, I obviously mis-read the situation again.

From: Allie Rainsbury

You're already forgiven. I don't want to dwell on anything, I just needed to let you know where the boundaries lie.

And it wasn't too formal? I spent ages composing it last night but I'm not much of a writer.

From: Scott Cooper

You were perfectly clear.

From: Allie Rainsbury

OK. Good, I'm glad. Then let's talk no more about it. I'm happy to move on if you are?

How's Tess doing?

From: Scott Cooper

She's coping as well as usual, thank you.

I have some work to get on with, Allie.

From: Allie Rainsbury

Sure, of course...

As usual, my offer is still there: If there's anything I can do then I'd be happy to help.

From: Scott Cooper

We're fine, thanks. We can manage by ourselves.

From: Allie Rainsbury

Right. Well then, I'll see you soon I hope.

From: Scott Cooper

Other commitments allowing, absolutely.

From: Allie Rainsbury

Scott?

We are OK, aren't we?

From: Scott Cooper

Never better.

From: Allie Rainsbury
To: David Marshall

David, are you free this evening? I could do with a hug x

Thursday

From: David Marshall
To: Allie Rainsbury

Hey, I've only just picked up your email!

Have I missed my chance? ☺

From: Allie Rainsbury

Not necessarily. Where were you yesterday? I called a few times.

From: David Marshall

I know, I'm sorry. I had my phone on silent from a busy afternoon of meetings and forgot to switch it back on.

You didn't miss much – I was so tired last night that I fell asleep on the sofa.

From: Allie Rainsbury

That sounds pretty hectic – although you do have a very comfy couch!

Want to make it up to me this evening?

From: David Marshall

Absolutely! I'll turn all equipment off and we can have a quiet night in.

From: Allie Rainsbury

That sounds lovely.

I feel pretty down and lonely this week so could do with your company please!

From: David Marshall

Ah sweetheart, we can't have that!

I'll do my best to cheer you up. At the very least I can guarantee that you won't be lonely ;)

From: Allie Rainsbury

Thank you x

From: Allie Rainsbury
To: Ann Rainsbury

Hey Mum,

How are you getting on today?

I'm feeling rather rubbish ☹ I might give you a call this evening for a bit of attention if that's OK?

Anyway, I should be doing some work now, but don't really have the energy.

Sorry, this is a rather aimless note! I just thought you might be about.

Love you, Allie x

From: Ann Rainsbury

Darling, what's wrong? Are you sick?

You need to look after yourself – you've been so busy fussing about me recently that you're completely ignoring your own health.

What are your symptoms? Love Mum x

From: Allie Rainsbury

Hello! I'm fine, really!

I just feel a bit listless. I'm being spoilt, that's all x

From: Ann Rainsbury

What's this to do with? How are things with David?

From: Allie Rainsbury

It's not boy trouble! ☺

Things with David are fine, I'm seeing him this evening. We're actually in a better place than we have been for a while.

I just feel sad. I can't explain it any other way.

From: Ann Rainsbury

Well there must be a reason!

What's making you upset? Who's making you worry?

From: Allie Rainsbury

I don't know. It's nothing.

Sorry, Mum, I'm clearly enjoying a bit of self-indulgent wallowing.

Nothing's wrong, really it isn't. I don't want you worrying.

From: Ann Rainsbury

Well I reserve the right to do so ☺

I shall interrogate you further over the weekend and we'll come up with a solution.

Call me later darling x

From: Allie Rainsbury

I will! Thanks for listening.

Sorry it was so rambling and incoherent x

From: Ann Rainsbury

Nonsense!

That's what mums are for! x

Friday

From: Julie Lawson
To: Allie Rainsbury

I don't suppose that Scott's foul mood this morning was anything to do with you...

From: Allie Rainsbury

Why do you say that?

From: Julie Lawson

So it was?!!

From: Allie Rainsbury

No! I wouldn't have thought so anyway. He has a lot on his mind at the moment, Jules – I'm sure it's the stress of everything that's starting to weigh heavily.

From: Julie Lawson

But...

From: Allie Rainsbury

But I did send him a rather stern letter a couple of days ago. He vented a bit and took out some of his frustrations with a rather unfairly biting critique of David.

From: Julie Lawson

Ah. And I'm guessing you told him to mind his own business.

From: Allie Rainsbury

In so many words. I told him not to be so judgemental. I just felt he'd crossed a line. I couldn't let it pass and risk him thinking that sort of behaviour was OK.

From: Julie Lawson

Right... well, that doesn't leave much room for doubt!

Is he not entitled to tell you how he feels then?

From: Allie Rainsbury

Not as harshly as that, no.

You never used to be David's number one fan but you didn't say the sort of things he wrote, even if they did cross your mind at some point.

From: Julie Lawson

Wow. Now I'm intrigued. What did he say?

From: Allie Rainsbury

He described David as selfish and self-absorbed. A player who doesn't care as much for me as he does for himself.

From: Julie Lawson

Ha! Good for him!

From: Allie Rainsbury

Julie!! Seriously, stop, or you'll be receiving a similarly worded letter of warning :P

He was being very unfair and very rude.

And anyway, he's completely wrong. David came round last night with a bunch of flowers and cooked me dinner.

So Scott doesn't know what he's talking about.

From: Julie Lawson

What a strange little triangle you have ☺

Poor Scott.

From: Allie Rainsbury

Poor who?!

Have you been reading any of this at all?

From: Julie Lawson

Absolutely – poor Scott. He's obviously still smitten with you.

From: Allie Rainsbury

No, no, no! Don't go starting with that theory again. He is not and never has been.

He just needed to be brought down to earth a bit; his head was getting too cloudy.

From: Julie Lawson

Well, mission accomplished there. I'll wager you've brought him crashing back. So go easy for a while; he's battered and bruised right now.

From: Allie Rainsbury

All this misplaced sympathy!

Of course I will be. You're way off the mark though.

CHAPTER 38

Monday 19 September

From: Allie Rainsbury
To: Julie Lawson

How were the kids this morning?

From: Julie Lawson

Surprisingly excited and happy. Which either suggests they're keen to learn something this year or they're bored of being at home and keen to get back to their school friends.

From: Allie Rainsbury

Surely the latter ☺

From: Julie Lawson

I fear so...

Ah well, at least I have a few nice photos of them looking smart and shiny in their uniforms. This is the first year that Cale is wearing a tie and he insisted on doing it all by himself. The result is... interesting.

From: Allie Rainsbury

Aw, how cute. Pictures please!

From: Julie Lawson

Hold tight and I'll send them over in a bit.

How are you?

From: Allie Rainsbury

I'm excited and happy as well as it happens!

I had a good weekend in Oxford; spending most of it with Mum as Dad was off playing golf with friends. She's really starting to bound around more now (comparatively at least).

On the train back to London I was looking out of the window thinking how lucky I am: Mum's recovering well, I feel on top of work and I'm seeing David this week. Things seem to be finally moving forward with the two of us. Everything is getting back to normal and it's all looking good!

From: Julie Lawson

A positive vibe to start the week with, hey?

I approve ☺

From: Allie Rainsbury

I've been taking some things too seriously recently, and that's probably in danger of wearing a bit thin.

Compared to lots of people, I've got it good.

From: Julie Lawson

I won't argue with that! Of course, that doesn't mean you're not allowed to be grumpy occasionally!

Just as long as it's not at me or in my presence :P

From: Allie Rainsbury

Ha! Fair enough.

Fancy lunch today?

From: Julie Lawson

If you can wait until 1 p.m. I have meetings until then.

From: Allie Rainsbury

Sure!

See you then. Now go away and let me get on.

From: Allie Rainsbury

What?! Is my good mood not proving infectious?

From: Julie Lawson

No, it's unnerving.

Besides, I enjoy my Monday sulk and don't want you barging in on it with your tip-tappy happiness :P

From: Allie Rainsbury

Ah, I remember when I used to be that grouchy...

Enjoy your tea.

From: Julie Lawson

I'm giving you a week before you revert back to moaning.

And that's being generous :P

Tuesday

From: Tess Cooper
To: Allie Rainsbury

Hi Allie,

It's Tess here (Scott Cooper's sister, from Devon?).

How are you? I hope you'll forgive the email, but I wanted to drop you a quick note to say hello and ask after your mum.

Take care, Tess x

From: Allie Rainsbury

Hi Tess! Of course I remember!

Mum's fine, thanks. She's doing very well at the moment, long may it continue!

How are you? It's really good to hear from you.

Write back! Allie x

From: Tess Cooper

I'm glad she's recovering so well. You must be so relieved – I can't imagine what you went through.

I'm OK thanks. I've been at a bit of a loose end since getting back from Devon to be honest; it was such a fun trip and so nice to get a change of scene that the time since hasn't exactly flown by.

From: Allie Rainsbury

Tess, you of all people must know what I'm going through.

Scott doesn't really tell me much about your illness; no doubt it's difficult for him to talk about.

From: Tess Cooper

Stupid Scott!

He's always been a bit closed off with his emotions. I hope you don't read too much into that. So many people think he's a stuck-up idiot because of it, I've always told him!

When we were teenagers I thought the same. I even remember telling my friends that we weren't related, that our parents had adopted Scott from an asylum in the Highlands! I suppose most brothers and sisters go through tensions at some point when they are growing up though. Do you have any siblings?

From: Allie Rainsbury

No, I'm an only child. I'm pretty sure that Scott thinks I'm spoilt because of it as well.

From: Tess Cooper

He definitely doesn't. He thinks very highly of you.

From: Allie Rainsbury

Aw, he's sweet really, I know that. Don't worry, I don't subscribe to the stuck-up theory!

From: Tess Cooper

Good, because beneath all of the stiff-upper-lipness is a very tender, kind and compassionate guy.

Even if I don't have to acknowledge that (the benefits of being a younger, sickly sister)!

From: Allie Rainsbury

☺! Definitely milk that for all it's worth.

I've already said this many times to Scott but he might not have passed on the message – if there's anything I can do then please let me know.

From: Tess Cooper

That's kind, thank you!

There's not a lot you can do, although if you don't mind getting the odd email once in a while then I'd be very glad to chat again.

I'm sure you're terribly busy, so don't worry if you can't reply. But it's always nice to talk, especially when I'm feeling a bit down or lonely and frustrated.

And you don't seem afraid to ask about my illness, which is quite refreshing really since so many people skirt around things with me these days.

From: Allie Rainsbury

That's exactly what I told Scott!

Of course, I'd love to talk again. And I'm never too busy for a chat.

From: Tess Cooper

I look forward to that then!

I'm going to go and do a bit of painting now I think – the sun is out and the garden looks very inviting.

From: Allie Rainsbury

How funny, I was painting in the garden a couple of weeks ago too!

I'm hopeless though. You'll have to show me yours sometime, so I can see how a real artist works.

From: Tess Cooper

And ruin the illusion I've built that I have any talent?

Hmm... Maybe ☺ x

From: Allie Rainsbury

Modesty runs in your family.

Chat soon x

Wednesday

From: David Marshall
To: Allie Rainsbury

Fancy catching a film later?

From: Allie Rainsbury

I'm jogging this evening.

How about you come over for the weekend and we can go then?

From: David Marshall

Jogging? Are you still doing that?

From: Allie Rainsbury

How many times have I told you that I've been out running? I don't think you listen to me at all sometimes!

From: David Marshall

Why not go another night instead? I'm free today!

From: Allie Rainsbury

I can't, David – unless you want to come along as well.

I've already told Chris to come round and I'm cooking him dinner afterwards. You're very welcome to join us.

From: David Marshall

You do realise that most men would raise some questions if their other half said that she was having another man over for dinner.

From: Allie Rainsbury

Don't be silly! It's Chris! Why don't you come? You haven't even met him yet!

From: David Marshall

No, that's OK. I'll phone around my friends and find something fun to do.

From: Allie Rainsbury

Because an evening with me is so boring?

From: David Marshall

Yes, that's it! ☺

I just don't want to intrude on a pre-planned evening, that's all.

I'm teasing – you have fun with your other bloke.

From: Allie Rainsbury

Well that's silly, but OK. It would be nice to see you if you change your mind.

What about the weekend – can we meet up then at least?

From: David Marshall

Sure. I'm busy on Friday but I can come down Putney way on the Saturday? We can catch the last of the autumn sunshine and wander through the park.

From: Allie Rainsbury

That sounds good. I'll make you dinner as well, how about that?

From: David Marshall

No, we'll go out for a meal – I don't mind treating you, once in a while.

From: Allie Rainsbury

Anyone would think you distrust my cooking!

See you Saturday, lovely (if not this evening) x

Thursday

From: Julie Lawson
To: Allie Rainsbury

Has the euphoria from the start of the week given way yet?

From: Allie Rainsbury

It's still holding firm! A couple of negative thoughts ran through my head when running last night, but I tried to banish them ☺

How are you?

From: Julie Lawson

Panicking that Cale's school uniform is going to be several sizes too small for him by the end of the term. His shirt sleeves are already stretched and it's not even day two!

From: Allie Rainsbury

He's growing up quick, isn't he!

From: Julie Lawson

Literally :S Especially considering his dad is such a short-arse. I don't know where this spurt is coming from.

From: Allie Rainsbury

I did warn you to stay away from the milkman ☺

You shouldn't be complaining – women love tall men!

From: Julie Lawson

It's my wallet that's protesting, not me!

Anyway, I don't want to think about Cale dating just yet. I have at least another five years before I lose him to another woman.

From: Allie Rainsbury

Hmm... that's optimistic. I think he'll be a real lady-killer too. He has a cheeky smile and a twinkle in his eyes. Girls will flock to him!

My bet is four years before Cale goes on his first cinema date! Two years for Elly ☺

From: Julie Lawson

My daughter is definitely not dating anyone. When she's 18 maybe she can exchange a letter or two with the eligible first born son of a prominent family. But nothing more than that.

From: Allie Rainsbury

Didn't you kiss someone in your school playground when you were eleven?

From: Julie Lawson

That was different! That was very innocent and a different time. Before kids really knew anything about anything!

Plus it was with Johnny Robertson. Everyone wanted to kiss Johnny Robertson!

From: Allie Rainsbury

Uh-huh.

From: Julie Lawson

You hush.

And, speaking of people everyone wants to kiss, how's Scott today? :P

From: Allie Rainsbury

That is a low blow, Julie! I shall not dignify it with a reply.

Besides, I wouldn't know – he hasn't replied to me much since I wrote him that email.

From: Julie Lawson

Ah, the infamous 'keep your nose out of my business despite the fact that I ask for your council' email?

It's almost as if he's taken offense, isn't it?

From: Allie Rainsbury

You will not ruin my good mood, sorry! I learnt to zone out from your witterings a long time ago.

From: Julie Lawson

That at least explains why you've gone so wrong then.

From: Allie Rainsbury

All I see there is a series of random letters :P

From: Julie Lawson

Ha!

Fancy grabbing lunch and listening to random noises as well?

From: Allie Rainsbury

You're on.

Friday

How's the painting going?

Well, I don't think my legacy will be garden-scapes, put it that way!

Funny. At least... I think that's funny?

I don't know how to take it.

Take what?

You mentioning your legacy. Writing as if it's a fait accompli that you're leaving us all behind.

Oh, I see! Sorry – I didn't even notice! I don't mean it like that. Or at least, not really. Everyone leaves a legacy eventually. It just depends when you check out.

You don't need to apologise, and I don't mean to nag!

As long as you're not accepting your departure time, that's all I mean. That you're always fighting to delay it.

Don't worry, I'm not accepting anything! ☺ There are lots of people in worse states than I am.

Isn't that accepting too? By saying that things could be worse, you're not concentrating on making them any better...

I know what you mean, except that I haven't lost that perspective either. I'm fortunate in many ways, unlucky in others; I'm damn sure going to beat the unlucky out of me! My leukemia isn't terminal and my attitude isn't anything but positive.

From: Allie Rainsbury

All right! That sounds more belligerent.

Sorry. I hope you don't think I'm lecturing.

From: Tess Cooper

No, no, it's good. Most people are sympathetic to patients; it's interesting to see a more aggressive approach ☺

From: Allie Rainsbury

Oh no! I'm sorry! I really didn't mean it like that!

From: Tess Cooper

If you can tease me then I can tease you ☺

What are you up to this weekend?

From: Allie Rainsbury

I'm up in Oxford with my parents. Nothing glamorous, but I always seem to look forward to it these days all the same.

From: Tess Cooper

And why wouldn't you – they're such lovely people!

I know one of the things Scott first liked about you was your commitment to your family.

From: Allie Rainsbury

Unfortunately, that seems to be one of the few things that he likes about me these days.

From: Tess Cooper

Why do you say that? What have you done to my brother? ☺

From: Allie Rainsbury

I haven't heard that much from him recently, that's all.

He's probably been busy with work. But, then again, this silence does happen to have coincided with a little talk I gave him last week.

From: Tess Cooper

Ah... this wouldn't be the 'David' email would it?

From: Allie Rainsbury

He told you about that?

From: Tess Cooper

Oh, he tells me most things. I might pretend to be this innocent little waif like thing, but I have the dirt on a lot of people! ☺

From: Allie Rainsbury

Well, what did he say? What did you say?

From: Tess Cooper

He said that you'd stood up for your boyfriend after he'd called him an idiot. I told him that I'd have done exactly the same!

From: Allie Rainsbury

You would have called David an idiot too?

From: Tess Cooper

No, silly! I'd have told Scott to shut up ☺

Besides, Scott shouldn't be saying that kind of thing anyway.

From: Allie Rainsbury

But he meant well. He was looking out for me.

And I haven't exactly been the easiest person to read over the past couple of months.

From: Tess Cooper

Well, I think it was for the best anyway. If that's how you feel then honesty is always the best policy. He needed to be told.

From: Allie Rainsbury

That's what I thought. I knew it made sense, however hard it was to say! I'm so glad you're in agreement ☺

From: Tess Cooper

I can always agree that Scott's a plonker ☺

Chat to you later, I'm off for my obligatory afternoon nap.

Speak soon Tess, nice catching up with you x

CHAPTER 39

Monday 26 September

From: Tess Cooper
To: Allie Rainsbury

Good morning! I started to feel a little bad after emailing you last Friday. My conscience was nagging me for some reason. Normally I'd dismiss it, but in this instance the feeling was annoyingly persistent.

Although I absolutely stand by my description of Scott as a plonker (obviously), in fairness I should add some depth and context to this.

He is notoriously hard-headed, of which you are no doubt well aware. He often comes across as stuck up (again as you know well). In both these ways, he's a plonker in the most negative of senses.

However he is also a plonker in a positive sense. He has a fantastic sense of loyalty and is brave to a fault. When he was 15 he and a friend were walking home from an evening out and were jumped on by four men. Scott wriggled free but, instead of running away and leaving his friend, he grabbed a nearby stick and hit two of them round the head with it. In the end it was Scott fighting them off and his friend who ran to get help.

He's an idiotic, hopeless romantic. On a business trip a few years ago he got talking to a girl at a conference in London. It turned out that she lived in Barcelona and was only in the country for two days. So the next week he flew to Spain and took her to dinner. He's impulsive in that sense – even if something seems unlikely, he'll still go for it.

He's stupid in so many ways. But most of those ways are incredibly wonderful, kind and thoughtful. So when I call him a plonker I do so with an overwhelming sense of love, affection and pride. Hopefully these two instances give you an idea why.

From: Allie Rainsbury

Interesting stories for a Monday morning!

And, for the record, I have never thought of Scott as being anything less than amazing. Your conscience can rest easy.

What happened with the Spanish girl?

From: Tess Cooper

She wasn't right for him. Apparently he knew inside five minutes of the dinner starting. But he had fun visiting Gaudi architecture all the same ☺

Are you free to chat today? I feel a bit guilty emailing you yet again, but it is nice to have someone new to talk with.

From: Allie Rainsbury

Tess, you need to stop asking me if I'm free. And definitely don't feel guilty! I'm never so busy that I won't be able to respond.

From: Tess Cooper

I shall take advantage of that then!

How are you? How's David? I haven't really asked about you two yet.

From: Allie Rainsbury

Perhaps because it's a slightly awkward topic?

From: Tess Cooper

I rarely feel awkward asking personal questions ☺ Why would it be awkward anyway?

From: Allie Rainsbury

Well, with Scott being your brother.

From: Tess Cooper

Ah, I see.

You reckon Scott fancies you.

From: Allie Rainsbury

No! No!

No!

Does he?

From: Tess Cooper

Yes. You know that.

I'm not supposed to tell you. But since I'm not revealing anything new by saying so, I think I've managed to skirt round that rule!

From: Allie Rainsbury

Wow. I don't know what to say... I honestly don't.

He's really sweet and totally gorgeous. Any girl would be lucky to have him.

But...

From: Tess Cooper

You're going out with David. I know, I know!

I can't believe you'd pick someone else over my brother! We are no longer friends ☺

From: Allie Rainsbury

I'm sorry! If you'd told me at the start of the year that someone like Scott would be interested in me, and not only that, but that I wouldn't be able to do anything about it...

From: Tess Cooper

A nice position to be in.

From: Allie Rainsbury

Not for Scott so much. I don't know. I feel bad.

Let's change the subject, please! How about you? Any boyfriends? ☺

From: Tess Cooper

No, no one for me right now. I was seeing someone a while ago, well before I was diagnosed. It didn't work out.

From: Allie Rainsbury

How come?

From: Tess Cooper

He wasn't right for me, nor me for him come to that. A nice man, but it wasn't enough really. It's a more complicated recipe than that.

From: Allie Rainsbury

Far too complicated for my understanding anyway!

Well, I think you're well out of it! Better to be single and find the right guy than stay in a relationship with the wrong one.

From: Tess Cooper

Agreed!

There are moments when I'm lonely and down and could do with a hug, but that's what red wine was invented for ☺

From: Allie Rainsbury

Hmm… I must feel lonely and down quite regularly :P

I have a meeting to go to now, Tess, sorry; chat again very soon, OK?

From: Tess Cooper

Oh, sorry! Absolutely, go – talk later x

From: Allie Rainsbury

Stop apologising!! ☺

Tuesday

From: Allie Rainsbury
To: Julie Lawson

I'm worried…

From: Julie Lawson

Why? What's up?

From: Allie Rainsbury

It's your birthday in just over a week and I've heard nothing about what's being planned.

This leads me to deduce that either a) I haven't been invited or b) I'm meant to be organising something and have forgotten to do so.

From: Julie Lawson

Ha! You should have gone for the obvious final option:

c) Julie feels far too old to celebrate anything and will instead sit in a corner weeping for her lost youth.

From: Allie Rainsbury

Of course! How silly of me not to choose that one.

What's the real plan, old girl? ☺

From: Julie Lawson

Very little! A few drinks with a few friends in Putney's finest establishments. George is looking into reserving a room at the Boathouse; although, unless I miraculously magic up 20 new friends between now and next Wednesday, that won't be necessary.

From: Allie Rainsbury

It's not the quantity, it's the quality.

And, although my opinion might be slightly biased, I'd suggest that the quality of your friends is second to none.

From: Julie Lawson

They're OK I guess...

From: Allie Rainsbury

Ha! Your memory is going, you've clearly forgotten all the good times!

From: Julie Lawson

☺! And with enough alcohol I can dull the memory of this birthday as well!

It's all very depressing, this 'getting older' thing.

From: Allie Rainsbury

The last week of mid-thirties. You must be feeling sad, true.

From: Julie Lawson

Hey! I have several years left of mid-thirties, thank you very much!

From: Allie Rainsbury

36 is late thirties. If this was a maths test then you'd be rounded up to 40 ☺

From: Julie Lawson

Your present better be un-bloody-believable :P

Wednesday

From: Allie Rainsbury
To: Tess Cooper

Almost through the first half of the week! Thank goodness - I feel so tired.

How are you?

From: Tess Cooper

Hello! Sorry for the delayed reply, I'm not having the best of days myself today. I was horribly ill this morning and to top it off am feeling thoroughly drained now as well.

From: Allie Rainsbury

Oh Tess, I'm so sorry.

I'm not tired at all really, I keep forgetting that you're going through something that should make me just keep quiet.

That's a testament to how incredible you are – I always feel as if we're just talking normally.

From: Tess Cooper

We are! I've told you before, I'm not looking for sympathy and I definitely don't want a conversation that's anything but normal.

I'm feeling a bit fragile today. But it's manageable – I've had worse hangovers ☺

From: Allie Rainsbury

Really? Maybe you should sign off and get some rest? Maybe some sleep will help?

From: Tess Cooper

Absolutely not! I could do with the distraction, I'm at risk of becoming utterly bored otherwise.

I'm in bed, I'm alone and the only phone calls I've had today have been from my brother and the hospital.

From: Allie Rainsbury

Why from the hospital? What's going on?

From: Tess Cooper

Just confirming dates on my next appointment. Nothing exciting. I keep telling you!

From: Allie Rainsbury

Hmm, OK.

What about your brother?

From: Tess Cooper

He called to check in. There was no news there either. He phones twice a day – it drives me round the bend ☺

From: Allie Rainsbury

Aw, that's sweet though. You love it really!

From: Tess Cooper

I do, I know. My friends and family have been great, but Scott's my knight, that's for sure.

Anyway, tell me what's new with you, before the conversation starts going down a dangerous route again ☺

From: Allie Rainsbury

Does he know I'm chatting to you?

From: Tess Cooper

I've mentioned it, yes. He didn't seem that interested though.

From: Allie Rainsbury

Or maybe he just doesn't want to think about me at all.

From: Tess Cooper

Give it time. He'll be back on form again soon, I'm sure.

From: Allie Rainsbury

Anyway! My news isn't much since we last spoke.

I spent Monday evening at David's watching a terrible documentary about bees and why they're so crucial for the planet to maintain its natural equilibrium. I still have no idea what the answer is. I find programmes like that rather boring, but David likes to watch them; or at least convinces himself that he should be watching them. He thinks my tastes are low-brow, which isn't true at all – they're just different!

Then last night I went for a run with Chris; we're getting rather good now, at least compared to how we first started a few months ago. I got back home, chatted with my parents and watched *America's Next Top Model*.

There – you're up to date. Quite the page-turner.

From: Tess Cooper

That all sounds fun – can definitely relate to the intellectual snobbery that guys pull out. You just know as soon as your back's turned they switch over to MTV!

Much applause for your fitness efforts too. I used to love running, although I don't really get the chance at the moment. I shall get back into it as soon as I've fought this thing off.

From: Allie Rainsbury

Absolutely! We'll have to go on some jogs. No doubt you will put me to shame, but it will be nice to have a running partner who doesn't stop to 'tie his shoelaces' every two minutes. Honestly! If he wants to pause for breath, he should just say.

From: Tess Cooper

There you go, you see? We're agreed that guys are both snobs and unable to admit any weakness.

We've done well today ☺

From: Allie Rainsbury

And I feel so much more energised for it. Character assassination obviously makes for good therapy.

From: Tess Cooper

It does, definitely. Although I think I'll get a bit more rest now all the same.

Thanks for your time again, Allie.

From: Allie Rainsbury

Yes, rest up and get some sleep x

Thursday

From: Allie Rainsbury
To: Scott Cooper

I haven't heard from you in a while now. I know that you're upset with me, Scott. Why don't we talk about it?

From: Scott Cooper

I'm not upset with you. What gives you that impression?

From: Allie Rainsbury

Because you've hardly said a word to me since I sent you that long email.

From: Scott Cooper

I've been very busy, that's all. It is a rather hectic time of year in this industry – I'm sure I don't have to tell you that.

From: Allie Rainsbury

Because I've been speaking to your sister and she mentioned that I might have offended you.

From: Scott Cooper

When did you speak to Tess?

She's got confused there I think, I didn't say anything of the sort.

And besides, she shouldn't be passing on that kind of information.

From: Allie Rainsbury

I've emailed her a bit recently, that's all.

OK – well, maybe I've got the wrong end of the stick... I just don't want you to feel bad and, if I have offended or upset you, I want to apologise. I never meant to do so.

From: Scott Cooper

Relax. You haven't.

Being blunt (since this is one topic I think I'm still allowed to speak freely on) I haven't thought about you at all recently. Work commitments and Tess have needed all of my time and energy.

From: Allie Rainsbury

She did mention that she was feeling a little tired yesterday. What can I do?

Would she like some company, do you think? Could I go and see her maybe?

From: Scott Cooper

Tess's very capable of inviting people over if she wants visitors. Ask her, you don't need to go through me.

From: Allie Rainsbury

OK, I will. I wanted to check with you first though.

Have there been any more updates from the hospital?

From: Scott Cooper

Allie – again, why don't you ask her?

She's not ashamed of her battle; she'd be very happy to share that information with you.

From: Allie Rainsbury

I know she's not ashamed of it! I didn't mean it like that! I only thought... you might want to talk about it as well?

I'm just trying to help, Scott, however I can. However little that may be.

From: Scott Cooper

Well, you're not helping.

I'm confronted by Tess's illness every time I walk through the door in the evening. Why you think I would want to talk about it during the day as well is beyond me.

From: Allie Rainsbury

I thought it could be a good outlet! Months ago, you told me that you could 'just listen' and not judge. I'm only offering the same here. That's all I'm trying to do.

From: Scott Cooper

That was different. I don't need you to listen to anything.

Why was it different? Because you didn't know I had a boyfriend then?

What was your offer in that case? A subtle chat up line – is that what you're saying?

You didn't even want to help me, you just thought of the best way to turn my head?!

From: Scott Cooper

If I had wanted to turn your head I'd have acted like a cretin and got you drunk. That seemed to work well for David after all.

From: Allie Rainsbury

Thanks, Scott.

I don't know what else I can do to demonstrate friendship and support. And, to be honest, I'm beginning to wonder if I should even bother any more.

From: Scott Cooper

Great. Don't. Just leave me alone.

Friday

From: Ann Rainsbury
To: Allie Rainsbury

Hello darling,

Just to let you know that I've sent you a text with Robert and Mary's phone number in case you need to get hold of us. Reception out there is pretty terrible apparently, so you might need to use the landline to get through.

Hopefully it won't be too cold and isolated on their farm – especially since they're your father's friends more than mine. Although I suppose I'm fond of Mary; she always looks for a chance to tell an embarrassing story about your Dad's University days ☺

I'm so glad that you're giving yourself the weekend off and unwinding. I was terribly worried after your emails a couple of weeks ago, you did sound awfully down. But you were back on form last weekend I thought and happier with everything, David included.

Anyway, must dash. Much love and make sure you enjoy yourself!
Mum xx

From: Allie Rainsbury
To: David Marshall

Are you about next Wednesday? It's Julie's birthday and we're having a few drinks in Putney to celebrate.

From: David Marshall

You're kidding? Wednesday is the one evening next week that I can't do – I'm away.

From: Allie Rainsbury

Oh, that's a shame.

Typical, the only day you can't do!

From: David Marshall

It really is. I feel terrible. I don't want your best friend thinking badly of me! Can I make it up to her and George by buying them dinner on the Friday instead?

From: Allie Rainsbury

Hmm... I can ask.

Am I invited too? ☺

From: David Marshall

Only if you don't eat any of my chips :P

Are we still getting together on Sunday?

From: Allie Rainsbury

Yes, definitely. Although I must admit I'm praying for rain. Remind me again why I agreed to let you teach me tennis?

From: David Marshall

You'll be fine, don't worry! It's about time I got you interested.

From: Allie Rainsbury

I'm just worried I'll hit you with a tennis ball!

Don't be silly and stop worrying; there's no chance of that happening!

CHAPTER 40

Monday 3 October

From: Julie Lawson
To: Allie Rainsbury

How was your weekend?

From: Allie Rainsbury

It was ok thanks!

I played tennis yesterday though and hit David in the eye with a tennis ball.

From: Julie Lawson

What?! Why did you do that?

From: Allie Rainsbury

I didn't do it on purpose, Julie! Obviously!

He was teaching me the stupid game.

From: Julie Lawson

Ah, OK, so you hit him in the eye as a thank you... I see.

From: Allie Rainsbury

Ha. Ha.

He wasn't happy :S

From: Julie Lawson

I can only imagine...

What happened exactly?

From: Allie Rainsbury

He kept telling me to bounce! Bounce the ball, bounce around… Bounce, bounce, bounce!

That's all he said for about half an hour!

None of it seemed to make any difference and only served to get me worked up. After a while I was so annoyed that I decided to swing my racket as hard as possible. It was an unfortunate irony that this coincided with the one time I managed to hit the ball.

It flew straight at his head, smacked him square in the face and he crumbled to the floor. There was a second of stunned silence followed by what I can only describe as a high-pitched scream.

From: Julie Lawson

That. Is. Bloody HILARIOUS!!

From: Allie Rainsbury

It was mortifying! The players in the court next to ours stopped their game to check on him.

You would have thought he'd been mown down by a machine gun!

From: Julie Lawson

Ha! That's too funny.

Did he talk to you for the rest of the day or were you given the silent treatment?

From: Allie Rainsbury

I got a couple of curt responses before making an ill-advised comment about keeping his eye on the ball.

The day went downhill pretty quickly from there.

From: Julie Lawson

Priceless ☺

Tuesday

From: Allie Rainsbury
To: Tess Cooper

Hey Tess, how are you feeling this week?

I was wondering, if you happened to be free one evening, if I could come by and visit?

Teignmouth seems ages away now and it would be nice to catch up properly.

From: Tess Cooper

Hi Allie! I've had a busy week already.

An old school friend came on Sunday and we went to see *The Lion King* in the West End. It was incredible (although still not as good as the film ☺)!

I'd love you to visit. How about Friday evening? I have a hospital trip between now and then so might need a day or two to recover from that.

From: Allie Rainsbury

Friday sounds great. Only if you feel up to it though, OK? I'll completely understand if you're too tired.

Is anyone going with you to the hospital? I'm happy to come along if you'd like?

From: Tess Cooper

You're very kind, Allie.

Scott's taking me, as he always does. I suspect the doctors think we're actually conjoined twins ☺

From: Allie Rainsbury

Ha!

OK – well, it sounds as if you're in the best hands possible.

Look forward to seeing you on Friday!

From: Tess Cooper

Ditto.

Although you must promise me one thing first please...

From: Allie Rainsbury

Of course...

From: Tess Cooper

Devon was a few weeks ago now, and I've lost a bit more weight since then. It's a combination of things: mostly a lack of appetite from all the medication I'm on.

Anyway, it's not a big deal, and that's why I'm telling you now. I don't want you to be shocked and I don't want to talk about it.

It's something I can manage, but not something I want to be confronted by – if that makes sense?

From: Allie Rainsbury

Tess, I'm sure you'll look as beautiful as always.

Besides, what girl ever wants to discuss her weight? ☺

From: Tess Cooper

True!

Thank you, Allie! I really am excited about seeing you.

From: Allie Rainsbury

You leave me speechless, Tess.

You are, without doubt, one of the more incredible people I've ever met.

From: Tess Cooper

Stop being silly ☺

See you soon – make sure you bring lots of gossip with you! x

Wednesday

From: Allie Rainsbury
To: Julie Lawson

Happy Birthday!!!!

You are cordially invited to a free lunch and all the attention you want! ☺ x

From: Julie Lawson

Aw, thank you! That's very sweet. I accept! ☺

From: Allie Rainsbury

How's your morning been so far?

What presents have you got?

From: Julie Lawson

Ha! You seem to be far more excited than I am.

George gave me a white jumper that I like so much I might not exchange. Elly got me a corkscrew; I'm not sure what sort of message I should read into that. Cale gave me a handmade card with an IOU token that he'd written. He didn't actually specify what it was he owed me though, so he's either not really understood the concept or he's being rather tight.

From: Allie Rainsbury

Or he's a tactical genius? ☺

Are you looking forward to this evening?

From: Julie Lawson

So-so.

Part of me wants this whole day done and dusted; another wants to bathe in the attention and enjoy all the free drinks that are coming my way.

From: Allie Rainsbury

Is that a hint?

From: Julie Lawson

No, never!

It's a demand if anything :P

From: Allie Rainsbury

I guessed as much ☺

Come on then, birthday girl – get your coat! Let's start things off with a glass of wine and an early lunch in the Firestation...

From: Julie Lawson

It's 11 a.m.!

From: Allie Rainsbury

You mean you want to wait a while longer?

From: Julie Lawson

I meant, what took you so long? I've been sitting with my coat on for the last hour.

See you downstairs in two minutes!

Thursday

From: Julie Lawson
To: Allie Rainsbury

Are you in work today, sweetheart?

From: Allie Rainsbury

No. I should be really, but I just didn't feel up to it.

From: Julie Lawson

Well, I don't blame you.

Is there anything I can do?

From: Allie Rainsbury

No, you've been brilliant already!

I'm so sorry to ruin your evening, Julie. Everything always seems to revolve around my dramas and it's very unfair on you.

From: Julie Lawson

Don't be ridiculous! It's not your fault.

From: Allie Rainsbury

Maybe. With all the warnings that everyone gave me, I've only got myself to blame.

From: Julie Lawson

Nonsense! Don't you let him make you feel like that. Don't you dare!

From: Allie Rainsbury

How's George's hand?

From: Julie Lawson

Swollen! That's the first punch he's ever thrown. He's still shaking ☺

From: Allie Rainsbury

Tell him he's my hero please.

From: Julie Lawson

He's mine too ☺ I'll let him know.

Are you sure you're OK?

From: Allie Rainsbury

I'll be fine. Honestly. I'm going to think things through and I'll be in tomorrow.

From: Julie Lawson

Make sure you walk in with your head held high.

And call me if you need any company this evening.

From: Allie Rainsbury

Thanks Jules, love you lots.

From: David Marshall
To: Allie Rainsbury

Allie, this might sound crazy to you now, but I can explain things.

Can we talk? Love, David.

Friday

From: Tess Cooper
To: Allie Rainsbury

Hello! How has your week been?

From: Allie Rainsbury

Hey Tess! Not great for the past couple of days, but all good really.

How are you?

From: Tess Cooper

I'm OK. Have felt horribly sick the last few days and very weak and pathetic as a result. Today seems to be one of the better days though.

Why has your week been tough?

Scott has said that work is really busy for him at the moment, so you're no doubt having the same number of projects thrown at you.

From: Allie Rainsbury

No, it's not work related. It rarely is with me ☺

And certainly not a big deal in comparison to you feeling sick.

From: Tess Cooper

Allie, everyone's problems are only measurable within the context of their own lives.

Stop feeling sorry for me and tell me what's going on.

From: Allie Rainsbury

I have told you how great you are, haven't I?

From: Tess Cooper

Of course you have! ☺

Now are you going to tell me or is it too private to share?

From: Allie Rainsbury

It was my friend Julie's birthday on Wednesday and we went out in the evening to celebrate. We started off in Soho Square for a couple of drinks before moving on to another bar just off Old Compton Street.

That's where I saw David, having a drink with another girl. No doubt he'd have tried to explain his way out of the situation if he'd spotted me coming in – but he was far too busy kissing her to do that. It actually took me a while to digest the scene. By that time, both Julie and her husband George had followed my eyeline and seen the same thing.

I still don't really know why I walked over to where they were sitting. I suppose something inside me wanted to see his face; to find out what excuse he'd come up with. I even had to tap him on the shoulder before he turned and noticed me there. For a second, a fleeting instant, he held a look of panic. But it was gone in a flash. Replaced in a blink by smug resignation. He looked me straight in the eye and shrugged, before saying, 'What are the chances of that?'

I've never been good at thinking on my feet so, hard as I tried to come up with a biting one-liner, nothing came to mind. I just turned to walk away.

It was only then that David made a move towards me. That was a mistake; he should have stayed where he was. Instead, George walked over, moved between us and told him, 'I think this is what Allie meant to say'. Then he punched David in the face.

We were asked to leave after that.

From: Tess Cooper

Wow! That's a far more interesting story than I thought I'd get!

But still, a horrible one for you to endure.

Are you OK?

From: Allie Rainsbury

Actually, I really am.

When George threw that punch, it was like he'd shattered the illusion I'd been carrying, as well as David's jaw. I looked down on the floor and saw David for what he is: a pathetic guy, lost in his own vanity.

I'm pleased to be free.

From: Tess Cooper

Still want to come over?

From: Allie Rainsbury

Absolutely!

From: David Marshall
To: Allie Rainsbury

Please don't ignore me. You'll end up imagining things far worse than are actually true.

CHAPTER 41

Monday 10 October

From: Allie Rainsbury
To: Julie Lawson

How's George's hand?

From: Julie Lawson

It's on the mend!

Now that the shock of the whole thing is receding I'm trying to keep his ego in check. He thinks he's suddenly a hybrid of Bruce Lee and Superman.

From: Allie Rainsbury

Aw... Well, to me he is!

From: Julie Lawson

Don't tell him that. He's one step away from buying a cape and going out in the evenings to fight crime.

How was Oxford?

From: Allie Rainsbury

It made a nice refuge.

It felt like David was sending me a text message every couple of minutes, so it was good to turn off the phone and relax at home.

From: Julie Lawson

Unbelievable. He's honestly trying to wriggle his way out of this?

From: Allie Rainsbury

I know! Don't worry though. I won't be fooled again.

From: Julie Lawson

I wouldn't let you be.

Are you planning to speak to him at all?

From: Allie Rainsbury

And say what? And hear what, for that matter?

No, I have no desire to listen to another list of lies. Whatever he wants to say, he can keep practising in front of the mirror.

From: Julie Lawson

I think that's a wise decision. The guy would just drip his words in honey and try to make them stick.

Leave him staring at his own reflection; in time, he'll start to despise himself as much as we do ☺

From: Allie Rainsbury

Hmm... I'd have thought that day is a long way away.

Thinking about it now, I can't understand how I put up with his narcissism for so long. Whenever he stayed over he'd always take twice as long in the bathroom in the mornings as I did. And he once kept me waiting for half an hour on an evening out in order to top up in a tanning salon! At the time he said it was all for me, so that I'd be proud to be with him. But it wasn't about me at all, was it? Everything was always about him.

From: Julie Lawson

This really is the best thing that could have happened to you, Allie.

I mean, granted, the circumstances may have been a bit of a shock, but I'm so happy he's been found out for the dirt-bag that he is.

From: Allie Rainsbury

Agreed.

If that's what most men are like then I'm better off alone anyway.

From: Julie Lawson

All guys aren't like that, but you are better off alone than with David, that's for sure.

1. How often did he buy you flowers?

2. How often did he surprise you with anything?

3. When did you last really laugh together?

4. Did he ever even tell you how special you are?

From: Allie Rainsbury

Bastard!! Never!

He didn't do any of that stuff!!

From: Julie Lawson

Well then, there you go. You can wait until you find someone who does.

You deserve that.

In the meanwhile, you'll have a bit of free time and I can invite you over for a glass of wine a bit more often. From my perspective, it's a great result.

From: Allie Rainsbury

I suppose that's one positive at least... ☺

Thanks Jules x

From: David Marshall
To: Allie Rainsbury

I missed you over the weekend, especially since I had to go to the hospital and get an x-ray. Turns out that idiot oaf has broken my jaw. All over a misunderstanding.

If you give me a chance to explain things I won't press charges.

Tuesday

From: Chris Trail
To: Allie Rainsbury

Hey there, honey, are you about tonight for a catch up?

From: Allie Rainsbury

Yes, absolutely. Are we running or relaxing?

From: Chris Trail

Well, you sound rather more upbeat than I was expecting!

I was anticipating a blubbing wreck; I'm slightly thrown...

From: Allie Rainsbury

That's what everyone keeps saying. I'm really fine!

Perhaps that will change in the coming weeks when I realise that another Christmas has come around and I'm single and dateless :P

From: Chris Trail

Ah, OK – it's a period of denial then. Yes, that makes more sense ☺

Well, I'd date you of course, but that would be out of the question.

From: Allie Rainsbury

So I've missed my chance finally? Typical! The one eligible guy that I know and he's newly spoken for ☺

From: Chris Trail

Newly spoken for yes.

Although, in truth... the problem would lie more around the fact that I'm newly gay.

From: Allie Rainsbury

...?!!

Say again?!

From: Chris Trail

You read right the first time! ☺

I had planned to tell you all at Julie's birthday but someone else selfishly stole the show :P

From: Allie Rainsbury

What? But you should have said anyway!

Why haven't you told me before?

What do you mean you're newly gay?!

From: Chris Trail

Ah, yes – sorry, I should clarify that. I've always been gay, I'm just newly declared.

I suppose I've always known but, rather shamefully, have never had the inner or outer strength to admit it.

I mean, if you remember, I had that rather boyish-looking girlfriend at University, but just never felt anything.

From: Allie Rainsbury

But you could have talked to me?

I've always debated it with friends, but thought that you'd have told me anything like that! It's the only reason I ever assumed you were straight!

From: Chris Trail

I'm sorry...

After telling myself though, I always promised that I'd tell my parents next. And, since you know how conservative they are... Well, it's always been a very difficult subject to broach, put it that way. I should have told them ages ago, but it gets to a certain point and you just feel that the chance has gone.

From: Allie Rainsbury

Well, this is huge! How did they take it? When did you tell them?

From: Chris Trail

Last week. I had to.

They took it rather badly, unfortunately.

But give it time, I'm hopeful they'll come around to the idea.

From: Allie Rainsbury

Wow.

Massive, huge, wow!

I really don't know men at all, do I?

From: Chris Trail

Maybe not...! But you were the one who gave me the strength to do this.

What you've been through with your parents recently made me want to be honest with mine. And with myself.

Plus, I met someone and fell head over heels! It's the classic boy-meets-boy story ☺

From: Allie Rainsbury

You still should have told me, Chris.

From: Chris Trail

I know. I should have.

I'm sorry, I was just scared. I wasn't sure how you'd react.

From: Allie Rainsbury

You're my best friend! If you're happy than I'm happy!

Obviously! You big, gay plonker! :P

Who is he?!

From: Chris Trail

Well actually... it's Pablo.

From: Allie Rainsbury

Pablo?

Who's Pablo?

From: Chris Trail

Our guitar teacher!

From: Allie Rainsbury

What? The short little balding guy? That Pablo?!

From: Chris Trail

Allie!! He's the perfect height. He's like a pocket-sized Phil Collins ☺

From: Allie Rainsbury

Wow! There's no accounting for taste is there? ☺

That's great! I mean, that's fantastic!

And are you happy?

From: Chris Trail

Blissfully so.

Happy and contented and – whisper it softly – not a little bit in love!
☺

From: Allie Rainsbury

Ah Chris! I'm so excited for you!

Right we are definitely meeting up this evening. Come round and tell me everything about him.

From: Chris Trail

Deal! We do have lots to chat through after all.

From: Allie Rainsbury

Lots!

Until later then, lovely. I need a cup of tea after all this.

From: Chris Trail

Tea now. Drinks tonight!

Wednesday

From: David Marshall
To: Allie Rainsbury

Allie, I need to speak to you in a professional capacity.

Please can we book in a meeting this afternoon to discuss Christmas marketing campaigns with your accounts?

From: Allie Rainsbury

No.

From: David Marshall

So you are alive!

I'm afraid I must insist. It's business critical. I shall be forced to raise the matter with your superiors if you refuse.

From: Allie Rainsbury

Raise away.

From: David Marshall

Do not test me on this, Allie. I can make life very awkward for you here if you're not careful.

From: Allie Rainsbury

David, I cannot believe it's taken me this long to figure out just how pathetic you actually are.

How exactly do you plan to make things awkward for me? Is that a threat?

Would you like me to escalate the matter, approach HR and inform them of this or would you rather back down and crawl back into the hole you came from?

From: David Marshall

Why are you being so mean to me?

Why won't you listen to me?

From: Allie Rainsbury

David, I'm not being mean, I'm just being honest.

You make my skin crawl and the fact that I was ever attracted to you makes me feel rather ill.

There's nothing you can say that will make me revise this opinion.

From: David Marshall

So everything we had was just a joke to you then?

From: Allie Rainsbury

Leave me alone.

Don't call me, don't text me, don't email me.

From: David Marshall

I changed everything for us, Allie! I even took a punch for you!

Give me one more chance to prove what kind of man I am… please?

From: Allie Rainsbury

I already know what you are.

You're a liar, a creep and a coward. And you're not worth my tears or my time.

From: David Marshall

But you still feel something…

Despite the fact you're hurting now, despite your emotions running high...

Despite lashing out with words you don't mean, you still want me...

From: Allie Rainsbury

Ps. Your haircut is the office joke.

From: David Marshall

Oh, go screw yourself, Allie!

How immature and spiteful can you be?

Fine, if you want to play it like that, I'll leave you alone. Who are you going to run to though, answer me that? Who'll even look at you?!

I gave you a chance and you've blown it. You'll never get a guy like me again.

From: Allie Rainsbury

Thank God for that.

Thursday

From: Allie Rainsbury
To: Tess Cooper

Hey Tess, how was your hospital check up yesterday?

From: Tess Cooper

It was OK – the usual prodding and poking!

How are you, more importantly?

From: Allie Rainsbury

You're just like Scott, aren't you – always deflecting attention! If you want to talk about it some more then I'm here to listen.

I'm fine, thanks, no big eventful news. Just coming to terms with spinsterhood again!

From: Tess Cooper

There really isn't much to tell! Besides, what little news there is generally makes me slightly depressed; either at the thought of additional treatment or at the possibility that none of it might work. I'd rather think happy thoughts and not dwell on the stuff I can't control ☺

Hurrah! I have a fellow single sister to moan about men with!

From: Allie Rainsbury

Hmm... that's not quite how I celebrated my new-found status, but OK! Hurrah!

From: Tess Cooper

Positivity Allie. Don't let the bastard get you down ☺

Do you want to organise another get together? I had a great time on Friday.

From: Allie Rainsbury

Ooh, that might help cheer me up. Yes, I'd love to!

How about next Tuesday?

From: Tess Cooper

Agreed!

From: Allie Rainsbury

Great, looking forward to it!

How's Scott, by the way? I don't really speak to him these days, for one reason or another.

From: Tess Cooper

Well, that's not true! You don't speak to him for one reason only... And that one reason isn't around anymore.

You should give him a call.

From: Allie Rainsbury

Ha! Maybe :P

As long as he's well anyway, that's the main thing.

From: Tess Cooper

That's exactly what he says about you!

As long as she's happy. As long as she's OK.

Well? Are you happy? Are you OK?

I'm getting to see you, aren't I?

We're planning an amazing evening, aren't we?

Of course I'm OK, of course I'm happy!

From: Tess Cooper

Such flattery will buy you time, nothing more.

We can discuss things further when you come visit on Tuesday x

----

From: Peter Rainsbury
To: Allie Rainsbury

Hi sweetheart,

Thanks for the phone call last night.

Your mum and I were so sorry to hear about you and David. He seemed like a very nice man, although, if truth be told, I never thought that you seemed entirely comfortable with him. Whether or not that contributed to your break up, I'm not sure – I have never been a good judge of that kind of thing. After all, I only worked up the courage to ask your mother out after knowing her for two years first.

Anyway, I suppose I can't offer much advice or solace really. A break up must always be hard and I'm sure you both had your reasons. All I will say is that, if it was his doing, then he obviously doesn't appreciate what a wonderful woman you are. And, if it was your doing, then I'm sure it was for the best.

We're here for you if you need us, remaining very proud (and ever so slightly protective) of our beautiful, talented daughter.

With love, Dad x

Friday

From: Julie Lawson
To: Allie Rainsbury

So, have there been any more updates, or has he finally got the message?

From: Allie Rainsbury

Nothing in two days!

I think the whole sorry chapter could be drawing to a close at last!

From: Julie Lawson

Thank goodness for that, I was starting to worry.

Horrible, idiot man.

From: Allie Rainsbury

Absolutely! Although part of me was gearing up for a proper fight. I even thought of various insults and saved them in a Word document, just in case.

From: Julie Lawson

Ha! Well, that's an emphatic victory then – you haven't even used all your material and he's already backed down.

From: Allie Rainsbury

True! And it is for the better, because I'd have just been talking to him, however abusive and angry the conversation would have been.

Really, I don't want anything to do with him, I don't want to speak to him, think of him or see him.

From: Julie Lawson

Hmm… a tough task with you both working at the same company.

Has he wandered up to your floor yet?

From: Allie Rainsbury

Actually no, I haven't seen him. I'd imagine it will stay that way too – David surely wouldn't risk the scene it would cause.

Coincidently or otherwise, I got a very sweet, supportive email from Garry telling me to hang in there. That, while it wasn't his business, he'd heard about everything. He told me not to worry, that he'd try to ensure that any dealings I have with David will be minimal, and that he never liked him anyway.

From: Julie Lawson

Really? Garry wrote a sweet note? Your boorish boss wrote something sensitive?

Why doesn't he like David?

From: Allie Rainsbury

He always found David a chauvinist, apparently ☺

From: Julie Lawson

Ha! No way!!

That's funny.

From: Allie Rainsbury

It just goes to show, doesn't it? Maybe people's true colours are pretty different to the ones they dress themselves up in.

From: Julie Lawson

I suppose so! A strange world though.

So what are you going to do with yourself, now that you've bested David and got some time on your hands?

From: Allie Rainsbury

I'm not sure. I'm thinking about throwing myself into work.

From: Julie Lawson

Wow. How strange will that be? ☺

From: Allie Rainsbury

I know!

Unless you fancied a cup of tea first?

CHAPTER 42

Monday 17 October

From: Chris Trail
To: Allie Rainsbury

How would you like to do the Royal Parks half marathon with me?

From: Allie Rainsbury

I'd like to do it in a car, with the air con on.

From: Chris Trail

Come on, let's give it a go!

We've done so much training now that we should be able to manage it.

From: Allie Rainsbury

Occasional jogging does not equate to marathon preparation!

From: Chris Trail

Half-marathon.

It's practically a sprint!

From: Allie Rainsbury

Chris, for someone who is so naturally inept at exercise, your positivity is as worrying as it is misplaced.

Now, changing the subject to more sensible matters, when am I going to meet Pablo?

From: Chris Trail

You've already met him!

If I remember correctly, you were busy rolling your eyes while he played the guitar for us :P

From: Allie Rainsbury

I wasn't rolling my eyes, I was moving them to the rhythm!

And anyway, I mean a proper meeting! When do I get to see him officially as your boyfriend and grill him on everything and anything?

From: Chris Trail

Hmm... sometime in the vaguely distant future?

Perhaps if you agree to this run, then I'll be more inclined to set something up.

From: Allie Rainsbury

Christian! How many times this year have you resorted to blackmail?

From: Chris Trail

Short of you simply saying yes to something, it's the only viable alternative ☺

From: Allie Rainsbury

:P

Who are you running for?

From: Chris Trail

Me!

What do you mean?

From: Allie Rainsbury

What charity are you running for, you plonker?

From: Chris Trail

Oh, right... I hadn't even thought about that. It was more a personal achievement thing.

From: Allie Rainsbury

Touching.

I need to think about it. If we do decide to run then we should definitely have a cause behind us.

From: Chris Trail

OK, sure; agreed!

Does that mean you're in?

From: Allie Rainsbury

It means maybe. Let me talk to a couple of other people first.

Tuesday

From: Allie Rainsbury
To: Tess Cooper

Hi! Are we still on for this evening?

From: Tess Cooper

Yes, absolutely! If you're still able to come, that is?

From: Allie Rainsbury

Yes, of course, I'm looking forward to it.

Plus, there's something I wanted to ask you as well.

From: Tess Cooper

It's not about Scott, is it? Because I probably shouldn't get involved in that. I wouldn't want to confuse things between the two of you.

From: Allie Rainsbury

No! It's nothing to do with Scott. Not that there's anything to talk about there anyway.

I'm considering running a half-marathon and wondered how you'd feel about me running it for Cancer Research.

From: Tess Cooper

Wow! That would be a terrific achievement.

From: Allie Rainsbury

It would be terrifying more than terrific I think.

But what do you reckon? A good idea?

From: Tess Cooper

A fantastic idea! I'm very flattered ☺

How can I help?

From: Allie Rainsbury

Well, you can help me register this evening for a start.

And pull together a list of potential sponsors.

And calm me down when I realise what I've committed to.

From: Tess Cooper

Consider it done! I shall write a particularly pathetic sounding email and tug on people's consciences. We should be able to raise lots... providing you finish of course ☺

That is the big stumbling block, yes.

From: Allie Rainsbury
To: Chris Trail

OK. I'll do it. But you have to run it with me – no running off into the distance and leaving me by the roadside.

Now bring me Pablo! ☺

Wednesday

From: Scott Cooper
To: EMEA Sales; EMEA Marketing; Group Finance

Dear all,

Following the largely positive reaction that we received from our away day earlier this year, we have decided to follow a similar structure again with the upcoming one.

In the morning, we will convene at Mile End Climbing Wall (the largest in Europe!). We are all constantly striving to scale new heights in our day jobs, and this will give us an opportunity to work towards this literally by reaching the top of the wall. For those worrying about attacks of vertigo, fear not, this is an optional exercise, but as ever I would encourage you all to take part.

It should be another fun-filled, energetic morning and give us the focus needed to review the year so far in the afternoon.

The afternoon session will be in a pub across the road; while alcoholic drinks won't be available until 5 p.m. (apologies) a free bar will be in place for the evening.

I hope you will all be able to stay and help celebrate what has been a successful year so far.

Regards, Scott Cooper

From: Allie Rainsbury
To: Scott Cooper

This isn't another set up for me to make an idiot of myself, is it?

Hi darling,

How are you? I'm slightly tired today, but I can put that down to having a few of the girls over yesterday. We were debating whether or not to hold a Christmas fête in the village again this year. I think the general consensus is that we should, especially since it was so well received and attended last time.

This does of course mean that there is now a lot of organising to do in rather a short time, but I needed another project to get on with! Your father isn't overly happy about it and thinks I should be resting but as I pointed out to him, I was basically resting for several weeks during my coma. I've had a lot more sleep than he's enjoyed this year.

Anyway, that's that. But speaking of your father (and as part of my worried mother routine ☺) I wanted to share a little secret with you: When he and I started going out, my parents weren't particularly keen on the idea. They viewed him as slightly poor stock, which is terribly ironic as they were far from upper class themselves. And my friends weren't sure either. They thought that he was too quiet, that I'd find him boring, that he simply wasn't quite right. I didn't listen to any of them, because I knew something that no one else did. I knew what I wanted. I knew that, from the moment I saw him, I wanted him to ask me out. So, people could have said anything to me and it wouldn't have mattered – I wasn't going to let him go!

I suppose I'm telling you that because I never got the sense you were ever that certain over David. You never gazed at him adoringly; if anything it was slightly quizzical. You've done the right thing splitting up with him, darling. One day you'll find someone and you'll be sure.

I hope you don't think I'm shoving my nose in – I know that you'll figure everything out yourself anyway. But, if nothing else, it was a nice little story to share.

With love, Mum x

Thursday

From: Julie Lawson
To: Allie Rainsbury

What would you say to the offer of a blind date?

From: Allie Rainsbury

I'd say that there's no way in hell!

From: Julie Lawson

I guessed as much. Thought I'd ask all the same though since George mentioned him.

From: Allie Rainsbury

What's he look like?

From: Julie Lawson

Ha! ☺

I honestly couldn't tell you. I tried to get a description out of George and the most detail that I got was 'normal looking'. But a nice guy apparently.

From: Allie Rainsbury

Well, that would be a change. But I think I'll decline all the same.

It's a bit soon and my head's not in that place yet. Sorry!

From: Julie Lawson

Not a problem. I figured you'd be a 'no' anyway.

From: Allie Rainsbury

I just don't think I'd be able to get through a date at the moment without questioning everything that the man in front of me was saying.

From: Julie Lawson

You don't need to explain yourself, hun!

As long as you're still keeping positive, that's all I care about!

From: Allie Rainsbury

Very much so ☺

From: Julie Lawson

Good!

A shame though – you'd have liked his estate; it has indoor and outdoor swimming pools!

From: Allie Rainsbury

His estate?!

From: Julie Lawson

Well, OK, I made that up.

But it got you interested, didn't it?

From: Allie Rainsbury

Ha! No!!

Only out of curiosity anyway :P

From: Allie Rainsbury
To: Ann Rainsbury

Hey Mum,

Thank you for your email! I didn't know that about you and Dad. And you're right, it is a lovely story – one to keep me warm on this horribly cold day! I wish I could relate to it myself.

You're right as well about David; I never felt certain in the way that you seemed to. Maybe I looked at him quizzically because I was confused. Confused about why I was with him and not with someone else perhaps.

I'll see you this weekend. We'll chat more then (although not about this! ☺)

Love, Allie xx

Friday

From: Julie Lawson
To: Allie Rainsbury

Looking forward to this evening?

From: Allie Rainsbury

Very much!

I spoke to Chris last night and he sounded terribly nervous.

From: Julie Lawson

So he should be! This is a big moment for him, especially since he didn't tell us anything for so long.

From: Allie Rainsbury

I see you're going with your usual take-no-prisoners approach then...

From: Julie Lawson

I play it as I see it ☺

I'll be on my best behaviour, don't worry. As long as they're happy, right?

From: Allie Rainsbury

Exactly. And from what he's told me so far they seem to be.

How's George about it all?

From: Julie Lawson

Couldn't care less. All he said was that he wished he'd put a bet on Chris finding a man before you did ☺

From: Allie Rainsbury

Cheeky bastard! He only gets a free pass for his heroics for so long.

Tell me when you're ready to leave and we'll head down.

From: Julie Lawson

Shall do!

CHAPTER 43

Monday 24 October

From: Julie Lawson
To: Allie Rainsbury

Happy Monday! It's freezing today!

From: Allie Rainsbury

It's horrible out, hey? It's dark and cold and miserable.

And it's raining in my heart.

From: Julie Lawson

Oh dear!

Positivity seems to have deserted you on this wintry morning.

From: Allie Rainsbury

It has. I feel really down today. I felt down yesterday as well. I came back a bit early from Oxford, got changed into my pyjamas and curled up on the sofa in front of *Love Actually.*

From: Julie Lawson

Great choice of film! ☺

From: Allie Rainsbury

Well, yes, it did cheer me up for a bit, that's true.

But then I started thinking about how unfair it was that I wasn't going out with the Prime Minister and started feeling sorry for myself again.

From: Julie Lawson

I don't think you'd want to go out with David Cameron, sweetie. For one, he's not really your type and for two, he's married with kids.

From: Allie Rainsbury

Plus, I never want to go out with anyone called David ever again!

Jules, I feel so rotten. It's been a tough, tough year in lots of ways but I thought that the one bright spot was that I'd finally managed to get hold of a great guy. It turns out I wasn't even close.

From: Julie Lawson

Hey, come on now! We've been through this. You couldn't have done anything more than you did – you were right to give David a chance; to try and make things work. It's not your fault that he turned out to be such a nasty piece of work is it?

From: Allie Rainsbury

Maybe. Maybe not.

Maybe I'm just hopelessly naïve and gullible. You wouldn't have fallen for his acts. George never trusted him. Scott couldn't stand him – he tried to warn me against him from the start.

From: Julie Lawson

It's always easier looking in than looking out.

And Scott had other reasons not to like David, so you can't beat yourself up for not listening to him.

From: Allie Rainsbury

But it's so difficult not to. Every day I end up thinking about what I should have done, what I should have said. How different everything could have been.

From: Julie Lawson

There's nothing you can't change if you want to. These aren't the end credits to a film. Life goes on.

You'll get another chance.

From: Allie Rainsbury

At what though?

From: Julie Lawson

That's what you need to figure out, hun.

From: Allie Rainsbury

I think I'm going to take a couple of days off and mope. This attempt at positivity is all well and good but it does rule out the possibility of being self-indulgent.

From: Julie Lawson

What are you going to do? Bury your head beneath the covers and refuse to come out of bed?

From: Allie Rainsbury

Oh, that sounds good. Yes, maybe that!

From: Julie Lawson

Hmm... actually that does sound good! But it isn't really what I meant.

Don't hide away, that's the message I was going for.

From: Allie Rainsbury

I'll text you from beneath the duvet.

Tuesday

From: Julie Lawson
To: BMT UK OpCo

Dear all, please be advised that Allie Rainsbury is feeling genuinely unwell today and won't be in the office. Forward any urgent queries onto Garry Blackman.

Thanks, Julie Lawson

Wednesday

From: Julie Lawson
To: BMT UK OpCo

Allie Rainsbury is ill again today; suffering terribly.

In her absence please continue to direct all questions to Garry. Thanks, J.

Thursday

From: Julie Lawson
To: Allie Rainsbury

Feeling better? :P

From: Allie Rainsbury

A little... thank you for your concern :P

From: Julie Lawson

And did you manage to draw any conclusions?

From: Allie Rainsbury

A few!

I've definitely concluded that my efficiency levels would increase dramatically if the working day was allowed to start at 11 a.m.

From: Julie Lawson

Uh-huh... a restful couple of days then :P

From: Allie Rainsbury

Very much so ☺

I watched a lot of *Grey's Anatomy* and thought about very little.

From: Julie Lawson

But wasn't the point of the 'retreat' for you to think about things and find your positive side again?

From: Allie Rainsbury

That would have proved too intense.

Besides, I think my mind was just tired from over-thinking everything anyway. It needed to be switched off for a while.

From: Julie Lawson

Ha! Whatever works for you, hun! Glad that you're re-engaged now at least.

From: Allie Rainsbury

I'm back to fully focused, yes. Which is a good thing as I have a big year-end customer presentation to give in a week's time – until this morning I'd completely forgotten about it.

Time to transform into a conscientious employee.

From: Julie Lawson

Fine, message received! I'll leave you be.

Make sure to include lots of bright colours. Words don't matter so much if you make them sparkly; that's pretty much all I remember from my marketing module at University!

From: Allie Rainsbury

Your classmates must have felt very threatened by your intellectual superiority.

From: Julie Lawson

:P

Good to have you back x

Friday

From: Allie Rainsbury
To: Tess Cooper

Hi Tess, sorry I've been so quiet the past few days. It's terribly busy at work at the moment, but that's no excuse I know.

Are you free this evening by any chance? I'm off to Oxford tomorrow morning but have no plans later if you happen to be about?

From: Tess Cooper

Hi – not to worry! Work sounds constantly busy there; Scott is forever on his BlackBerry when he's not in the office.

From: Allie Rainsbury

Oh, he is still around then, is he? I thought he'd vanished off the face of the earth!

How are you doing?

From: Tess Cooper

I'm fine thanks. Looking forward to seeing you!

With everyone being so hectic, it's just been me and my parents this week so I'm starting to feel ever so slightly stifled. I'm dreading the holiday season.

From: Allie Rainsbury

Do you have a big family Christmas planned?

From: Tess Cooper

No, not at all!

In fact, for the last few years we've just gone to a local hotel and spent the day there. At least then you can pretend that you're all together as a family, while actually spending the majority of the time in your own hotel rooms.

Ho, ho, ho...

From: Allie Rainsbury

☺! As long as you have a movie channel available and make the most of room service then I'm sure you'll make it through.

I, on the other hand, will no doubt have to endure a 6 a.m. alarm call and help prepare half a ton of vegetables, then steel myself for a day of cards, Trivial Pursuit and the Queen's Speech!

From: Tess Cooper

Aw, that sounds nice though (early morning start aside).

It's certainly more traditional than us anyway!

From: Allie Rainsbury

True... and really, for the first time in many a year, I suppose I am actually looking forward to it!

Must dash to another meeting now, sorry. Need me to bring anything over later?

From: Tess Cooper

Just your gossip, thanks! x

CHAPTER 44

Monday 31 October

From: Allie Rainsbury
To: Julie Lawson

How was your weekend?

From: Julie Lawson

I spent most of Sunday covered in pumpkin. Other than that, it was OK.

I honestly think that teachers should be made to do the homework they set, so they can fully understand the chaos some of their assignments cause. Carving a pumpkin might sound fun in theory, but in practice Cale lost interest after drawing a very bad cat (yet still demanded that yours truly carve the thing in infinitesimal detail), while Elly nearly chopped her thumb off three times before completing what can only be kindly described as a big hole.

From: Allie Rainsbury

I'd forgotten about Hallowe'en! I suppose I should pop out at some point today and pick up some sweets.

From: Julie Lawson

Yes, you definitely should – I'm passing by your flat this evening with a large troop of kids in tow!

From: Allie Rainsbury

That sounds demanding! How many kids?

From: Julie Lawson

Twelve, I think. I wasn't honestly left with much option – Elly invited her friends before even raising the idea with me. I thought she was winding me up until the first set of parents phoned, asking what time they could drop their children off!

From: Allie Rainsbury

Cunning. Well played, Elly!

From: Julie Lawson

I know – she knew exactly what she was doing! It was properly devious of her.

I couldn't have been more proud ☺

From: Allie Rainsbury

☺! I'll see you tonight then! Should I have a glass of wine ready as a treat for you as well?

From: Julie Lawson

That's very tempting! But no, don't worry – I think it's all going to be rather fast moving. The more doors knocked on, the more chocolate gathered!

From: Allie Rainsbury

How cute. How mercenary.

From: Julie Lawson

I don't know what else this holiday teaches them!

See you later!

Tuesday

From: Allie Rainsbury
To: Julie Lawson

Bastardy kids!!

From: Julie Lawson

I hope you're not referring to mine?

From: Allie Rainsbury

No, not yours – they looked really sweet! Was Cale meant to be a pirate?

From: Julie Lawson

Sort of. He insisted on wearing his favourite Spiderman costume as well so the whole look became slightly confused.

So which kids are you talking about?

From: Allie Rainsbury

After you left another group came around, who sounded at least 13 judging by the depth of their voices.

This horrible boy screams out 'Trick'! and I hear them all cackling away. I called back 'Treat' and ran to get some sweets.

I'm halfway to the kitchen when he shouts, 'Nah, you're all right', and starts pouring olive oil through the letter box.

From: Julie Lawson

No! That's not nice.

What did you do?

From: Allie Rainsbury

I wasn't sure what to do. I mean, I always thought that a trick was simply an idle threat, didn't you? I never imagined that someone would actually take it up as a viable option. It seemed a bit unfair.

Elly spent all of last week learning how to make a coin disappear. She may have interpreted 'trick' too literally, but at least it wasn't sinister.

Did you open the door and confront them?

From: Allie Rainsbury

Yes! Eventually, once I actually processed what was going on. I was outraged.

From: Julie Lawson

So what happened? Did you shove them off your doorstep?

From: Allie Rainsbury

Yes!

Well, I mean, yes, that's what I was going to do. But no – I slipped on the olive oil and fell over.

They ran off laughing.

Wednesday

From: Ann Rainsbury
To: Allie Rainsbury

Hello darling!

I know you're coming up this weekend, but can't remember if I've told you that I'm having my girls over again on Saturday. We're going to run through all the recipes we need for our Christmas stall.

An official taster would be very useful?

Love, Mum x

From: Allie Rainsbury

I'm sure I can manage that! ☺ I can try to bring a couple of friends if you need more feedback? x

From: Ann Rainsbury

Absolutely!

Which friends? Any 'special' ones, I need to know about? ☺

The more the merrier anyway! Tis the season after all!

From: Allie Rainsbury

No, Mother, nothing you need to know about.

And it is definitely not the season yet – stop siding with the department stores! Honestly, I walked into one of them last weekend and half the shop was dedicated to Christmas.

From: Ann Rainsbury

Quite right! It's a wonderful, magical time of year. I'm all for it!

From: Allie Rainsbury

Humbug x

From: Allie Rainsbury
To: Julie Lawson; Chris Trail; Tess Cooper

Would any of you be interested in coming up to Oxford this weekend?

Short notice I know, but my mother's running a biscuit stall in her village fête and wants to practise her cooking in preparation.

Free samples of delicious (or otherwise) baked goods…!

From: Chris Trail
To: Allie Rainsbury

I'd love to! (It's definitely your mum cooking, not you, right? ☺)

From: Tess Cooper
To: Allie Rainsbury

Oh, yes please! Are you sure that's OK?

From: Julie Lawson
To: Allie Rainsbury

Ah, sounds fun! We don't actually have any plans for the weekend but not sure I can subject your mum and dad to the kids as well.

From: Allie Rainsbury

Of course you can! They haven't seen Cale and Elly in ages; Mum would be thrilled to have them there!

From: Julie Lawson

Hmm... double check first maybe?

If you're sure it's OK then we'll pop up for the day.

From: Allie Rainsbury

Of course it's OK! The house will be properly bustling.

I'll call home tonight and warn Dad; that should give him enough time to find a good hiding place ☺

From: Julie Lawson

Ha! Well, let me know – we really won't be offended if it's too much for them.

Ps. Remember to pack your harness for tomorrow. And whatever you do, don't think about the previous away day :P

From: Allie Rainsbury

At least it's on dry ground this time!

But thanks for the confidence boost all the same :P

Thursday

From: Chris Trail
To: Allie Rainsbury

Hey Allie, I feel a bit cheeky asking this, but is Pablo invited this weekend as well? It's only because I mentioned it last night and he seemed rather jealous.

Completely understand if not.

From: Allie Rainsbury

Out of office reply: Allie is climbing the wall today. Literally rather than figuratively for once.

She will be checking her emails intermittently.

From: Allie Rainsbury
To: Chris Trail

We already assumed he was coming. I spoke to Mum last night and she's looking forward to meeting him x

From: Chris Trail

Really? Fantastic, thank you. He'll be so excited!

Let the biscuit eating commence! ☺ x

Friday

From: Allie Rainsbury
To: Scott Cooper

You didn't need to do that. I don't know if that was for my benefit or not, but thank you.

I don't even know what's going on with you these days. I ask Tess occasionally but she doesn't like to share too much and of course I don't want to pry. I know you asked me to leave you alone but it seems like it's been such a long time now that I can barely remember why we argued in the first place. I miss you.

I don't expect you to say yes, but you're very welcome to come to Oxford this weekend. You must know that I'm picking Tess up en route.

At the very least I hope you can reply and that we can start becoming friends again. I really would like that.

With love Allie x

From: Julie Lawson
To: Allie Rainsbury

So did you manage to scale Everest? ☺

From: Allie Rainsbury

Pretty much! It was certainly another interesting away day...

From: Julie Lawson

You fell off, didn't you?

From: Allie Rainsbury

Actually, I didn't! :P I was very careful albeit really, really slow. I didn't quite make it to the top and was stuck in one particular pose for about 20 minutes when it suddenly dawned on me how far I was from the ground. But, basically, I retained a modicum of dignity – I think.

From: Julie Lawson

I can't wait for the photos, again! ☺

From: Allie Rainsbury

Anyway! The more interesting session was in the afternoon this time.

From: Julie Lawson

The dry, business part you mean?

From: Allie Rainsbury

Exactly!

Scott started it off by summarising the company performance across the year so far, what the rest of our targets were, what we were trying to achieve collectively in the future... that kind of thing.

From: Julie Lawson

Sounds fascinating.

From: Allie Rainsbury

So boring! Hence he tried to keep it as light-hearted as possible. Which is the interesting bit!

To make sure people didn't fall asleep he highlighted the management team's strengths and weaknesses by comparing them to animals. He compared himself to an ostrich – burying his head in the sand was a weakness but being able to thrive in tough conditions was a strength.

Garry was compared to a dog, because he was all bark and no bite; or something like that anyway. There was a kangaroo, a monkey and a lion at some point as well; I forget now what they represented. But it was all done in good humour.

Then he came to a slide with David's name displayed – it had a photo of a rat! Strengths: Enjoys multiplying. Weaknesses: Often deserts.

There was a collective intake of breath, before he moved on with the rest of the afternoon.

From: Julie Lawson

Really?!

Was David there?

From: Allie Rainsbury

No, although the presentation was distributed afterwards.

From: Julie Lawson

That's funny!

Good old Scott!

From: Allie Rainsbury

Good old Scott... stupid old Allie.

From: Julie Lawson

Hey, no crying there please – that milk has long since spilt.

From: Allie Rainsbury

I know, I know. I'm not reading anything into it.

I shouldn't be, should I?

From: Julie Lawson

...

So we'll see you at your parents tomorrow?

From: Allie Rainsbury

:P! Fine!

See you there, anytime from 11 x

CHAPTER 45

Monday 7 November

From: Scott Cooper
To: Allie Rainsbury

Thanks for your email. I'm sorry, I didn't pick it up until Saturday.

From: Allie Rainsbury

That's OK! I didn't think I'd even get a reply.

From: Scott Cooper

Tess seemed to have a good time at the weekend.

From: Allie Rainsbury

Did she? I'm glad. There were over a dozen people in the house; lots of chatting, lots of biscuit making, lots of wine. She must have been shattered by the end of it; especially since Mum collared her early on and made sure she was active in the preparation as well as in the tasting!

From: Scott Cooper

Tired, but happy.

Thank you again. It's appreciated; especially by her.

From: Allie Rainsbury

Scott, you don't need to thank me – you make it sound pitying and that's not the reason I chat to her. Tess is fun and interesting and gives me far more sensible advice than I give myself.

Shouldn't I be the one thanking you anyway? That was quite a speech you gave on the away day.

From: Scott Cooper

One of the advantages of being David's senior is that there's little he's likely to do.

How are you coping? It couldn't have been a very pleasant experience.

From: Allie Rainsbury

I'm fine, really! I'm better off for it.

I guess Tess told you everything?

From: Scott Cooper

She did, yes.

I'm sorry.

From: Allie Rainsbury

Well, if I'd listened to you in the first place I wouldn't have had to go through it. You warned me against him from the very start, I was just too headstrong to listen! ☺

From: Scott Cooper

Or too lost in lust.

From: Allie Rainsbury

No! No, it wasn't that. Not really…

It's difficult to explain now and it seems so silly. I suppose I was just scared of losing what I had. Haven't you ever felt that way before?

From: Scott Cooper

I've never cared about losing something I don't want.

So, no.

From: Allie Rainsbury

I'd forgotten how blunt things can be when talking to you!

I'm not explaining myself very well.

Maybe if we go for a drink I'll try to be clearer. ☺ It's been ages!

From: Scott Cooper

Listening to you talk about David, now that you don't get to see him?

No, thank you, but I'll pass.

From: Allie Rainsbury

I won't bring him up at all! I couldn't care less about him. It would be good to see you.

From: Scott Cooper

I can't, sorry. Things are too busy right now.

From: Allie Rainsbury

OK… well, if anything changes then let me know? I miss you.

From: Scott Cooper

As you said on Friday.

Tuesday

From: Allie Rainsbury
To: Julie Lawson

I'm feeling rubbish again today.

From: Julie Lawson

You're not taking any more days off sick, I won't allow it!

From: Allie Rainsbury

I know... although I wish I could. I didn't want to get out of bed at all today.

From: Julie Lawson

Is this because your half-marathon is coming up and you've just realised how long 13 miles actually is?

From: Allie Rainsbury

No! Although that doesn't help.

I emailed Scott yesterday and we chatted for the first time in ages.

From: Julie Lawson

Right. And that's put you into a bad mood because...

From: Allie Rainsbury

Because I asked him if he wanted a drink and he said no. It was just a friendly offer and he still said no, that he was too busy.

From: Julie Lawson

Well, maybe it is just that? Perhaps he is busy. There have been lots of people scurrying around on this floor recently; I'm sure it's just work.

From: Allie Rainsbury

He could make time if he really wanted to. Besides, it was the way he wrote it. I might have asked him to swim in acid for all the warmth he replied with.

From: Julie Lawson

Perhaps he's being hesitant because he had feelings for you, and he got hurt more than you realised. Now he wants to protect himself a bit.

From: Allie Rainsbury

But Jules, that's just it! I think I have feelings for Scott too. I think maybe I've always had feelings for him.

And I can't say anything, can I? I can't tell him that now, after everything that's happened!

From: Julie Lawson

You can tell him, but I'm guessing he'd be a bit resistant to hearing that as well.

From: Allie Rainsbury

Because he hates me.

From: Julie Lawson

Aw, honey, he doesn't hate you!

Just cast your mind back. He pushed as hard as he morally could to suggest you choose him and not David. And you chose David.

From: Allie Rainsbury

But he never told me that! He never said outright, 'I like you'. In fact he denied it when I asked him. And I asked him a couple of times!

From: Julie Lawson

Allie, come on! Because he's a nice guy. What kind of man would actively break up a relationship? He's not built that way, and it's good that he isn't!

From: Allie Rainsbury

So I was meant to guess, was I? I was meant to drop everything because he smiled at me?!

From: Julie Lawson

Yes.

You were meant to choose him.

From: Allie Rainsbury

But that's so unfair! I didn't know that!

What can I do now?

What should I say?

From: Julie Lawson

I don't think there's much you can say or do right now.

He needs to be able to trust you – to trust your intentions. And that might take a while.

From: Allie Rainsbury

But how long? What if it never comes?

From: Julie Lawson

Well then, he's not the right guy. And you're not the right girl.

Sorry, hun, but that's all there is to it. There's no magic wand here.

From: Allie Rainsbury

I feel miserable. And stupid. And hurt.

From: Julie Lawson

Welcome to Scott's world.

Come on, meet me in the cafeteria; I'll buy you a cup of tea.

Wednesday

From: Ann Rainsbury
To: Allie Rainsbury

Hello darling!

I hope your week is going well and that you've recovered from the weekend. I've barely got my breath back I must admit, but thoroughly enjoyed it all!

We were so pleased to have everyone visit – what fun to have such a frenzied household! And Cale and Elly have grown so much! Elly looks incredibly like Julie I must say, a terribly pretty little thing. Such a lovely family. And it was good to meet Pablo as well. Your father and I thought he suited Chris perfectly; we're so pleased that he's found someone he can be himself with.

And Tess – what can I say about her? I hope I didn't fuss too much, but she does make one feel rather protective. I'm so glad she managed to eat something as she looked so frail, although of course her illness must be making her very weak. Aside from that though, you'd never be able to tell. She seems such a happy, bubbly young girl; awfully easy to get along with.

Anyway, I just wanted to thank you again for inviting them all; it was lovely to see you of course, but with so many people around it felt as though the Christmas fête had started already!

Love, Mum xx

From: Allie Rainsbury

Dear Mum,

I had fun too! You were out when I called on Monday but Dad mentioned that you and your girls were all pleased with the positive feedback! My personal preference was the caramel shortbread, but I think that they will all prove popular. Perhaps you should start baking batches now to ensure you have enough! ☺

Pablo and Chris do seem to work, don't they! And Tess is a sweetheart, she's incredibly brave and utterly selfless. She reminds me of you in lots of ways, those included. And Scott too – I've always thought that he has those attributes as well.

I have this charity run at the weekend that you laughed about so much (!) so I won't be able to visit. I'm still looking forward to our Spa visit the weekend after. I think I'll need it!

I'll call you when I've finished and let you know that I'm OK... fingers crossed!

Love, Allie xx

From: Allie Rainsbury
To: Scott Cooper

Hi, are you about today?

From: Scott Cooper

In meetings for most of it, sorry.

From: Allie Rainsbury

Oh dear, work never seems to stop for you!

I was just wondering what your plans were for this weekend? I'm running a half-marathon in Hyde Park and thought, if you weren't doing anything else, that you might like to come and watch?

From: Scott Cooper

Let's see.

I might not be able to on Saturday though.

From: Allie Rainsbury

Tess is coming as well...

From: Scott Cooper

I know. I'll see if I can make it – unlikely though.

I have to dash.

Thursday

From: Chris Trail
To: Allie Rainsbury

Are you doing stretches under your desk? ☺ Do you think we should do one final training run this evening?

From: Allie Rainsbury

I'm starting to feel a bit ill actually. I honestly don't know how I've managed to put myself in this position.

How many people don't finish?

From: Chris Trail

I've no idea! That won't be us though, don't fret. In fact, I'm sorely tempted to place a cheeky little wager on us finishing among the elite runners!

From: Allie Rainsbury

Christian, if we stood on the finish line and waited for everyone then we still wouldn't manage that.

From: Chris Trail

You're just determined to be a ray of sunshine, aren't you? ☺

From: Allie Rainsbury

At the moment, I'm just determined not to throw up.

From: Chris Trail

Go onto the website and take a look at the route. If nothing else you can make a note of where the toilets are.

From: Allie Rainsbury

You speak as if I'll be alone. I plan on grabbing onto your t-shirt and letting you drag me around!

From: Chris Trail

I shall be a mere speck on your horizon! ☺

From: Allie Rainsbury

You'd better bloody not be! And I'm not even remotely joking, Chris! You got me into this ridiculousness, you're getting me through it!

From: Chris Trail

☺! See you this evening. A few kilometres, nothing more.

From: Allie Rainsbury

Of course nothing more!

From: Chris Trail

You get terribly cross when you're stressed, don't you?

From: Allie Rainsbury

Sod off.

Friday

From: Tess Cooper
To: Allie Rainsbury

Just to let you know, I'll be standing by the main entrance gates to Hyde Park on Saturday. I'm going down with a few friends.

We may or may not have made you and Chris a banner ☺

From: Allie Rainsbury

That's sweet.

Does the banner read, 'There's dignity in last place'?

From: Tess Cooper

Ha! Or something similarly uplifting.

You'll be great, don't worry.

From: Allie Rainsbury

'You can worry, don't be great' would be more consoling at the moment.

As long as I finish, then that's all that matters.

From: Tess Cooper

Finish, shminish! I'm proud of you just for taking part!

From: Allie Rainsbury

I have to finish! Otherwise I'll lose all the sponsorship money!

From: Tess Cooper

Allie! I have leukemia! Whether you finish or not, if I can't get people to feel sorry enough for me to donate a promised fee, then I'm not doing my job very well.

One cough and they'll pay ☺

From: Allie Rainsbury

Ha! I hadn't thought of it like that. So, you're basically saying it doesn't matter if I even do the race or not?

From: Tess Cooper

Oh no! That part's crucial. I want something to laugh at :P

From: Allie Rainsbury

You and 50,000 other spectators!

Is Scott coming, do you know? I did mention it to him earlier in the week.

From: Tess Cooper

I don't know. I don't think so though. He's awfully busy etc etc.

Why, would his presence make you run faster? ☺

From: Allie Rainsbury

Probably – the less time he got to see me red, sweaty and lurching ungracefully, the better!

See you tomorrow...

From: Tess Cooper

We'll find you afterwards and hose you down!

CHAPTER 46

Monday 14 November

From: Julie Lawson
To: Allie Rainsbury

How are the calves?

From: Allie Rainsbury

I'm still shaking! It took me half an hour to put my socks on this morning.

From: Julie Lawson

Ha! But at least you made it. That's fantastic!

From: Allie Rainsbury

I accept your praise and modestly agree with it ☺

Really, the whole day was pretty inspiring. There were absolutely masses of people crowded over the whole course, cheering us along all the way.

Plus, I ran most of the distance behind a man dressed as an elephant which although adding to the sense of carnival, got pretty hallucinary towards the end.

From: Julie Lawson

Ah, it sounds great! I'm just annoyed we had to miss it, especially since the sun was shining.

So the two of you ran together?

From: Allie Rainsbury

Right up until the final hundred metres, when Chris told me he was going to sprint to the finish line.

From: Julie Lawson

How competitive!

So he left you trailing at the very last?

From: Allie Rainsbury

Well no... he was so exhausted that he missed his step and fell over.

From: Julie Lawson

No!! That's hilarious!

Was he OK?

From: Allie Rainsbury

He was fine!

I should probably have stopped to ask instead of hurdling over him, but he didn't go down that heavily and I was far too tired to wait ☺

From: Julie Lawson

I'm laughing at the scene I've got pictured! ☺

And was Tess there? And Scott?

From: Allie Rainsbury

Tess was there, yes. She was with a few other friends who all shouted very loudly as we went past them.

Scott wasn't able to make it unfortunately :S

From: Julie Lawson

Ah, well, it's great that you had a support group though. Anyway, I doubt you were looking your glamorous best by the end of it – maybe it's a good thing he didn't come.

From: Allie Rainsbury

True...

I think I'd have accepted the humiliation though, if only to see him for a bit.

From: Julie Lawson

Try not to think about him.

You've just run 13 miles!! That officially makes you a hero ☺ x

Tuesday

From: Tess Cooper
To: Allie Rainsbury

Hello, my special marathon-running friend!

How are the injuries? ☺

From: Allie Rainsbury

Healing slowly! Give it a year and I'll be back to full fitness.

From: Tess Cooper

Just in time for the next one.

From: Allie Rainsbury

Please, no... I don't want to think about that.

From: Tess Cooper

Ha! I don't blame you.

Happier thoughts then – I'm having a little Christmas party at my flat next Thursday evening and you are one of an incredibly select number of people to get an invitation.

It's nothing major, just a few drinks and some pretentious finger food! Are you able to make it?

From: Allie Rainsbury

You mean I've reached the inner circle of friends already? ☺

Let me leaf through my busy social diary first to check availability...

Of course I'll come!

From: Tess Cooper

Great! Oh good, I am glad – it should be fun.

Just beware of my uncle, he's notorious on the dance floor, so I'd advise you to keep your distance.

From: Allie Rainsbury

Ha! I wouldn't worry; I can barely walk, let alone dance.

From: Tess Cooper

A prepared excuse already? Very clever!

From: Ann Rainsbury
To: Allie Rainsbury

Hello darling,

Are you still coming up here on Thursday evening?

I'm terribly excited about our Spa day although I do hope you haven't gone to too much expense or trouble; I feel very spoilt (especially as it's coming up to your birthday soon – I should be the one organising treats for you). I won't put up too much resistance though ☺

Let me know if your plans change, but if not then we'll see you up in Oxford.

With love Mum x

From: Allie Rainsbury

Hi Mum,

Yes, I'm still coming to collect you!

I'll stay over on Thursday night and then we'll head down to Hertfordshire on Friday morning for a weekend of relaxing massages. I can't wait either! ☺

Love Allie x

Ps. You coming along is birthday present enough for me!

Wednesday

From: Scott Cooper
To: Allie Rainsbury

My sister tells me you hardly broke a sweat. I'm very impressed...

From: Allie Rainsbury

Ha. Ha.

I finished the race – that's all I care about :P

From: Scott Cooper

I was being sincere. There weren't any prizes handed out for aesthetics, were there? Just making it around is achievement enough.

From: Allie Rainsbury

Oh...Then, thank you!

It would have been nice to see you there, but understand that you don't have much free time these days.

From: Scott Cooper

I'm proud of you for doing it.

I wanted to say well done, that's all.

From: Allie Rainsbury

Proud enough to buy me a congratulatory drink? ☺

From: Scott Cooper

Success has its own reward.

From: Allie Rainsbury

That's virtue!

Would it really be so bad to see me?

From: Scott Cooper

Of course not.

But I can't, sorry – it's just not a good idea.

From: Allie Rainsbury

Why not? I don't understand.

What are you afraid of? I'm asking you for a drink, nothing more than that!

From: Scott Cooper

When were you thinking?

From: Allie Rainsbury

Whenever!

Are you free this evening?

From: Scott Cooper

I have a date tonight.

From: Allie Rainsbury

As in... a date? Like a proper date?

With who?

From: Scott Cooper

With someone I've seen a couple of times recently. You don't know her.

From: Allie Rainsbury

Why haven't you said anything? Tess hasn't said anything.

Are you sure? How many times have you seen her?

From: Scott Cooper

Allie, this isn't something I want to get drawn into a discussion over. Suffice to say that us meeting up for a drink wouldn't be very helpful at the moment.

From: Allie Rainsbury

I can't believe you wouldn't tell me something like this!

Where did you even meet her? I thought you were too busy with work to do anything else?

From: Scott Cooper

Maybe I shouldn't have emailed you. I'm sorry.

I have to go now.

From: Allie Rainsbury

Wait though – I'm just...

Have feelings her?

From: Scott Cooper

That's just gibberish I'm afraid.

I have to go; we'll chat another time, I'm sure.

From: Allie Rainsbury

Have you got feelings for her?!

From: Scott Cooper

That's really not your business...

But yes, I like her.

Thursday

From: Julie Lawson
To: Allie Rainsbury

I ask this in trepidation while cowering slightly but... have you calmed down yet or are you still ranting and raving?

From: Allie Rainsbury

Sorry, I suppose I did drip bile down the phone line somewhat, didn't I?

I'm calmer now. Whether it's all the paracetemol or if the fight's just gone out of me now though, I'm not sure.

Maybe a mixture of the two.

From: Julie Lawson

Ah hun, don't be like that!

I think I prefer the fire-spewing dragon from last night to the passive depressive of this morning.

Did you speak with Tess after you called me?

From: Allie Rainsbury

Yes, and she confirmed the worst ☹

From: Julie Lawson

What did she say exactly?

From: Allie Rainsbury

Well, she wasn't very forthcoming really. I managed to get a name out of her but not much more. She's said all along that she doesn't want to get involved; I can understand that.

From: Julie Lawson

A sensible stance, I'd agree.

And the name of this wanton would be...

From: Allie Rainsbury

Rosie.

Exactly the kind of pure, pretty, evocatively English name that you're compelled to like.

I hate her.

From: Julie Lawson

Ha! I would never have guessed ☺

Well, my advice from last night still holds – don't overthink anything. Who knows what this is? A fling, a friend, a fiancée to be – you can't control it so don't let it control you.

Whatever regrets you have, this is probably the best way of consigning them to the past.

From: Allie Rainsbury

It's good advice. I know that. It's just not advice that I want to hear!

From: Julie Lawson

I understand. But sweetheart, at some point, you're going to have to listen – for your own sake.

Scott's moved on; you have to try and do the same.

From: Allie Rainsbury

This feels horrible.

It's so far from where I hoped things would finish, I don't know whether to laugh or cry.

From: Julie Lawson

Go and get yourself pampered. Relax and enjoy the weekend with your mum.

Sounds like it's much kneaded ☺

From: Allie Rainsbury

Wow...

Definitely cry.

Friday

From: Allie Rainsbury

Out of office reply: Hi, I am now out of the office until Monday.

Please contact Garry Blackman if this honestly matters. Thanks, Allie.

CHAPTER 47

Monday 21 November

From: Julie Lawson
To: Allie Rainsbury

So, what would this morning's positivity scale read, if one was inclined to do so?

From: Allie Rainsbury

Fair to middling ☺

From: Julie Lawson

Really? That's galaxies better than the eternally gloomy and despairing outlook of Friday!

From: Allie Rainsbury

It's amazing what a dosage of deep-tissue massaging and a jacuzzi can do for a girl's state of mind.

From: Julie Lawson

Ha! So it was good then?

From: Allie Rainsbury

It was as pleasurable as the previous weekend was painful.

The whole hotel was very luxurious – there were even little bowls of fruit and nuts in the relaxation rooms. Not that this was the highlight, but still.

From: Julie Lawson

Fancy! ☺

And your mum enjoyed it as well?

From: Allie Rainsbury

She didn't want to leave.

She flirted with the masseuse, had an exfoliating facial, and fell asleep in her mud bath. She spent the weekend walking around in a bathrobe and giggling excitedly; it was so nice to see ☺

From: Julie Lawson

Aw, that's sweet! She loved every minute I bet.

And did you talk to her at all about... recent revelations?

From: Allie Rainsbury

No. I was going to, but thought against it in the end.

For one, it might have made her worry and I didn't want to put a damper on anything. And for two, I've decided that (as usual :P) you're right – I do need to be positive.

I moved on from David. It's time to move on from Scott too.

From: Julie Lawson

Great! Well done you. Definitely support that decision!

From: Allie Rainsbury

Thought you might :P

Meet up for lunch later? I need to do some work now – I have a yearly review meeting on Wednesday with Waterstone's and the presentation is somewhat threadbare at the moment.

From: Julie Lawson

Positive and diligent? This is a Monday morning, right? :P

From: Allie Rainsbury

Less diligent, more panicked into action by the impending deadline.

From: Julie Lawson

Ah... that sounds more like it ☺

Good luck! See you at lunch, trooper x

Tuesday

From: Julie Lawson
To: BMT UK OpCo; BMT EMEA OpCo

Dear all,

Important message from your Christmas Committee!

This year's Christmas party will be held on Thursday 15 December at the Riverside Café in Hammersmith (please see map attached for directions).

Can everyone RSVP to me by Monday 5 December.

We asked various people around the office (anonymity is secure) and alcohol was top of most Christmas wish-lists. No doubt a large cheer shall go up at the news that there will be a FREE BAR throughout the evening.

Dress code is smart casual. Chariots can be arranged and expensed, however please let me know if you need one and I will organise the bookings.

Merry Christmas, The Social Committee ☺

From: Allie Rainsbury
To: Julie Lawson

Please don't book me into a cab with Garry again this year. I still have the recurring nightmare of him mooning other cars and throwing up on my shoes.

From: Julie Lawson

But it made such a good story!

Are you not curious as to how he could up the stakes this year? ☺

From: Allie Rainsbury

Not even the tiniest bit.

From: Julie Lawson

Ha! Don't worry; I wouldn't do that to you, I promise! George is looking after the kids so I'll be able to stay out later this year. We can head back together.

From: Allie Rainsbury

So the odds of suffering a babbling wreck vomiting in my cab are still high then...

From: Julie Lawson

Oi! I can't be associated with such drunken behaviour!

From: Allie Rainsbury

Umm... no, of course not.

I'll pack my Wellingtons all the same :P

Wednesday

From: Allie Rainsbury
To: Julie Lawson

Bugger! Buggery, bugger!

Can you access my computer?

From: Julie Lawson

I should be able to, if you let me know your password.

Why, what's up? Where are you?

From: Allie Rainsbury

On a train to Reading, to my meeting with Waterstone's!

I've left all of the handouts for my presentation at home. Help!

From: Julie Lawson

How did you manage that? What else did you even need to remember?!

From: Allie Rainsbury

Julie, is now really the time for recriminations?

I remembered the chocolate selection I bought them for Christmas.

From: Julie Lawson

Brilliant.

What do you need me to do?

From: Allie Rainsbury

You're a life-saver!

Go into my computer, print off six copies of the presentation (in colour), ideally have them bound and covered, then courier them up to Reading as soon as possible.

From: Julie Lawson

You're joking, right?

What time does your meeting start?

From: Allie Rainsbury

In just under half an hour.

From: Julie Lawson

Allie! How can I possibly get half a dozen copies to you in 30 minutes? Don't be ridiculous!

Did you not store it on a USB stick?

From: Allie Rainsbury

Yes! Of course I did. You know, despite your frequent views to the contrary, I'm not a complete buffoon.

From: Julie Lawson

Well then, can't you just use that?

So they don't have handouts, so what? Tell them you'll email them copies of the presentation and use one of their projectors to present it to them in the meantime.

And stop stressing!

From: Allie Rainsbury

Fine. OK. That could work.

You're right, sorry. It's only because this is a big meeting; their top brass are gathering for it and Garry will be there too, looking on.

I really want it to go well!

From: Julie Lawson

Take a few deep breaths and calm yourself down.

It will all be fine, I'm sure – they'll be too busy looking at the screen to worry about looking at any silly handouts anyway.

From: Allie Rainsbury

Right… right.

Thank you!

From: Julie Lawson

You're welcome ☺

Now go kick some butt!

From: Allie Rainsbury
To: Julie Lawson

Jules? You don't happen to have the key to my desk drawer, do you?

From: Julie Lawson

Focus on your presentation!

No, I don't.

Why?

From: Allie Rainsbury

That's where I've left the USB stick.

Thursday

From: Julie Lawson
To: Allie Rainsbury

Obviously, I'm concerned. Clearly, I feel for you.

Naturally, I want to hear everything!

From: Allie Rainsbury

I don't think I've ever been so embarrassed :S

I think I might be in serious trouble, Jules. Garry was, understandably, not impressed.

From: Julie Lawson

Ah, he'll be fine. He's all bark and no bite, remember?

Did you have to postpone it in the end?

From: Allie Rainsbury

Sort of.

I mean, I was panicking so much when I got to their offices that I couldn't even think straight.

I thought the best approach might just be to try and push on through.

From: Julie Lawson

Right...

What did that mean in practical terms?

From: Allie Rainsbury

It meant that we were led to the boardroom and exchanged pleasantries with their team for a few minutes, before Garry introduced me to the room.

Then I stood up and tried to deliver the presentation from memory.

From: Julie Lawson

No. No, you're kidding.

You wouldn't have done that!

From: Allie Rainsbury

It worked initially, although I suppose that might have been because they were so confused.

Everything unravelled very quickly though; I couldn't remember what their best-selling book was, so referred to it as 'Book X'. At the time, for some reason, I was rather pleased with that tactic so started apportioning letters all over the place.

After a couple of minutes I told them that they'd got an F market share and that Book X brought in D pounds of revenue.

Someone actually started taking notes.

From: Julie Lawson

Oh God, I don't want to hear anymore...

What happened then?

From: Allie Rainsbury

Garry stepped in and suggested that it might be G per cent better if I sat down and shut up.

His face had changed to that dangerous shade of crimson he gets when he's either annoyed or drunk. And I'm pretty sure he wasn't drunk.

Friday

From: Scott Cooper
To: Allie Rainsbury

Did I offend you last night? You seemed to walk off in something of a huff.

From: Allie Rainsbury

Not at all – why would I be in a mood? Or do you mean because the only time you speak to me all evening is to mock me in front of your new girlfriend?

From: Scott Cooper

I wasn't mocking you, Allie, I was teasing.

And she's not my new girlfriend.

From: Allie Rainsbury

Introducing me to Daisy as 'our company's best public speaker' wasn't funny or nice.

From: Scott Cooper

It's Rosie actually.

And I'm sorry, I didn't know you were so precious all of a sudden. It wasn't meant nastily, I just thought it was a funny story.

From: Allie Rainsbury

Oh, sorry, Scott, excuse me for feeling so sensitive when my job is on the line. Quite apart from the fact that my confidence has been beaten in most other areas recently.

I can't think why I'm not so fast to laugh at myself all the time!

From: Scott Cooper

Don't be dramatic. Garry told me about it yesterday and he was struggling to keep a straight face himself.

From: Allie Rainsbury

Great! Even better. I'm so pleased that you have your own little boys' club where I can be the butt of all your jokes.

What a hilarious figure of fun I am.

From: Scott Cooper

I didn't mean it like that.

From: Allie Rainsbury

Whatever, Scott. It must be so difficult for you, mustn't it?

Life must be such a bloody chore when everything comes so easily to you.

From: Scott Cooper

Allie, I only meant it as a joke.

If I was thoughtless or insensitive then I really am sorry.

I didn't mean to upset you.

From: Allie Rainsbury

I have to go.

Please thank Tess for a lovely party when you see her this weekend.

CHAPTER 48

Monday 28 November

From: Scott Cooper
To: Allie Rainsbury

I've been feeling bad all weekend.

In retrospect, I can absolutely see how you could have interpreted my comment as insulting.

It was thoughtless, needless and uncalled for. My unreserved apologies.

From: Allie Rainsbury

What a coincidence.

I was just composing a quick email to you, admitting that I'd over-reacted somewhat ☺

From: Scott Cooper

Hmm... that's very generous.

In all honesty, I'm not very convinced that you did, but I'm certainly relieved that you're gracious enough to see it like that.

From: Allie Rainsbury

I was also going to say, having thought about this carefully over the weekend, that I'd really like us to be friends again.

In between all the ups and downs of the past few months, I'd like to think that, for the most part, we've been there for each other.

We've forgotten that recently though, and despite being more to blame for this than you are, perhaps we can try and remember again now?

From: Scott Cooper

I've never not viewed you as a friend, Allie.

But I know what you mean. For my part, I know I've been very unapproachable. Again, I'm sorry; this can't exactly have helped.

From: Allie Rainsbury

How about it then? Whatever feelings weren't expressed or have been unrequited, friendship hasn't been one of them.

I've told you several times that I miss you, and I do – I really, genuinely do. Smart remarks included ☺

From: Scott Cooper

What unrequited feelings have you had?

From: Allie Rainsbury

Scott? Let's agree to bury that sort of conversation, shall we?

I'd like us to be able to catch up as friends. I'd like to know what's going on with you.

I'd even like to meet Rosie again ☺

From: Scott Cooper

But you'll be so hard pressed to make a better impression the second time around.

From: Allie Rainsbury

:P!

Agreed?

From: Scott Cooper

OK, mate; you're on.

Friends it is.

Tuesday

From: Ann Rainsbury
To: Allie Rainsbury

Hello darling,

I won't make this long as we have several batches of biscuits in the oven and I'm petrified that they'll burn if I take my eye off them for too long. We've already managed to ruin one load when your father offered to help and mistakenly iced all the cupcakes with salt. The girls, several sweet cups of tea later, ordered him out of the kitchen. I have my suspicions that it was all a clever ploy to ensure he's kept away from further tasks!

Are you still coming up with Tess on Friday? Will it just be the two of you this time? We've made up both the spare rooms, but there's always plenty of space on the couch or the floor. I'm sure you know by now that everyone's welcome!

Also, your father has asked me to ask you what you'd like for your birthday. And really, what you'd like for Christmas as well! I have a couple of ideas but I'm worried that they might be a little dull, so if you have any ideas then please let us know.

Really looking forward to seeing you — apparently there'll be a Santa's grotto this year!

Love, Mum xx

From: Allie Rainsbury

Hey Mum,

I'm still trying to work out how those two things are linked! ☺

Yes, definitely still coming up! I've asked a few others as well, but most people are busy this weekend unfortunately. I know Cale and Elly were especially disappointed, so I think I'll leave out the detail of there being a grotto, it might send them over the edge.

Ideas for my birthday (since I know that the words 'please don't worry about getting me anything' will fall on deaf ears!):

1. A book (not one from BMT Publishing)

2. Anything from Jigsaw (size 10 generally, size 12 just in case)

3. A first-class ticket to Australia

If pushed, I'd emphasise that I'm particularly keen on options one and two.

Love, Allie xx

Ps. Be sure to point out the salted cupcakes to me, they don't sound the most appealing (unless you try to pass them off as pretzels ☺)!

Wednesday

From: Julie Lawson
To: Allie Rainsbury

This should make you feel very special…

A letter, marked for your attention, was thrust at me this morning from the kids ☺

From: Allie Rainsbury

Ah, really? How sweet! Should I guess at it being a birthday card or a Christmas one?

From: Julie Lawson

I shall quote verbatim:

'Dear Auntie Allie,

Here is a list of things we most want for Christmas. Please do not wory about getting them all. If you do want to thouh then that is fine.

We have bean good. Love Elly and Cale xx

From: Allie Rainsbury

Ha! My heart is glowing with warmth.

What are they asking for?

From: Julie Lawson

As far as I can tell, various games that end in DS. I'll hand it to you at lunch and you can have a chuckle ☺

I've added spelling lessons to the list.

From: Allie Rainsbury

☺!

See you at lunch (unless I'm frog-marched out of the building before then)!

From: Julie Lawson

Ah, of course! I'd forgotten about your catch up with Garry. Have you prepared anything for it?

From: Allie Rainsbury

No.

Although ironically I do have a copy of that customer presentation printed out. I was going to try and appeal to his Christmas spirit.

From: Julie Lawson

Ha! Honestly, don't worry. These things happen - I'm sure Garry will be appreciative of that.

In fact, if I remember correctly, he missed his first external meeting here because he overslept.

From: Allie Rainsbury

Ooh, really? I didn't know that! Should I bring that up do you think?

From: Julie Lawson

No! Do not bring it up!

I'm only mentioning it to give you a clearer perspective on the whole thing.

Hold your hands up to an error in judgement, take his feedback on board and then forget about it.

From: Allie Rainsbury

Forget the feedback?

From: Julie Lawson

Forget the incident!

From: Allie Rainsbury

Ah, OK.

Right... see you in the canteen!

From: Julie Lawson

Plonker ☺ x

Thursday

From: Scott Cooper
To: Allie Rainsbury

Hi there,

Tess's at the hospital today but she wanted to ask if you'd be able to collect her at 3 p.m. tomorrow instead of 2?

Does that make sense?

From: Allie Rainsbury

I think I can just about decipher it! ☺

From: Scott Cooper

Great, thanks.

I know she's really excited about going up to Oxford again.

From: Allie Rainsbury

Good! It should be fun.

Is everything OK? The hospital trip is a planned appointment, right?

From: Scott Cooper

Yes, everything's fine. Thanks for asking. Just a few of the usual tests and checks.

From: Allie Rainsbury

OK. Because she's seemed in good spirits to me over the past few weeks...

From: Scott Cooper

She loves Christmas, so maybe that's helping a bit.

From: Allie Rainsbury

It must be that then, yes! ☺

461

From: Scott Cooper

She puts on a show sometimes too... Tess wears a brave face for her friends that she won't let slip very often.

After chemotherapy, when she's ill, hurting and everything seems so stark and real, she's broken down before. She's cried and sworn and cursed the unfairness of life.

From: Allie Rainsbury

Scott, I'm so sorry... I forget.

From: Scott Cooper

That's the point really. She wants you to.

They're moments, nothing more – just glimpses into her mind. As many positive thoughts as she has, inevitably she carries a host of negative ones too.

From: Allie Rainsbury

That must be hard.

From: Scott Cooper

That's when it's hardest and scariest. For her and me. Both of us feel petrified that she's giving up and letting this bloody disease win.

From: Allie Rainsbury

She won't give up. There's no way that will happen.

From: Scott Cooper

I hope not.

Anyway. This is a cheery conversation!

So you're OK to pick her up still?

From: Allie Rainsbury

Absolutely! 3 p.m. on the dot ☺

Scott? You'll let me know if you want to talk more, won't you?

From: Scott Cooper

When have you ever known me to want to talk more? ☺

Of course I will.

Thanks again x

Friday

From: Allie Rainsbury
To: Scott Cooper

Happy Friday!

By the way, I meant to say yesterday that you're invited to Oxford as well. I wasn't sure if you were up to anything or not this weekend.

From: Scott Cooper

That's kind, but I can't I'm afraid.

Besides, I'd hate to intrude on a girls' weekend away!

From: Allie Rainsbury

It's not a girls' weekend at all – I'm sure my father would be thrilled to have another man around for company.

You should come!

From: Scott Cooper

No, honestly, that's OK. I'll pass.

Thank you though.

From: Allie Rainsbury

What else are you going to do? Sit around all day and stare out of the window?

Better to enjoy the spirit of a warm community gathering and all the sugar you can eat! ☺

From: Scott Cooper

Rosie's taking me to the ballet on Saturday.

A matinee performance of *The Nutcracker*.

From: Allie Rainsbury

Oh. Yes, of course she is...

Well, that's nice then. How cultured!

From: Scott Cooper

That's what she said! I immediately thought of pretentious and dull, but apparently I'm wrong.

From: Allie Rainsbury

I'm sure you'll enjoy it when you're there.

Have a lovely time! x

From: Scott Cooper

Thanks, you too x

From: Julie Lawson
To: Allie Rainsbury

Have a great weekend!

I'm really upset that instead of coming to a fun festive fête, we have to entertain my in-laws! Talk about two extremes!

From: Allie Rainsbury

Stupid festive season! Everyone Christmassy and cheery and oh-look-there's-mistletoe-happy.

From: Julie Lawson

Scott?

From: Allie Rainsbury

No! Shush.

Thinking you're so clever :P

From: Julie Lawson

Scott ☺

I'll call you later!

CHAPTER 49

Monday 5 December

From: Julie Lawson
To: Allie Rainsbury

Happy birthday week! ☺

How did it all go?

From: Allie Rainsbury

Ha! Thank you ☺

It went really well. The whole village braved the cold and made an effort to pitch in, so we had various stalls selling homemade food, hand-knitted jumpers and strange looking (labelled 'quaint and authentic') knick-knacks ☺

Include the grotto and, rather bizarrely, a water tub and a coconut shy, and it was a pretty big event.

Mum and her girls had sold out of their biscuits by mid-afternoon, which they were very chuffed about.

From: Julie Lawson

Oh, that sounds such fun; I'm jealous.

What was the role of the water tub?!

From: Allie Rainsbury

It was a very ill-conceived game which involved throwing a ball against a target that, when hit, tipped our local priest into the pool.

Unfortunately, the design lent itself far too favourably to the thrower and the Father was being launched into this freezing water almost every time anyone had a go. The poor man had to be taken away after an hour or so because he was too cold to clamber back up to his seat.

How about you? Did you make it through unscathed? ☺

From: Julie Lawson

Just about, although I could have done with that water tub!

Cale and Elly presented their grandparents with their infamous Christmas wish list, which went down like a lead balloon since I'd phoned my mother-in-law just last week to suggest scarves and gloves as potential present ideas.

She looked at the list and then sternly implied that I had deliberately given her false information to set her grandchildren against them!

From: Allie Rainsbury

Ha! If she's that worried then she can splash out on a couple more presents surely?

From: Julie Lawson

That's what she said she'd have to do.

It was around then that my father-in-law went into a mood with me as well ☺

Tuesday

From: Julie Lawson
To: Allie Rainsbury

Is it me or is the workload finally starting to drop off?

From: Allie Rainsbury

I hadn't noticed either way.

Why, should I be easing up a bit? Am I working too hard?

From: Julie Lawson

Hmm... in your case, I wouldn't worry too much :P

Besides, you're the apple of Garry's eye. It doesn't matter what do you does it? ☺

From: Allie Rainsbury

Hey, that's not true at all!

Although, in fairness, he could have been much sterner with me over that fiasco of a presentation.

From: Julie Lawson

I told you it wouldn't be a big deal.

Want to sneak out for an early lunch? Celebrate your final day of being 31 with a glass or two of white wine... ☺

From: Allie Rainsbury

Meet you in the Firestation in an hour?

From: Julie Lawson

See you there!

From: Ann Rainsbury
To: Allie Rainsbury

Hello darling,

Just to let you know that we raised £268 for charity from all the biscuits we sold! That's even more than we had hoped for, so everyone is rather pleased with themselves. Thank you so much for all your help and support!

Your father is outside at the moment, walking around the garden rather despondently. It does seem slightly barren I suppose, but then I don't know what else he expects at this time of year. He told me this morning that things could only get worse if it started snowing. I dutifully nodded away of course, but secretly I'm hoping for a white Christmas, however hard that might hit the garden.

It turns out that Father Adrian has a nasty cold but nothing more than that. We're all very relieved because he does give such a lovely sermon. It would have been terribly impersonal if someone else had delivered it on Christmas morning.

Happy Birthday for tomorrow! We shall speak to you then!

Love Mum xx

Wednesday

From: Scott Cooper
To: Allie Rainsbury

Happy birthday, Allie. Hope you have a great day x

From: Allie Rainsbury

Thank you!

I'm feeling very special with all these birthday wishes ☺

From: Scott Cooper

It's quite right that you should do too.

You're a special person after all; and almost entirely in a good way :P

From: Allie Rainsbury

:P!!

I feel like a five-year-old saying this but – you're invited to my party this evening!

From: Scott Cooper

You don't give much notice on your invitations, do you?

I can't make it I'm afraid.

From: Allie Rainsbury

Off to the opera this time, are we?

From: Scott Cooper

Funny girl...

I have got you something though. I'll leave it with Tess to give you.

From: Allie Rainsbury

You didn't need to do that! You coming would have been present enough.

But what is it? ☺

From: Scott Cooper

It's just a token... don't get too excited.

Enjoy your evening x

From: Allie Rainsbury

Thank you, that's very thoughtful.

Enjoy yours too x

From: Chris Trail
To: Allie Rainsbury

Happy Birthday, you old hag!! ☺

Are we still celebrating this millstone – sorry, milestone – at the Duke's Head?

From: Allie Rainsbury

At least this hag hasn't found any grey hair yet :P

Yes, it's still at the Duke's Head!

I'll be there from 6 p.m.

From: Chris Trail

Hey! That was a rogue hair! It was stress related!

Mean old bat :P x

From: Allie Rainsbury

☺!

Thursday

From: Julie Lawson
To: Allie Rainsbury

I know I said this many a time last night, but I feel it needs repeating once more – wow, what a complete arse!!

I hope you're still laughing about it all.

From: Allie Rainsbury

Pretty much, yes!

A little mortified that I've yet again managed to make a scene on an evening out, but aside from that I'm fine.

From: Julie Lawson

It's not your fault though!

Your crazy life just seems to throw these incidents up! ☺

From: Allie Rainsbury

Well, I do wish it wouldn't!

He cut a pretty pathetic figure didn't he?

From: Julie Lawson

He was hammered! I thought he was going to fall over. And when he tried to hand you that present? The nerve of the man!

What did he imagine would happen by turning up?

From: Allie Rainsbury

Who knows what goes through David's mind.

Who cares?

Let's change the subject! Fancy a cup of tea downstairs?

Absolutely! ☺

From: David Marshall
To: Allie Rainsbury

Dear Allie,

I spent a long time debating whether to track you down. I knew that you might react as you did, but with it being your birthday as well as the season of goodwill, just thought it was worth a try.

I really do have to let you go though, don't I?

Love, David x

From: Allie Rainsbury

I went a long time ago.

I wish you hadn't come.

From: David Marshall

Did you get my present? I can't even remember now if I gave it to you?

From: Allie Rainsbury

The tree lights, you mean? Yes, I got them.

You shoved them at me just before you were escorted out for being too intoxicated.

From: David Marshall

A light for each day that I've loved you.

From: Allie Rainsbury

Considering they were a packet of thirty, that makes little to no sense.

I suppose that's par for the course with you though.

From: David Marshall

Ah, come on, Allie! Each week then!
Roughly.

From: Allie Rainsbury

David, go away.

I wish you hadn't turned up. I really wish you hadn't emailed me just now.

I wish you didn't work in the same building and that you're not ever a part of my life again.

From: David Marshall

So that's a definite no then?

From: Allie Rainsbury

That's a CAST IRON NO.

If I have to tell you this one more time then I'll have no choice but to get HR involved.

I don't know how much clearer I can be.

For your sake, I sincerely hope that you understand.

From: David Marshall

Fine!! Understood.

It's a shame you can't learn to forgive, but then I suppose that sums up your selfishness.

Bye, Allie.

Ps. Put the lights in the internal mail please, they were my only set.

Friday

From: Allie Rainsbury
To: Scott Cooper

Thank you so much!

Tess handed me your card on Wednesday, but I only opened it last night.

From: Scott Cooper

You're very welcome. It's nothing really but hopefully, at the very least, you'll find it a useful lunch.

From: Allie Rainsbury

I can't believe you remembered!

From: Scott Cooper

I almost mentioned it a while ago but thought it might have been slightly presumptuous.

Now I just figure that you've been postponing things for long enough.

From: Allie Rainsbury

Ha! I suppose I have.

The Literary Editor of *The Times Magazine* though! How do you know him?

From: Scott Cooper

Ben's a University friend. We shared a house in our second year and have kept in touch.

I gave him a call and explained your background. He's very happy to meet up and chat about any options that may be open to you.

From: Allie Rainsbury

But what do I say? I'm not really qualified, am I?!

From: Scott Cooper

Don't say that for a start...

It's lunch, not an interview, so don't stress!

Ben can give you some advice, answer any questions you have and, if you're keen, perhaps introduce you to a few other people who could further help.

From: Allie Rainsbury

I'm still nervous... but in a good way! ☺

I'm really looking forward to it!

From: Scott Cooper

Good – I was worried you'd view it as patronising.

Happy Birthday again.

And you're OK? After Wednesday evening?

From: Allie Rainsbury

You heard about that? You must think I'm such a prima donna!

From: Scott Cooper

Do you need me to have a word with David?

If he's hassling you then I'll make sure he stops.

Just say the word.

From: Allie Rainsbury

No, really, please don't.

It's fine. He's history, and ancient history at that.

From: Scott Cooper

If you're sure...

The offer remains, if you ever want it.

Enjoy the weekend.

From: Allie Rainsbury

You too, mister! x

CHAPTER 50

Monday 12 December

From: Allie Rainsbury
To: Julie Lawson

Did you know that the weather forecast is predicting snow this afternoon?!!

From: Julie Lawson

You sound awfully cheery today – good weekend?

From: Allie Rainsbury

I spent Sunday decorating a tree with my parents, which was fun.

Plus, we have just two weeks until Christmas!!

The thought nearly had me skipping to work!

From: Julie Lawson

Baubles tend to be more traditional decorations than parents.

From: Allie Rainsbury

Funny :P

Did you brave the shops in the end?

From: Julie Lawson

Yes, although I'm not sure I want to be reminded! I spent most of Saturday in Westfield while George took the kids ice skating.

It might have taken five cups of tea, involved three arguments with other shoppers and needed a strategic elbow to the ribs of at least one sweet little old lady, but I got the whole horrific ordeal out of the way in one fell swoop.

From: Allie Rainsbury

Well done you! That's less confrontation than last year ☺

I'm taking the cowardly route and postponing the inevitable crush for as long as possible. Maybe I'll wander up the high street one evening this week and see if I can get anything there.

From: Julie Lawson

Make sure it's not tomorrow...

You're still coming to the school nativity, aren't you?

Elly has a speaking line as one of the wise men and Cale is dressed as a bush.

From: Allie Rainsbury

Of course I am!

I'm intrigued to see Cale's costume, if nothing else ☺

From: Julie Lawson

Hopefully egg cartons look good from a distance...

Tuesday

From: Tess Cooper
To: Allie Rainsbury

Your mum will be pleased to know that her biscuits have all gone already!

From: Allie Rainsbury

Already?! And you must have taken at least ten packets home with you! You're getting an appetite back, I take it? ☺

From: Tess Cooper

A little yes, and they are delicious!

But it's more Scott, I promise.

And Rosie – I see her munching on one every time she's here.

From: Allie Rainsbury

Oh...

Well, they were made for eating I suppose!

Does Rosie visit very often then?

From: Tess Cooper

She's been over quite a bit recently.

Between us though, she's annoying the hell out of me! She speaks to me as if I'm five years old.

From: Allie Rainsbury

I didn't know they saw so much of each other.

From: Tess Cooper

Three times a week maybe?

I think she's a bit dull. They never seem to talk about anything.

From: Allie Rainsbury

Wow. Scott must be keen if he's seeing her that much.

I had no idea.

From: Tess Cooper

I'm not so sure. He seems to be going through the motions to me.

Rosie is way too possessive; he only sees her so much because she's constantly pushing him and he's too much of a dolt to say no.

From: Allie Rainsbury

You're clearly her biggest fan ☺

From: Tess Cooper

I can't pretend I'm that, you're right.

It's a just shame that you two never got together – at least then I'd approve!

From: Allie Rainsbury

Thank you! But I don't think that was ever fated to happen.

Besides, Scott would have got too jealous; I'd have come over for a date with him and ended up chatting with you ☺

From: Tess Cooper

Which we should do anyway.

Are you free before Christmas? If so, pass by for a catch up and an empty plate of biscuits?

From: Allie Rainsbury

Absolutely! Can you do next Tuesday?

This week's booked full with shopping, school plays and the office party.

From: Tess Cooper

Of course! Think of all the stories you'll come armed with; Rosie won't stand a chance.

From: Allie Rainsbury

Stirrer! :P

Wednesday

From: Allie Rainsbury
To: Scott Cooper

Are you going to the Christmas party tomorrow?

From: Scott Cooper

Maybe.

From: Allie Rainsbury

Maybe?! There's a free bar! What more do you need to think about?

From: Scott Cooper

I'm debating whether the free bar outweighs the inevitable need for mindless small talk.

From: Allie Rainsbury

You sir, are a Grinch.

You can't not come! It's only once a year!

From: Scott Cooper

That is a consolation I suppose.

We'll see. I might come along for a while. I'm staying at Rosie's tomorrow though so even if I do pass by, it won't be for long.

From: Allie Rainsbury

Again? She's got you round her little finger, hasn't she?

When did things start getting so serious?

From: Scott Cooper

They're not serious. It's only the second time I've been over to her flat!

From: Allie Rainsbury

But she's been staying with you a lot more often though.

From: Scott Cooper

How do you know that?

Actually, forget it – stupid question. Why would you ask?

From: Allie Rainsbury

It just cropped up in conversation, that's all.

It seems you're halfway down the aisle already.

From: Scott Cooper

I don't know what you're talking about.

From: Allie Rainsbury

It's pretty obvious! Do I need to write you a joint Christmas card? It's ridiculous!

From: Scott Cooper

You have no right to be annoyed, Allie.

Or insensitive for that matter.

From: Allie Rainsbury

How am I being insensitive? I just made an innocent observation, that's all! What's the big deal?

From: Scott Cooper

You really don't get it, do you?

I don't even know what you're implying any more.

I have no idea what goes on in your head.

From: Allie Rainsbury

Oh for goodness' sake, stop being so precious!

I'll see you at the party. Or not.

Hopefully you'll be more relaxed across the bar than you are across a keyboard.

Thursday

From: Julie Lawson
To: Allie Rainsbury

Remember that we're sharing a cab back this evening, before you jump in it without me!

From: Allie Rainsbury

I'm not even sure I'm going to go now.

From: Julie Lawson

Huh? What do you mean?

This is the best night of the year for office gossip! Where else would you rather be?

From: Allie Rainsbury

In stupid Rosie's position!

From: Julie Lawson

Who?

What are you talking about?

From: Allie Rainsbury

That calculating, overbearing tyrant that Scott's supposedly dating! I don't like how she's trying to worm her way into his affections so quickly.

What's the rush, for goodness' sake?!

Why can't he see that she's no good for him?

From: Julie Lawson

You've never even met her!

From: Allie Rainsbury

I've seen her! Once. Briefly.

Anyway, Tess doesn't like her, and I have a healthy respect for Tess's opinion.

From: Julie Lawson

...when it coincides with yours :P

Look, stop being ridiculous. Come along. Have a drink.

Forget the things again that you did so well to forget. It's Christmas!

From: Allie Rainsbury

It doesn't much feel like it.

I don't want to be surrounded by smiling and laughter when I feel annoyed and depressed.

From: Julie Lawson

I'm coming up to fetch you at 4 p.m. and we'll go and get changed.

From: Allie Rainsbury

I'm not going.

From: Julie Lawson

Yes you are. We're going to get drunk and we're going to make idiots of ourselves on the dance floor.

If that doesn't sound like Christmas then I don't know what does!

From: Allie Rainsbury

I'll be in a mood the whole night and rubbish company.

From: Julie Lawson

I'm used to that :P

Anyway, you're darn sure not leaving me to go by myself! I just won't allow it.

From: Allie Rainsbury

But it's all so unfair!!

From: Julie Lawson

Tell me about it through a wine glass.

See you this afternoon, you shiny, happy person :P x

From: Allie Rainsbury

Fine. I'll come along and get drunk at least.

I'm not making an idiot of myself though, on the dance floor or anywhere else.

I wouldn't want to give stupid Scott the satisfaction.

Friday

From: Julie Lawson
To: Allie Rainsbury

How's the head?! ☺

From: Allie Rainsbury

Ow... severely ow!! How about you?

From: Julie Lawson

I've felt better!

Do you remember much from last night?

From: Allie Rainsbury

I have vague memories of cocktails, karaoke and dancing, in no particular order!

It all got pretty hazy past our second bottle of wine :S

From: Julie Lawson

Hmm... we drank far too much, didn't we?

It was a fun evening though!

And, of course, you put on quite the performance ☺

From: Allie Rainsbury

What's that supposed to mean?

From: Julie Lawson

You don't remember asking the band if you could request a song?

From: Allie Rainsbury

I didn't, did I?! Ha! What did I ask for?!

From: Julie Lawson

'I Will Always Love You'.

From: Allie Rainsbury

No!! ☺

That must have stopped the party in its tracks!

Did the band actually play it?

From: Julie Lawson

Um... yes.

From: Allie Rainsbury

Oh dear! That's a bit embarrassing.

Ah well. My musical choice will no doubt be mocked for months to come! ☺

Have you heard any other stories yet?

From: Julie Lawson

Allie?!

Can you really not remember anything?

From: Allie Rainsbury

What do you mean?

From: Julie Lawson

The band played the song, but only because you insisted on grabbing the microphone and dedicating it to Scott, before launching into a truly horrible rendition...

From: Allie Rainsbury

What are you talking about?

From: Julie Lawson

You clambered up on stage and told everyone that you had an announcement.

You told us that you wanted to sing a song to Scott Cooper, the only man you've ever loved.

From: Allie Rainsbury

WHAT?!

From: Julie Lawson

The worst bit was when you started sobbing halfway through the second verse.

From: Allie Rainsbury

WHAT?!!!

ARE YOU JOKING?!

From: Julie Lawson

At least I think that's what you were doing. You might have been trying a medley of sorts. It was difficult to tell.

From: Allie Rainsbury

Why didn't you stop me?

From: Julie Lawson

I was too busy laughing. And cheering; I was cheering for you too.

Sorry...

From: Allie Rainsbury

OH MY GOD!!

What do I do?! I thought I got some funny looks this morning.

What do I do?! I don't believe this!

From: Julie Lawson

I wouldn't worry too much. It's a Christmas party – people are expected to get drunk and do stupid stuff!

Apparently a girl from Finance fell over near the bar.

From: Allie Rainsbury

Brilliant! That just puts me in the shade then, doesn't it?! That's the competition to me squawking a slow love song to the entire office? Someone slipped?!

Please tell me this isn't happening!

From: Julie Lawson

Well, I think it added to the entertainment! ☺

Laugh it off! It's not a big deal!

From: Allie Rainsbury

That's rather easier for you to say.

How did Scott react?!

From: Julie Lawson

I don't really know. He wasn't applauding though, if that's what you mean.

He left soon afterwards.

From: Allie Rainsbury

Probably scared there'd be an encore.

What am I going to say to him? He'll be furious!

From: Julie Lawson

He'll be fine! He'll do what everyone else will do and put it down to too much wine.

Stop panicking. It's quite funny really!

From: Allie Rainsbury

Hilarious.

From: Julie Lawson

By the time you come in on Monday it will all be forgotten.

Half the office are on holiday and the other half have their minds there!

From: Allie Rainsbury

I'm hiding under my desk until then.

From: Allie Rainsbury
To: Scott Cooper

I fear I might have embarrassed you almost as much as myself last night...

No more drinks for me for a while! ☺

CHAPTER 51

Monday 19 December

From: Scott Cooper
To: Allie Rainsbury

I need to know where your actions came from.

From: Allie Rainsbury

You wouldn't be willing to accept 'the vineyards of Southern France' as an answer would you?

From: Scott Cooper

Really? You're going to laugh about this?

Do you even begin to realise how difficult that was for me?

From: Allie Rainsbury

Of course I do, Scott! You think you're the only one walking around the office with your head down?

I'm incredibly embarrassed, but other than laugh about it what would you have me do?!

I'm truly sorry if I've made things awkward. If it's any consolation then I'm sure your colleagues will forget about me as readily as you have.

From: Scott Cooper

What's that meant to mean exactly?

From: Allie Rainsbury

You just don't seem to have much time for me anymore, that's all. Not now that Rosie's on the scene.

From: Scott Cooper

You're unbelievable, Allie!

From: Allie Rainsbury

Why is that such a bad thing to say?!

From: Scott Cooper

What do you want from me?

From: Allie Rainsbury

I want you!

From: Scott Cooper

What does that mean? What are you saying?!

From: Allie Rainsbury

You want me to spell it out?

From: Scott Cooper

Yes, I want you to spell it out!!

I waited for you for months! I basically threw myself at you!

You chose David.

From: Allie Rainsbury

I did not choose David! However blunt you felt you'd been, I was never sure there was a choice to be had. I stayed with him because you never directly told me how you felt!

From: Scott Cooper

I don't see how I could have been any clearer!

So what was this? Alcohol? A dare? What drove you to sing out these new-found feelings in front of everyone?

From: Allie Rainsbury

Of course it wasn't a dare!

And no, it wasn't alcohol! I mean, I doubt very much I'd have done what I did when sober, but...

It's how I feel.

From: Scott Cooper

I have given you so many chances to tell me how you feel, Allie.

Only a month ago you told me that you'd like to try and be friends.

From: Allie Rainsbury

I did! I do want to be friends!

I just... I want you too.

From: Scott Cooper

For God's sake!

You're so selfish!

You've spent months saying nothing and now you say that? After all this time? Now that I'm seeing someone?

From: Allie Rainsbury

I'm just telling you how I feel.

At various times this year I've been scared and stupid and I don't expect you to understand that.

But you wanted to know and I'm telling you now – I can't get you out of my mind.

And I don't expect you to do anything with it. But there you go.

You're all I think about.

From: Scott Cooper

I wish you'd taken me to one side at the party said this in private.

From: Allie Rainsbury

Me too...

From: Scott Cooper

I could have told you in person that it's too late.

Tuesday

From: Chris Trail
To: Allie Rainsbury

Raspbury! A very Merry Ho-ho-ho to you!!

From: Allie Rainsbury

Ah Chris – your emails never fail to make me smile.

How are you, lovely?

From: Chris Trail

Feeling exceptionally festive and deliriously happy!

It helps that today is my last day of work for the year! ☺

From: Allie Rainsbury

I am immediately jealous.

How have you managed that?

From: Chris Trail

Surprisingly easily. It turns out I'm actually not very important to operating efficiency over the company's busiest week of the year.

No doubt I'll be very worried about this in January when it's dark and cold and miserable. But since everything is glittery and magical at the moment I couldn't care less!

From: Allie Rainsbury

The magic of Christmas indeed.

So what are you going to do with yourself for three weeks?

From: Chris Trail

Actually, I'm going to go skiing with Pablo!

We've booked a little chalet in Austria and are spending Christmas Day over there.

I didn't mention it to you as I knew you'd be busy...

From: Allie Rainsbury

And you wanted some alone time with your soul mate ☺

It's OK, you can say! That sounds amazing! I hope you have a great time. When are you off exactly?

From: Chris Trail

On Thursday! I am practically hopping with excitement!

We fly back on the 28th – let's make sure we meet up for New Year though?

From: Allie Rainsbury

Absolutely!

Are you busy Wednesday evening as well? You could spend it with me, a bar and a few mulled wines?

From: Chris Trail

I honestly couldn't think of anything I'd rather do!

The Duke's Head?

From: Allie Rainsbury

Of course! ☺

You can tell me how much you're looking forward to Pablo serenading you on the nursery slopes x

From: Chris Trail

Allie, Allie... I'm good enough on the guitar now to serenade him :P

See you later hun x

Wednesday

From: Tess Cooper
To: Allie Rainsbury

Thanks again for coming over last night, and for the Christmas present – whatever it is! ☺

I hope it wasn't too awkward for you.

From: Allie Rainsbury

Ha! Was the biscuit tin too much of a giveaway? ☺

Whatever awkwardness that there was, I had coming my way.

At least Rosie wasn't there as well!

From: Tess Cooper

I haven't seen Rosie for a few days, thank goodness! Maybe a week's peace and quiet is her gift to me? ☺

I wanted to check you were OK though?

I hate seeing so much tension between my brother and you.

From: Allie Rainsbury

I'm fine, Tess, honestly I am!

I'm really sorry – that's the last thing you must need, a moody Scott stomping around the house!

From: Tess Cooper

Oh, don't apologise! It reminds me of when he was a stroppy teenager!

Anyway, I'm not in the firing line – you're the one getting the cold shoulder.

And despite singing him a song no less! What more does he want? ☺

From: Allie Rainsbury

☺!

He wanted me to hire a band a few months ago.

From: Tess Cooper

Well he should stop looking backwards and start thinking forwards!

Like I said last night, I've tried talking to him but a grunt seems to be his standard response to any question at the moment.

From: Allie Rainsbury

Please don't push him on it. The last thing he'd want is to be interrogated any further. I think the best policy for me now is to leave him alone.

From: Tess Cooper

Rubbish. He's crazy about you!

From: Allie Rainsbury

You're very sweet, but in this instance, wrong.

He's made it pretty clear that whatever window of opportunity existed has long since closed.

From: Tess Cooper

He's just being a stubborn idiot. He's just being Scott!

Don't give up just yet.

From: Allie Rainsbury

Tess, please don't speak to him, OK? I don't want him feeling harassed. Promise me you won't?

From: Tess Cooper

Fine, I won't!

Although I still don't agree with you!

Just don't get too down x

From: Allie Rainsbury

Why would I feel down? Without Scott I wouldn't have met you, and we wouldn't have become the friends we are today ☺

Whatever I might have lost, that's something good I've gained!

From: Tess Cooper

How wonderfully cheesy ☺

From: Allie Rainsbury

It's that time of year, I'm allowed to be!

So I'll see you after Christmas then? We should meet up again, if you're free.

From: Tess Cooper

Sounds good!

I have a hospital appointment on the 27th but don't have many plans after that.

From: Allie Rainsbury

I'll give you a call and we'll organise something fun.

I'm so positive about the year ahead for you, Tess. I know that you're meant for great things x

From: Tess Cooper

Thank you!

I'm fighting back against this stupid cancer! However much it thinks it might be beating me. I don't like losing at the best of times – this is one fight I'm determined to win ☺ x

From: Allie Rainsbury

Absolutely you will xx

From: Tess Cooper

Chat soon, Allie.

Merry Christmas to you and your family x

From: Allie Rainsbury

Merry Christmas to all of you too x

Thursday

From: Julie Lawson
To: Allie Rainsbury

If I hear 'Do They Know It's Christmas?' one more time I'm going to scream.

From: Allie Rainsbury

Office radios should be banned, I agree!

Personally, I've reached boiling point on 'Mistletoe and Wine' – it seems to have been on continuous loop for the last hour.

From: Julie Lawson

Ha! Another annoying classic.

At least it makes a change from having 'I Will Always Love You' on the brain though :P

From: Allie Rainsbury

Hey! That's not nice.

From: Julie Lawson

Sorry, couldn't resist!

It's the final, funny Allie story I have to keep me going until the New Year! ☺

From: Allie Rainsbury

I'm so glad I've been able to keep you entertained :P

From: Julie Lawson

Well, of course you have! In a good way though.

Fancy one more cup of cafeteria tea? My treat!

From: Allie Rainsbury

I'm not sure – I'm almost too insulted to accept!

From: Julie Lawson

Meet downstairs in five minutes ☺ x

From: Allie Rainsbury

See you there ☺ x

From: Ann Rainsbury
To: Allie Rainsbury

Hi darling,

Your aunt and uncle arrived today with a flurry of gifts and activity. We've put them in the spare bedroom that you normally stay in, I hope that's all right. It has an en suite toilet, and we thought your uncle will probably make more use of it than you would!

I can't believe it's Christmas again already – another year has gone by in a flash! I suppose I did miss some of it though, so perhaps that's the reason! When I think about what your father and you went through, how you looked after me and all the attention you both lavished, well... I feel very fortunate.

You've been wonderful. You really have. And in case I forget, or get too emotional when you're up here, I just wanted to say that now. I'm so lucky to have you as a daughter. And so proud.

Anyway, silly me is getting all worked up even writing this, so I'll stop there I think. We're so looking forward to seeing you. We just need you here and we'll have our full complement!

I promise that we'll keep card games to a minimum, or at the very least keep your glass full if you're forced into playing ☺

With much love, Mum xxx

From: Peter Rainsbury
To: Allie Rainsbury

Hi sweetheart,

Thought I'd take the chance to echo your mum's sentiments too.

I'll be brief since you no doubt have work to finish off.

I couldn't have got through this year without your support. Not even close.

See you up here on Saturday, I'll pick you up from the station.

Love, Dad xx

From: Allie Rainsbury
To: Ann Rainsbury; Peter Rainsbury

Dear Mum and Dad,

Thanks for your notes!

What a year indeed! It's been, for me, both more traumatic and more inspiring than any other. It's certainly helped me grow up in many different ways and put various events and previous priorities into perspective.

Thank you for being the amazing, wonderful parents that you are.

I'm looking forward to the coming year. I've learnt a lot about life, love and friendship over the last twelve months; I'm excited to be moving ahead with those lessons in mind!

Before that though, I'm looking forward to spending a fun Christmas with both of you... and finally winning a hand or two at rummy! ☺

With love,

Your daughter, Allie xx

Friday

From: Allie Rainsbury
To: Julie Lawson

Am I the only person in work today?

Has everyone else taken the day off? This is outrageous! Anyone would think it's a public holiday!

It's not is a public holiday, is it?!

From: Julie Lawson

No, it isn't, don't worry!

Technically I'm working from home.

From: Allie Rainsbury

Practically you've already opened a bottle of white :P

What's going on with your hectic household then?

I'm envisaging a traditional family scene with Elly and Cale looking at their presents under the tree ☺

From: Julie Lawson

Ha! Because we're just that picture-book perfect!

They're all outside at the moment. Unless he's fallen over, I think George is trying to show them how to make snow angels.

Want to sneak out early and come over for some mulled wine?

From: Julie Lawson

Hello?

From: Julie Lawson

HELLO?!...

From: Julie Lawson

Have you left already?!

From: Allie Rainsbury

Sorry...

Scott's in the office as well...

From: Julie Lawson

Really?!

How do you know that?

Have you seen him?

From: Allie Rainsbury

He's standing in front of me...

From: Julie Lawson

What?!

What do you mean?

From: Allie Rainsbury

He's standing in front of me, holding flowers...

From: Julie Lawson

WHAT?!!!

From: Allie Rainsbury

I think they're roses...

From: Julie Lawson

What's he saying?!

What's he saying?!?!!

From: Allie Rainsbury

Jules, I'll have to raincheck your mulled wine...

From: Julie Lawson

Why?!

What's going on?!!!!

From: Allie Rainsbury

I'll tell you later... I promise!

Merry Christmas to you all ☺

Xxx

Acknowledgements

With thanks to many. In particular to Nathalie Biggs for all her help and support along the way. Also to my family: Peter Thomas; James, Kathy, Max and Beatrix Rainsbury; Craig, Liz, Ellie and Cale Watson-Black; Christine, John, Ellie, Telly, Leo and Pascale Biggs (for her website design and creative advice). To Holly Roberts for her editing skills and Judith Fisher at Regent Typesetting. To Fliss, Steven and Midas PR. And finally, friendship thanks (among others) to Hugo Matcham, Adam Benson, James and Clare Clowes, Chris Millward, Heather Traill, Dom and Nadia Gibberd, Andy and Helen Clowes.